TRANSFORMATION OF A VALLEY
The Derbyshire Derwent

Heage Windmill.

TRANSFORMATION
of a
VALLEY

text by
BRIAN COOPER

photographs by
NEVILLE COOPER

'We see nothing till we truly understand it'
John Constable (1776–1837)

SCARTHIN BOOKS
1991

© Brian Cooper and Neville Cooper 1983
First published by Heinemann Educational Books Ltd 1983

New Edition published by
SCARTHIN BOOKS, CROMFORD, DERBYSHIRE
1991
Reprinted 1992

ISBN 0 907758 17 7

Printed and bound by
PRINTHAÜS
NORTHAMPTON

Contents

Preface

This is not a treatise on industrial archaeology, nor is it a history, nor even a guide book. It is the story of a valley, and the way in which it changed with the passage of almost three hundred years.

The river that flows through that valley penetrates the first of Britain's national parks, and within easy reach of its waters dwell some twenty-five million people. Even with its edging of limestone and gritstone, rising east, west and north, it comprises an area that is relatively small—fifty miles by twenty-five; yet within it lies scenery of exceptional beauty. Because of this it attracts visitors: people who have no knowledge of its history, who know little or nothing of industrial archaeology, and who rarely consult a guide book. This story is designed to be read by them, in the hope that, through it, they will discover another Derwent Valley from the one they come to see or the one they already know.

Experts will find nothing entirely novel in these pages. The facts have been recorded in innumerable books, pamphlets and articles written by specialists, who have concentrated on their individual fields of research; and anyone who follows such pioneers owes them an immeasurable debt of gratitude. What we have tried to do is to assemble these facts into a fresh kind of pattern, to link them and explain them in such a way that those with no prior knowledge can understand them, and to guide such readers to those places, often hidden away in odd corners of the valley, where they may, in crumbling walls, in hollows in the ground, or in buildings still throbbing, though with a different type of life, read and interpret the facts for themselves.

Because this is a story, we have not interrupted its flow with footnotes, but since every reader has the right to know where the evidence originates, a complete bibliography is given at the end, and we have detailed the sources of the extracts we have quoted. The photographs are all the authors', except where acknowledgement is otherwise made.

Finally, our thanks are due to innumerable people who have opened their doors to us, added their funds of knowledge to our own, allowed us to take photographs from cottage doors and gardens, and assisted us in other ways too numerous to mention. We would like to thank, in particular, Dr Robert Gittings for a great deal of invaluable help and encouragement; Professor Donald Cardwell for his meticulous reading of the typescript and many helpful suggestions; Dr Richard Hills for much in the way of expert technical assistance; Mr Christopher Charlton for making available to us his wealth of information on Arkwright at Cromford and the textile industry in Derbyshire; Mrs Winifred Wellington for her unwavering faith in the book and its authors; and our publisher, Alan Hill, for his immediate interest when the work was first suggested.

Brian Cooper,   Neville Cooper,
Mansfield   *Kings Bromley*, 1981

List of Illustrations

To supplement information given in the text, map references are given in brackets for most of the sites discussed.

All the sites are to be found on the new series of Ordnance Survey Maps, 1:50000, and the four maps required are

Sheets 110 Sheffield and Huddersfield
         119 Buxton, Matlock, and Dove Dale
         128 Derby and Burton upon Trent
         129 Nottingham and Loughborough

The grid letters are, in each case, SK.

It would, perhaps, be prudent to add that a number of the sites are on private property; and, while the majority of owners are only too willing to welcome visitors, it is a matter of courtesy to seek their permission before proceeding.

List of Maps

Map References of Places Mentioned in the Text but not Illustrated

FOR
the millions who travel, every year, through the valley

1   Ghosts

This black ruin looks out, not yet covered by the soil; still indicating what a once gigantic Life lies buried there! It is dead now, and dumb; but was alive once, and spake . . . Here was the earthly arena where painful living men worked out their life-wrestle—looked at by Earth, by Heaven and Hell . . . How silent now; all departed . . . [yet] here and there, some real human figure is seen moving: very strange, whom we could hail if he would answer—and we look into a pair of eyes deep as our own, imaging our own, but all unconscious of us, to whom we, for the time, are become as spirits and invisible.

Thomas Carlyle: *Past and Present* (1843).

One day in the early years of George III's long reign, a swarthy, thick-set man in his early thirties must have ridden down the steep hill from the moor and reined in his horse among the scattered cottages of Cromford. It was perhaps not the first of his visits, nor was it to be his last; but those who watched him would have noticed that he looked about him with perceptive eyes, and those to whom he spoke might have detected, behind his asthmatic voice and broad Lancastrian accent, an unusual interest in this small and very isolated community.

He had, almost certainly, already noted its isolation. The tracks around and through Cromford had not yet yielded to the turnpike trusts; the improved road to London approached no closer than Brassington, five miles to the east; the direct route to Derby ran at an angle over the moors, and there was no valley road except that brief stretch which clung to the river as far as Matlock Bridge. To Derby was fifteen wearisome, unpaved miles, to Nottingham twenty-six.

Such isolation may perhaps have drawn this man to Cromford, may have been a part of its undoubted attraction, but he must have taken note of other, equally favourable features. Knowing that this was an area peopled for the most part by miners and smelters of lead and calamine, and that these were visibly contracting occupations, he may well have ridden down the hill to the river and the fifteenth-century packhorse bridge. He would have looked with interest on the lead-smelting mill with its squat, smoking chimneys and its waterwheel for blast, and would have eyed, maybe with a sense of mistrust, the swift-flowing waters of the Derwent below: those waters that, half a century before, Daniel Defoe had described as a 'fury of a river', and that William Adam, eighty years on, was still to see as 'a powerful and rapid stream; impetuously rushing over its rugged and broken bed, giving birth to sounds more like the swell of a heavy sea, rolling in upon a rocky shore, than the flow of a river of such magnitude'.

The Derwent Valley.

Market Place and Greyhound Hotel, Cromford.

Turning his horse by the bridge, he may have ridden by the river to Matlock Bath, noting with approval that here, no more than a mile from the last of Cromford's cottages, society, in spite of the wretched roads, was beginning to penetrate the wildness of Derbyshire to indulge itself in the thermal waters. Here too the Derwent flowed, this time through its gorge, slower and smoother, but gathering pace. Perhaps he viewed it again with wariness, even indeed with a shrewd, misgiving shake of the head.

Riding back through the village, up the slope towards Wirksworth, he may well have turned aside to seek gentler waters, and found them in the brook that flowed down the secondary valley from Bonsall; and it would be a pleasant flight of fancy, if nothing more than that, to think that before he rode out of Cromford, he dismounted close to the foot of the hill, dabbled his fingers in the channel that drained away water from the lead mines, and discovered to his own abundant satisfaction that the stream was mild, almost tepid to the touch.

But if all this is fancy, one thing is sure: this man from the north would return to the village with a mind full of plans. He would live within its bounds for a full twenty years, and die by the river, for all its fury, boasting he was rich enough to liquidate the whole of the National Debt; and what he was to do in those twenty years would transform not only peaceful Cromford, but the whole Derwent valley from Bamford down to its junction with the Trent.

The Derwent is not a long river. From its source to its mouth it measures no more than sixty miles. The Trent is three times, the Thames and the Severn both four times its length. It is an inland river, rising in the mountains and tapering out still more than fifty miles from the sea. Apart from its mile through the centre of Derby, it is a completely rural waterway; and though its source is on the very border of Yorkshire and its mouth, likewise, on the border of Nottinghamshire, it is a river contained within one county, that county being Derbyshire.

Rising amid the rocks and peat of the Pennines, two thousand feet up, close to Bleaklow Stones, it flows on a roughly north-west south-east axis till it merges in the Trent on the flatness of the Midland plain at Wilne. On its sixty-mile course, cutting Derbyshire in half, it gathers to itself a number of lesser streams: the Noe at Bamford, the Wye at Rowsley, the Amber at Ambergate and the Ecclesbourne at Duffield. A host of even smaller waters join it on the way: a succession of brooks, the Burbage and Bar Brooks, the Sydnope, the Bentley, the Bonsall and the Markeaton, trickling almost unnoticed into its bed; infinitely smaller than the Peakshole Water which swells the River Noe, and the Lathkill and Bradford, streams of some consequence, that never reach the Derwent, but lose themselves in the waters of the Wye.

It is a beautiful river, the Derwent, wild in the north, becoming gentler and graver and yet ever stronger as it flows to the south; then losing itself at last, calmly and quietly, in the greater complex of waters that runs from Trent into Humber and thence to the sea. Its source is dramatic only in its scenery, the mist and the rocks, the cotton grass and peat hags and deep gritstone gullies; its mouth is less than dramatic, a placid, unmarked, inconsequential channel; and yet, between the two, lie the great man-made lakes and magnificent dams, houses steeped in history like Haddon and Chatsworth, the awesome gorge above Cromford, the spreading beauty of the valley as it widens to the south, and the idyllic twin vales of the Lathkill and the Bradford.

In 1793, J. P. Malcolm, writing in the *Gentleman's Magazine*, described this part of Derbyshire as 'desolate'. 'For some miles,' he wrote, 'I saw but two or three habitations. What, indeed, but extreme wretchedness could induce a person to live exposed to the keen northern blasts that whirl round those bleak rocks?' There is a difference nowadays. Roads seam the Peak; it is a residential area for those who work in the cities, Sheffield and Manchester, Nottingham and Derby; and since 1950 the northern half of the Derwent Valley has been a part of the first national park to be created in

Britain, the Peak District Park. Though the railways have gone, millions of people pour into the area by road every year, because the valley possesses a variety of England's finest scenery, and it is, above all, easily accessible.

Within sixty miles of the Derwent lives nearly half the population of England. From its centre point at Cromford, Derby is only 14 miles, Sheffield 25, Nottingham 26, Manchester less than 50, Birmingham, Leicester and the whole of the Potteries within the same radius. The A6 runs beside it from Derby to Rowsley; the M1 approaches to within ten miles; the M6 to the west and the M62 to the north box in the whole area with high-speed roads, so that, even from London, Cromford is less than three hours' drive by the motorway.

Those who come here in summer to the White and Dark Peaks come to camp and to walk, to fish or to laze, to visit the great houses and stroll through their gardens, or simply to drive and to stop and then drive on again. They tend to congregate in the popular places: in Chatsworth House and its park, by the river at Matlock Bath, or beside the landscaped reservoirs high above Bamford; but most of them leave at the end of their stay unaware of the fact that in the limestone villages, on the harsh, open moorland crossed and crossed again by its dry stone walls, in among the trees or simply where the water laps the edge of the river, there lie other signs of another Derwent Valley, artefacts of the past which they have never seen, or, seeing, have passed by without understanding. These are sometimes so obvious, so close to main roads and of such massive bulk that men's eyes deny them; sometimes they lie a few hidden yards from the river, deep among the trees, amid the grass and summer flowers; at other times they have to be sought for, on foot, through twisted brambles, across tumbled stones and over what appear to be landscapes of the moon.

They are the remains of that brief stretch of time, thirty, forty years, when this Derwent Valley was in the forefront of history; and for those who have the vision to look back in time, to see the men and women who laboured beside them and hear once again the sounds of their labour, the places where they lie, the still, quiet places, have a magic all their own. These are places where things once happened in profusion, but nothing happens now; the solitary places, soundless, motionless, save when the wind stirs the branches of the trees, the rain darkens old stones, or from somewhere close by, beyond a screen of leaves, comes the roar of the Derwent foaming down a weir as it did in that same, that identical place two centuries ago.

Half a mile from the river, beyond Darley Bridge and shrouded by a wood, stands a solitary arch of massive proportions, a classical ruin on the fringe of the trees. The land in front dips away to a valley, ravaged and hummocked by abandoned tips of waste. This is the site of the Old Mill Close Mine, and the huge stone blocks, for all the world resembling some ancient temple, are the tumbled remains of the engine house at the head of Watts Shaft. For

Watts Shaft engine house, Mill Close Mine, Darley Dale.

all its immense size the building is only half the height it once was, and
deserted save for those who come in ones and twos to search for galena, for
calcite, barytes and fluorspar on the desolate ground. Yet this was once,
and not so long ago, a part of the richest lead mine in Britain. Here the great
iron beam of a steam pumping engine rocked up and down, ponderously
sucking water from hundreds of feet below. Other stone buildings then
clustered round it, but these have now disintegrated into nothing more
than rubble, and the great stone arch of the ten-foot window through which

one could see the giant 50-inch cylinder topped by its gleaming cast-iron cover now stands alone, more impressive in its solitude than ever it was when the mine was at work. To stand in its shadow on an autumn day with the flashes of sunshine and the changing pattern of light on the stones is to hear once again the clank of the beam as it rose and fell; to see in scudding shadows, if only for an instant, the miners, long dead, who clambered up the tracks, feeding the insatiable monster with coal; and to catch the sound perhaps, half a mile away and even closer to the river, of the great Cornish engine they nicknamed 'Jumbo' toiling at the head of the Warren Carr Shaft, lifting with its companions seven million gallons of water a day from nearly a thousand feet below the level of the river.

Stranded in the middle of a farmer's fields and set against a bank of tufted grass, which seems from a distance to diminish their height, stand two squat pyramids of sandstone and gritstone, thirty-five feet high, isolated landmarks in the wide-open spaces above the town of Belper. A hundred and fifty, two hundred years ago, the scene here must have borne a close resemblance to Dante's Inferno, for these are the stubs of the Morley Park Ironworks, the blast furnaces erected by Francis Hurt, the first of them dating from 1780. Here the huge bellows blasted air into the furnaces, here the smoke and flame billowed out from their vents, the stream of liquid fire that was molten iron cascaded from the tap-holes, and amid all the fury hammers rang on the anvils and coke, ore and limestone were tipped rumbling from the bank into the tops of the towers. Now all is quiet, apart perhaps from the cry of a lapwing over the fields, but to stand in this place beneath a louring sky is to feel oneself haunted by the sights and the sounds and the figures of the past.

Morley Park blast furnaces, Heage.

They glide back, these visions, in other places too: innumerable places close by the Derwent. At Leawood, now deserted, the narrow boats still creak along the Cromford Canal, and trains of waggons, with a clanking of chains, are still wound up the now-trackless incline at the foot of the Cromford and High Peak Railway. At Shardlow, now no more than a sleepy village backwater at the end of the Trent and Mersey Canal, the empty warehouses still ring to the sounds of transhipment, as corn, salt and cotton, ale, cheese and malt, and Mr Wedgwood's pottery are unloaded from the boats, stowed away for safety and loaded again. In the deep and beautiful valley of the Wye one can sometimes, if one believes Robert Blincoe who worked in this place, catch the anguished cries of the work-house children from the walls of Litton Mill; and streaming down through the quiet little village of Pentrich, one can sometimes catch a glimpse on a dark June night of that 'great multitude of false traitors' armed 'with swords, pistols, clubs, bludgeons and other weapons' who, a hundred and sixty years ago, did 'with great force and violence parade and march in a hostile manner in and through divers villages, places and public highways': the raggle-taggle remnants of the Pentrich Revolution.

But most of all, perhaps, one sees the sights, hears the sounds of that bygone age amid the bustle of Cromford. Through the dust and rattle and engine-noise of the limestone lorries that sweep round the bend from the Via Gellia to the A6 junction at Scarthin Nick, one can still see the ghost of that thick-set man who rode into the village down the hill from the moor. He still stands at the gate of his fortress mills, moves like a shadow through the rooms of the Greyhound, drives in his carriage down to Rock House, then across the packhorse bridge and up the gentle slope to look with pride on the walls of his half-constructed castle.

That man was Richard Arkwright. An itinerant hair-dealer when he rode down to Cromford, he lived to own his own carriage, to build his own castle, to create an industrial empire spreading from Derbyshire through Lancashire to Scotland, and to die a millionaire.

Within the span of two decades he changed his own fortunes and his pattern of life, and in the course of that radical transformation life and landscape were changed in the valley that he chose as his home. He stamped his own particular marks on the Derwent, its scene and its people: marks that time and nature, for all their slow, remorseless process of erosion, have not entirely succeeded in smoothing away.

2 Rich Wilderness

All Derbyshire is full of steep hills, and nothing but the peakes of hills as thick one by another is seen in most of the County which are very steepe which makes travelling tedious, and the miles long, you see neither hedge nor tree but only low drye stone walls round some ground, else its only hills and dales as thick as you can imagine, but tho' the surface of the earth looks barren yet those hills are impregnated with rich Marbles Stones Metals Iron and Copper and Coale mines in their bowells, from whence we may see the wisdom and benignitye of our greate Creator to make up the defficiency of a place by an equivolent as also the diversity of the Creation which encreaseth its Beauty.

Celia Fiennes: *Through England on a Side Saddle in the time of William and Mary* (1697).

And now I am come to this wonderful place, the Peak ... I cannot but ... desire you, my friend, to travel with me through this howling wilderness in your imagination, and you shall soon find all that is wonderful about it.

Daniel Defoe: *A Tour thro' the Whole Island of Great Britain*, Volume III (1726).

When, seventy years before Arkwright's arrival, Celia Fiennes, that redoubtable daughter of a Roundhead colonel, rode side-saddle over the tracks of Derbyshire, she needed courage. Though she clung to no rigid, pre-planned route and cheerfully turned aside to avoid the worst of the potholes, much of her journey must have been not merely uncomfortable, but often dangerous and desperately lonely. She wrote more than once of unending hills, of a landscape bereft of both trees and hedges, revealing nothing but dry stone walls. 'All Derbyshire', she observed with the rich satisfaction of a determined stoic, 'is but a world of peaked hills which from some of the highest you discover the rest like steeples ... and tho' they appear so close yet the steepness down and up takes up the time that you go it, as if so many miles'. Some of the slopes were so hazardous that she described them in typically forthright fashion as 'steep precipices'; and after making the comment that a traveller needed guides in all parts of the county, she went on to imply that these were difficult to find since 'the common people know not above 2 or 3 mile from their home'.

Derbyshire, indeed, had for long been regarded by those who explored it from the gentler, rolling lands of the south as little more than a bleak and cheerless limbo. It had been noised abroad, eighty years before, that to enter this region was to travel in constant fear of one's neck, and Lord Chesterfield, in displeasure at his wife's behaviour, had packed her off to the Peak: an action, said Samuel Pepys, 'which is become a proverb at court—to send a man's wife to the Devils o' Peake when she vexes him'.

As late as 1726 Daniel Defoe, though much of his journey lay within a couple of miles of the Derwent, still described the place as a 'howling wilderness ... the most desolate, wild and abandoned country in all England'; but Defoe, too, was a Southerner and not disposed to look with any kind of perception on a land that showed little of the growing trade and commerce that he believed at that time to be the glory of the nation.

Celia Fiennes was more discerning, for all that her main concern was to find a way from one place to somewhere quite different. She summed up the county with impeccable judgment as an endless series of dry stone walls encircling 'some ground' and a world of hills, to all appearances barren, yet impregnated with a wealth of stone and a greater wealth of metal; for the valley of the Derwent must have presented to her much the same pattern as it does to us today: a sixty-mile stretch that was predominantly agricultural, yet revealing among its sheep-walks and limestone villages the scattered evidence of small-scale industries: industries that in those days were interdependent and drew their inspiration from its four outstanding natural resources: mineral ores and stone from the bowels of the hills, wool from the backs of Woodland and Limestone sheep, and water from the river.

For those who live and also work in the valley, farming has, since before Saxon times, been the form of livelihood with the longest and most continuous tradition; and if its pattern has repeatedly changed with the years, yet the characteristic signs of its presence were just as much in evidence at

Dry stone walls, Litton.

the end of the seventeenth century as they are to us now and will be to those who travel the slopes around the Derwent in a hundred years' time. They can be seen deep in the heart of the valley, on the banks of the river. They climb up the faces of the limestone hills, and up still further to at least fifteen hundred feet on the gritstone. William Adam called them 'Derbyshire hedges', and the whole county seemed indeed, to Celia Fiennes, to be little else but mile after mile of them, straddling and straggling across the slopes. Living closer to the earth than the high-flown, semi-Romantic Adam, she described them more prosaically. To her they were nothing more than what they appeared to be: walls, stone walls, and ground in between.

In her time, there were not so many of them. Adam, traversing the county in 1840, would have seen far more, for the great age of Parliamentary Enclosure was only just beginning when Arkwright came to Cromford. Even so, there were enough to fill her vision of the landscape: a spider's web of grey across the pale green hills and the deeper green of dales, marking the boundaries of arable fields, holding in the livestock, withstanding the winds that tore across the moors and, once constructed, far more durable than the hedges and fences to be found in the south, needing no repair till long after those that had raised them had died.

When, towards the end of the eighteenth century, most of what remained of the county's common pastures were enclosed by Act of Parliament, these grey walls multiplied, cutting the land into a geometrical pattern of rectangular fields, intersected by roads driven straight as the walls, disregarding every trace of a previous boundary. This was the transformation, almost complete inside sixty years, which was merely commencing in Arkwright's time, and which led Edward Rhodes, taking note of the change in the 1820s, to write that parts of the county were 'everywhere disfigured with stone wall-fences'.

It was a ruthless change, too savage for Rhodes. Its features, he said, if not 'absolutely repulsive', were at least 'unlovely'; but if this newly-made, harsh, rectilinear landscape clashed with his notions of natural beauty, it was still nothing more than a somewhat different version, realized more swiftly, of a process already four hundred years old.

What Celia Fiennes saw were the walls that village people, monks and farmers on the hills had raised stone by stone from medieval times; but the landscape they created was never as stark as the one that Rhodes was so swift to condemn. These walls, built long before the first of parliament's commissioners ever set foot in the limestone villages, followed a different, more logical pattern. Built to enclose the old arable strips, which up to that time had grown rye and oats and less commonly wheat and barley, they undulated from side to side across the surface of the ground, following the lines of ridge and furrow traced by the plough or the time-honoured boundaries of common pasture; and the lanes that intersected them wound like adders, seeking a way round the balks and strips of the old open fields.

No-one knows for certain just how long men had been toiling to build them, but it seems likely they began to appear in quantity when the Derbyshire farmers, struggling to produce their crops on the difficult limestone of valleys and hillsides, began to develop an interest in livestock, particularly sheep which had long been reared on the gritstone uplands.

This slow, subtle change, which, in three hundred years, produced its web of stone walls, probably commenced in the late fourteenth century. The catalyst that first of all set it in motion was perhaps the Black Death which swept through the country in 1349, wiping out whole communities and producing, at least in the farming areas, a shortage of labour to work on the crop fields. This, coupled with the rise of the English wool trade, the growing profitability of wool-bearing sheep and the reduced amount of labour needed for stock farms, encouraged the enclosure of arable strips to provide grazing land for the constantly multiplying numbers of sheep.

The process was undoubtedly assisted by the monks. At least fifty years before the Black Death, the wealthy monasteries of the Midlands and the North had already begun to take to themselves extensive tracts of land in widely separated parts of the county. The abbeys of Darley and Combermere, Leicester, Roche, Rufford and Welbeck, to mention but a few, all acquired such land by gift or by purchase; and on these estates, often far removed from the abbeys themselves, they developed considerable economic assets: outposts called granges: monastic farms which were devoted almost purely to the raising of sheep. In another hundred years these granges were sending regular exports of wool to Florence and Flanders, and by Daniel Defoe's time a traveller could have ridden a Derbyshire circuit and seen at least fifty: vast sheep stations covering, each of them, hundreds of acres, their flocks penned in by the dry stone walls. By that time the monasteries had long been dissolved and the lands had passed to great families such as the Cavendishes, but they too continued to farm their sheep on the granges, selling the wool to the English clothiers who employed a host of varied domestic workers to turn it into broadcloth.

It would be wrong to say the granges raised nothing but sheep. They had their cattle too, but in much smaller numbers; and some of their walls, those contiguous perhaps to the buildings themselves, enclosed arable fields; but their main concern, irrefutably, was wool. As early as the end of the thirteenth century it was reported that the monks of Dunstable Priory had twelve hundred sheep on their grange at Bradbourne, roughly half way between Ashbourne and Wirksworth, and it was at least rumoured that another of these farms provided pasture for a flock of more than five thousand. Indeed, the limestone slopes round the valley of the Derwent and the gritstone heights climbing up to its headwaters must for long have presented the undulating, chequer-board appearance of a series of sheep walks, the walls merely serving to separate the one from its nearest neighbour.

Those who travel through the valley today can still find relics of this age of contracting arable and expanding stock farms that preceded the arrival of Arkwright at Cromford. The signs of arable, it is true, have almost disappeared. The curling patterns of ridge and furrow produced by the plough are difficult to discern from the level of the ground and have often been so obscured by later patterns of farming that they become visible only through the medium of aerial photography. Whole villages, along with their fields, have vanished; some, like Nether Haddon and Chatsworth, destroyed when the great ducal houses were rebuilt and their parks extended.

The relics that remain only serve to emphasize the problems of farming, in bygone days, on this difficult land. Nutrients tended to drain away swiftly from the limestone soil, and the farmer was continually faced with the problem of maintaining fertility. To keep his land in at least reasonable heart, he normally burnt limestone and treated the ground with lime. Most farms therefore had stone-built limekilns fuelled with wood or peat or furze; and though the vast majority have long since disappeared, many still survive, among them two in fields to the north of Monyash and Flagg near the head of Lathkill Dale.

The other great problem on the limestone was water conservation. It was met in many places round the Derwent Valley by deepening the ground above a natural spring. Thus the farmer made a pond, which was then progressively widened to provide a reserve of drinking water for livestock. Some of these ancient ponds, or meres as they were called, can still be seen today. A particularly fine example is that at One Ash Grange on the edge of Cales Dale south of the Lathkill.

Yet the most persistent, the most hardy of all surviving relics from this age of arduous arable farming has no connection with its problems, save that of finding shelter on the wind-swept slopes. The domestic buildings, the old manor farmhouses, stone-built and solid, probably raised on the site of an older timbered dwelling, still stand in great numbers all about the valley, seemingly impervious to three and a half centuries of wind and rain, frost and snow and the even more insidious erosions of man. Most of them were built in the early years of the seventeenth century when, right across the Peak, stone and slate were progressively replacing timber and thatch. Beside the River Bradford, and close to where it joins the Lathkill at Alport, is the village of Youlgreave. Here, up a side-turning off the main street, is Old Hall Farm. Built in a mixture of limestone and gritstone, with its hall and cross wing, its mullioned windows and stone-slated roof, and the year of its construction, 1630, engraved above the door, it represents one of the many styles of manor farmhouse that date from this age of arable farming close to the Derwent.

The stock farms, too, have left their traces on the valley. If the village flocks feeding on the common pastures are only part of memory, and if the multitudes of sheep cropping the grass round the old monastic granges have disappeared for ever, yet this age, when the hornless Old Limestone breed

Old Hall Farm, Youlgreave, 1630.

held sway around the Derwent, still comes to life in places scattered from the banks of the Lathkill to Peakshole Water on the fringes of Edale. The grange buildings have survived, like the manor farms, in sufficient numbers to sprinkle the surface of ordnance maps; and the rising ground to the south of the Lathkill, once divided between the abbeys of Leicester and Roche, has, within the space of a couple of miles, three medieval granges, One Ash, Calling Low and Meadow Place, which still exist and operate as present-day farms.

The first two are relatively difficult to reach, approachable only from the village of Monyash or the gorge of Lathkill Dale by cart-tracks and footpaths that once crossed their sheep walks. The easiest of the three for the visitor to reach is Meadow Place Grange, a quarter of a mile south of the river at Over Haddon, and approached by a zigzag path through the wood which is now a nature reserve. Here the old grey-stone farm, built around a square that is almost a courtyard, still looks toward the slopes where, on eight hundred acres of slowly climbing pasture, the sheep of Leicester Abbey were reared in an almost monastic isolation. There is a cloistered peace today around Meadow Place Grange; and when, on a Sunday evening in summer, the bells of Youlgreave church sound from a distance across the dale, one

Meadow Place Grange, Over Haddon.

can, through half-closed eyes, recreate a time when the sheep were lost to view in the failing light and the lay brothers walked to worship in their chapel.

That was the time when almost every village had its own sheepwash. Many, indeed, had more than one, and there was a period when Over Haddon parish had four. In those days of a prosperous woollen cloth industry, the cost of washing the sheep before shearing was more than offset by the higher price paid for wool that had been cleansed of dirt and grit. The washing was normally done at midsummer in a river or stream that offered a sufficient depth of water, and since it was necessary for one man to guide and handle each animal in turn as it came to the stream, some physical means was required of penning the sheep and releasing them one by one into the water. Stone-walled enclosures were therefore constructed on the banks of rivers, and the one which remains by the Sheepwash Bridge at Ashford-in-the-Water is photographed and painted by thousands of visitors in the course of a year, though more perhaps for the beauty of its setting than its archaeological interest. Here the A6 road from Bakewell to Buxton runs close to the Wye, and between river and road, at right angles to the bridge, is the stone pen from which the sheep entered the water. Sheep were washed at this spot

Sheepwash Bridge, Ashford-in-the-Water. On the left and attached to the bridge is the holding pen with ventilation holes round the base.

until very recent times; not merely flocks from Ashford, but from Sheldon, three hundred feet up the hill, and from Monyash and Flagg, some four miles away: a round trip of eight miles up and down the steep slope. Ashford is one of the most charming villages in Derbyshire, and no doubt most of the visitors who linger by the bridge are happy to do nothing more than watch the water as it flows through the flat, seventeenth-century arches; but a closer look at the walls of the sheep pen would reveal to them something worthy of notice. Stones appear to be missing, here and there, low down in the walls. Some people do, perhaps, notice the gaps, and dismiss them merely as holes left by stones that time has dislodged; but they are, in point of fact, nothing of the kind. They were purposely constructed, and at that precise height, to give air to sheep huddled close together inside the pen. In this way the odd sheep casualty, caused by suffocation, was avoided by a stroke of precautionary forethought.

At that time, too, almost every village could lay claim to a pinfold. This was a small enclosure, usually of stone, where the village pinner or pinder impounded sheep and cattle found straying on the crop fields. It was the pinder's duty to round up the offending animal, lock it in the pinfold and notify the owner by personal contact. Until such time as the animal was claimed, it was also his duty to feed and water it, an expense which he had the right to recover from the owner, along with a fixed charge for possible damage to standing crops. This charge was, in many villages, higher in summer than it was in the winter, since, as harvest time approached, the potential damage was likely to be greater. Once the owner had paid, the pinder released the animal into his care; but, if he refused to pay, the costs of damage and fodder could be recovered by offering the animal for sale.

Many pinfolds have disappeared, leaving nothing behind. The sites of others can, with difficulty, be traced, marked only by a rough, tumbled outline of stones. Still more of them exist, their origins now forgotten, serving as allotments, parts of gardens or, sadly, as dumps for a farmer's refuse; but some are still preserved, notably those at Hathersage and Hope. The one at Hathersage, unused for more than fifty years, is a square stone enclosure close by the church. At Hope, the village still has its pinder, and animals are still impounded in the circular fold on the Pindale Road. Close to the bridge over Peakshole Water, it measures some fifteen feet in diameter, has limestone walls that are six feet high and a wooden door fitted with a hasp and padlock. The pinder still has the right to recover his expenses, which nowadays include the cost of petrol for transport and a telephone call to notify the owner: justifiable expenses in view of the fact that, as recently as 1967, three hundred

Pinfold, Hope.

sheep were impounded in the fold. The sanctity of the pinfold was always strictly guarded. An owner who, sooner than pay the fixed charge, chose instead to break in and remove his animal, risked the imposition of a swingeing fine. This is true today at Hope, where the maximum penalty for such an offence is set at £500.

The sheepwashes, the pinfolds, or the sites they once occupied, have now to be sought for with the aid of old enclosure maps, oral traditions, and painstaking examinations of stony and often unpromising ground; but the dry stone walls still form a grey web against the green of the land, as they wander up the hillsides and down the steep slopes to the banks of the Derwent. They may not follow the same line as once they did; they may have been restored or even rebuilt, not once, but many times in the course of the years; but their purpose is still the same, to hold in the livestock, and if the numbers of cattle are greater today than they were at the end of the seventeenth century, the sheep now, as then, always seem to predominate. The walls were built for them, and for them they survive: a fact to which the creep holes still bear witness. These gaps, called in some places cripple holes, in others known as sheep creeps, are still to be seen, low down in the walls. Formed by the builder omitting a stone or a couple of stones, they allowed sheep to pass from one field to the next, though they were never made large enough for use by the cattle. Those that have survived from much earlier days can be distinguished by their size, for sheep are bred much bigger now than they used to be, and the very old creeps appear to have been designed for Lilliputian animals.

Yet, in many of these walls, no farmer would have dared to construct a creep hole; for, while some walls were built to save the crops from the sheep, far more were constructed to save the sheep themselves from a danger that was widespread around the Derwent Valley. That danger was bellanding, a Derbyshire term which meant that animals were poisoned by the grazing of pastures infected by lead.

This was a danger that sprang not so much from the actual mining of the ore, but from its subsequent treatment by running water to separate the lead from the dross, and from the process of smelting which released deposits that were highly toxic. Just how dangerous these could be was proved as late as 1966 when, at Marsh Farm near Hope, five cows and a number of other animals died of the belland. The farm was on the site of the old Marsh Green lead-smelting cupola, and it was later discovered that the poison had spread from an old furnace chimney which had been incorporated into the farm buildings and from slag heaps nearby which had been somewhat unceremoniously disturbed. The Marsh Green smelter had then been disused for some eighty-seven years, but the belland had survived in sufficient strength to prove deadly to the stock as they grazed the pastures. Bearing this in mind, it is easy to appreciate just how much greater the danger must have been in the early years of the eighteenth century, when the face of the valley was scarred by the workings of thousands of miners, and the lead ore was crushed, and then washed and smelted with few of the precautions that would now be imposed on production plants.

Generalizations are notoriously dangerous; yet armed with the knowledge that they can never be fully justified, one can sometimes discern in them elemental truths. It would not be strictly accurate to say that when Celia Fiennes jogged her way across Derbyshire, such parts of the Derwent Valley as were not given over to the farming of sheep were hummocked and hollowed by 'the subterranean wretches', as Daniel Defoe called them: 'a rude boorish kind of people . . . who they call Peakrills, who work in the mines.' It would not, however, be entirely false, and it would at least point the way to a truth which could hardly be disputed: that, apart from agriculture, the most widespread of all occupations in the valley was the mining and, after that, the processing of lead.

When Sir John Betjeman wrote that in the northern half of Derbyshire stone never seemed to be far below the surface, he was, in a sense, merely echoing the words that Celia Fiennes had written three hundred years before. Though the surface of the earth looked barren, she said, yet the hills were impregnated with rich stones in their bowels; and whereas, nowadays, the stones of great price are the limestone and fluorspar, in her time and Arkwright's the stone that could make a man rich beyond his always modest dreams of wealth was galena: lead ore.

It may well have been mined in Derbyshire before Roman times, for, as early as the year A.D. 79, Pliny the Elder wrote that 'in Britain lead is found near the surface of the earth in such abundance that a law is made to limit the quantity that shall be gotten.' It was certainly mined in the Derwent Valley in the second and third centuries. The excavation of pigs of smelted lead with Roman inscriptions, found on Cromford Moor and in the Matlock area, bears witness to this; and the mining continued through Saxon times. In the year 714 the abbey of Repton owned lead mines at Wirksworth, and they were clearly producing large quantities of ore because, a century later, the subsequent owner, according to his contract, was sending three hundred shillings' worth of lead every year to Christ Church at Canterbury.

The Danes, when they arrived, may perhaps have worked the Odin Mine at Castleton, though no evidence but the name has ever been adduced to support this contention; but, whether they did or no, mining appears to have continued in the valley without intermission, for the Domesday Book records five centres of activity: Wirksworth, Crich, Ashford, Bakewell and Matlock. These were not, strictly speaking, designated as mines, but as 'plumbaria', places where lead ore was refined, and they could well have been smelters, each in turn serving one or many mines. Certainly, by the twelfth century, more and more of the valley was being appropriated for the working of lead. This was the great age of church and castle building, and lead was required in ever larger quantities for drainage pipes and roofing, for fonts, vats and cisterns and the lining of coffins. Round about this time, probably when the central keep was constructed in 1175, Peveril Castle was roofed with lead, and by the middle of the fourteenth century Derbyshire and Somerset had become the two chief sources of lead in the country, and that which was mined around the Derwent Valley had assumed immense importance in the export trade.

All through the Middle Ages the getting of ore continued to grow, and when Daniel Defoe, in 1726, wrote of the Wirksworth men as 'bold, daring and even desperate kind of fellows' who 'search into the bowels of the earth' for lead, the number of mines must have run into thousands; yet, almost without exception, they were small-scale concerns in the hands of individuals or small groups of people. The great mining companies like London Lead had only recently been founded and were still in the process of testing their initial samples of Derbyshire ore. In the years that followed they leased mineral rights, London Lead in the Winster and Elton district, and by Ark- wright's time their injections of capital to cut drainage tunnels and import Newcomen steam engines for pumping the levels had done much to effect a major transformation; but, at the beginning of the eighteenth century, the pattern of mining was still dictated by those medieval laws, hallowed by ancient custom and privilege, that gave to every man, as they still do today, the unquestionable right to search and dig for ore wherever he chose, no matter who owned the land, provided he kept clear of churchyards and gardens, orchards and highways.

Many thousands of men on the slopes that climbed up from the waters of the Derwent, and above, on the windy, sheep-strewn pastures, chose to exercise that right; and the land, as John Byng wrote, became 'scoop'd by lead mines' as 't'owd man'—a term used, it seems, indiscriminately to apply to the miner, the workings, the ore and the waste—tramped out across the heights with his pick and his kibble to burrow, like some sharp-toothed, predatory animal, deep into the rock.

The kibble or wisket was a bucket, wicker basket or sometimes a goatskin bag that was used for carrying the ore to the surface. To extract that ore, a miner would in those days, more often than not, work the length of a rake vein, where it lay beneath the ground in a fissure or crevice that might be anything from a few feet to sixty feet wide, and stretching perhaps for several miles. He staked his claim by placing a stowce, a primitive hand winch, on the spot, and having worked the vein till he had sufficient ore to pay the necessary tribute to the local Barmaster, he then followed the line of it under- ground, driving at an angle deeper and deeper till ventilation problems forced him to return, like a mole, to the surface. At this point he sank another shaft and started afresh, throwing out the dead stone and waste as he pro- gressed, and so producing along the line of his narrow workings a pattern of hollows and hummocks on the ground, stretching far from the original point of his claim. He worked with a hand-pick, a chisel and a wedge, by the light maybe of a tallow candle secured to his leather cap by a lump of clay; and to free the ore along the line of his level, built a fire against the rock and then dashed water on the face to induce a crack. The ore was then crushed using hammers or a heavy stone roller drawn around a circular track by a horse. After that it was riddled or 'jigged' in wire sieves set in tubs of water, and then raked and washed in a 'buddle', a tilted wooden trough down which the water flowed, the heavy lead particles trickling down to the bottom of the slope.

Smelting was carried out in what were called 'boles', crude hollows in the ground, usually set on the windward sides of hills to produce the draught, or in primitive furnaces blown by hand or foot bellows and later by power transmitted from a waterwheel. One of these, near Wirksworth, was described by a visitor in 1729 as 'consisting only of some large rough Stones placed in such a Manner as to form a square Cavity, into which the Ore and Coals are thrown stratum super stratum [layer on layer]; two great Bellows continually blowing the Fire, being moved alternatively by Water.' These early furnaces were replaced in many cases, once the London Lead Company began to work its Derbyshire concessions, by the reverberatory or air furnaces known as cupolas, of similar type to the one at Marsh Green which eventually poisoned Mr Sidebottom's cows.

Since Daniel Defoe's time there has been so much activity in the lead mining fields, mainly at the instance of heavily capitalized companies, that these earlier workings are difficult to trace and have often been obliterated by the later, more intensive, methods of extraction; but signs and symbols of the age of 't'owd man' do remain to be seen, if a visitor to the valley knows precisely where to look.

In the south transept wall of Wirksworth church there is a tiny carving, dating probably from the twelfth century or earlier, of a Derbyshire lead miner, his pick in his left hand, his kibble in his right; and in the church at Great Longstone, by Monsal Dale, there are two perhaps even more significant carvings, set side by side: one of a dairymaid carrying a churn and the other of a crouching miner with a pick, symbolizing, it seems, the two major occupations pursued in early times by the people of the valley.

In Wirksworth too, the great centre of lead in the early eighteenth century, tucked away in a side street stands the Moot Hall, still the centre of jurisdiction for lead mining disputes and seat of the Barmote Court which administered the complicated lead mining laws. The building, it is true, dates only as far back as 1814 and is, architecturally, somewhat unimpressive, but the Barmote Court still sits at certain times in the year, and though its functions are now nothing more than traditional, to stand in the narrow street and see the collection of lead miners' tools carved on a plaque that flanks one of the windows is to waken memories of an age when the miners disputed, often with violence, the ownership of veins, and the Barmote Court possessed

T'Owd Man, Wirksworth Church.

what were virtually powers of life or death. In those not so far off days it could punish a miner convicted of stealing by impaling his hand to the winch above his claim and leaving him either to tear himself free or to die of starvation.

Inside the same hall is the standard brass measuring dish, made in 1512, and presented to the miners by Henry VIII as a master reference for calculating the 'lot' or levy of lead ore that was due to the king; 'this Dishe,' reads the inscription wrought on the side, 'to Remayne In the Moote Hall at Wyrkysworth hanging by a cheyne so as the Merchauntes or mynours may have resorte to ye same at all tymes to make the trew mesur at the same.'

Moot Hall, Wirksworth.

Wirksworth, like many other places round the valley, has its Bolehill, north-east of the town on the edge of Cromford Moor, a constant reminder of the primitive smelting techniques on the lead field; and the western part of the Moor itself, on the flank of the Cromford to Wirksworth road, lies pitted with workings, an uneven waste of hollows and hummocks and still-open shafts, half hidden, grassed over and interspersed with bushes, but still evocative of a time when 't'owd man' toiled away with his pick and chisel and struggled with his ore up a climbing shaft to the light of day.

But undoubtedly the most dramatic of all these remains of the early workings is Tideslow Rake. Half a mile along the lane that links Little Hucklow with Lane Head near Tideswell, the road dips into a hollow, and from here the Rake stretches away to the west, climbing steadily all of another half mile up to Tideslow Top, five hundred feet wide, a rough moon-landscape of grass-covered mounds and shadowy depressions. It is a high and lonely place, unaltered from the time, perhaps Celia Fiennes' time, when the miners, one by one, abandoned its workings; and to stand in the silence at Washhouse Bottom and look up the Rake between its edgings of trees, planted no doubt to save the sheep and cattle from the danger of belland, is to feel all around one the ghosts of that age when Daniel Defoe, crossing Brassington Moor,

Tideslow Rake, near the village of Windmill.

saw 't'owd man' appear from a hole in the ground, 'lean as a skeleton, pale as a dead corpse, his hair and beard a deep black, his flesh ... something of the colour of the lead itself'; when the Wirksworth ale-houses, thirty-seven of them, dispensed the 'transcendant Derby Ale', and a visitor to the town, happening to drop his gold watch in a saucer full of water, it 'presently turned green, curdled, and let fall a large sediment', the reason being, he said, that Wirksworth's water supply was drawn from the soughs, the tunnels that drained the lead mines under the town.

Wool and lead were, then, the staples of the valley; but farming and mining were not the only industries. These two spawned others. The farmers required ploughshares, scythes and sickles; the lead miners needed picks and chisels, and also wire for their ore-washing sieves; and to provide these necessities iron smelters and forges, slitting and rolling mills sprang into existence up and down the valley, using the water power offered by the Derwent and its tributary streams.

The requirements of the farmers were, it is true, mainly fulfilled by the rural smithies scattered in profusion through the limestone villages, but these smithies needed bar-iron and share-moulds for ploughshares, and one of the centres which developed to supply them was the complex of smelter, forge and rolling mills at Alderwasley between Cromford and Belper. Here, in one of the most beautiful parts of the valley, the forge, that William Adam described in 1851 as 'a black and gloomy object amongst such scenery', was already in existence ninety years before; and in the hands of Francis Hurt in the 1780s it grew into a considerable manufactory. Hurt, who inherited the family lead merchanting business, expanded the Alderwasley site; acquired, across the river at Crich, perhaps the richest lead-ore deposits in the county; became a part-proprietor of Meerbrook Sough, driven to unwater the Wirksworth mines; claimed his own wharf on the Cromford Canal; began to manufacture castings for cotton-mill machinery; married his son to Arkwright's daughter; and from his white Georgian mansion on the slopes above the river could, in his retirement, look across the valley to the conical hill at Crich that contained not merely caverns of lead-bearing ore, but the limestone quarried by the Butterley partners, Outram and Jessop, and later by George Stephenson: stone which was carried to the kilns at Bull Bridge and Ambergate on the steep-sloping, narrow-gauge railway lines.

The lead mines have now ceased to work and only the headgears, the spoil heaps and ruined engine houses remain as indications of long-exhausted wealth on the ravaged hillside; the complex of iron mills and furnaces is now submerged beneath a modern wire works; but the Meerbrook Sough, with the keystone of its tail arch still bearing Hurt's initials and the year of its construction, 1772, still pours out some seventeen million gallons of water every day, a proportion of which goes to swell the resources of Severn-Trent Water Board; and Alderwasley Hall, now adapted as a school, can still be seen, gleaming white among the trees, from the road that climbs up to Crich from Whatstandwell bridge.

Wire for the miners' ore-sieves came from Hathersage and Makeney. At Hathersage there seems to have been a wire-making works as early as the reign of Elizabeth I, for in 1566 Christopher Schutz, a German immigrant, developed a process for drawing iron wire and established there his own concern for that purpose. His interests apparently stimulated others, and the village became a centre for the drawing of wire and the manufacture of needles. At Makeney, Sir John Zouch of Codnor set up a similar establishment in 1581, presumably on what is now the old forge site by the Milford bridge. He was later closed down by William Humphray, the Assay Master of the Royal Mint, who had acquired the rights to Schutz's process and aimed to restrict its use to the Company of Mineral and Battery Works at Tintern, which had been operating under royal charter since 1568; but in spite of this the forge, presumably in other hands, continued to flourish, and in 1777, four years before its sale to Jedediah Strutt as a site for his cotton mill at Milford, it was large enough to occupy both banks of the Derwent, 'consisting of two Iron Forges . . . Also a Slitting and Rowling Mill, for

Iron and Copper . . . worked by Wears made at vast Labour and Expence, and executed with great Judgment.'

The site of the Old Forge at Makeney is now a garden centre, and those of the various wire works at Hathersage, though still recognizable, are often difficult to trace; but Dale Mill on Dale Road at the head of the village, though serving many different purposes in the course of its life and now occupied by a firm of joiners and house decorators, is reputed to have been originally a wire-drawing works. A gritstone building, three storeys high and seven bays wide, with a square stone chimney, it stands by one of the Derwent's tributary streams which supplied its water power. At one time it was used for making pearl buttons, and a resident of the village, living close by, maintains that these can still be found on the road to the mill.

Another group of workers who required supplies of iron were the nailers of Belper. Before the Strutts built their cotton mills below Belper Bridge, nail-making was for centuries the predominant local industry. It was first recorded in the town in 1313, though it may have existed even earlier than that, for the nails used in building St John's Chapel, founded in 1260 as a forester's chapel for Duffield Frith, are thought to have been made in the immediate vicinity. By 1700 the industry was firmly established, and the Belper nailers were conducting a considerable export trade to the American colonies, where their products were consumed in the building of houses and the fixing of horseshoes. The making of nails was domestic in the sense that the nailer would often employ the whole of his family, working in a small stone 'shop' or smithy attached or perhaps adjacent to his cottage. Here the rod-iron supplied by a middleman or 'factor' was heated in a hearth and then beaten into nails on a blacksmith's anvil; the women and children, so the legend goes, toiling beside the men, all stripped to the waist because of the heat. The factor organized the distribution of rod-iron and collected the finished nails, contracting with the nailer to receive a certain stipulated weight; though at harvest time, when the family could earn more in the fields than in their shops, he may well have had to wait some time for delivery. It is known, for instance, that in the mid-eighteenth century a Quaker merchant, explaining to one of his American customers the delay in dispatching a consignment of nails, wrote apologetically, 'Our nailors are so much out in harvest time'.

But, if the industry was basically domestic, it was dependent on its middle-men, and they, in their turn, had to buy rods of iron from the slitting mills. The forge at Alderwasley, in the days before Hurt, developed a not inconsiderable trade with the Belper nailers; and a further source of rod-iron supply was probably the slitting mill built by Edmund Evans in 1734 on The Holms, an island in the middle of the Derwent at Derby. The Holms, as an island, no longer exists, and the mill has disappeared, like most of the early water-powered sites in the city, under constant demolition and civic redevelopment; but, in Belper, one of the nailers' shops, built in stone and

Nailer's shop, Joseph Street, Belper.

roofed in slate, with a short, squat chimney, can be found near the top of Joseph Street, one of the streets of houses built by the Strutts for their cotton mill workers. Its diminutive size lends credence to the legend of the topless women nailers, when one appreciates the intensity of heat and sweat that must have been generated in such a miniature smithy.

If the farmers and miners had need of iron, they also needed stone: stone of the Chatsworth or Rivelin Grits that outcrop in a continuous series of escarpments or sharp, rocky edges stretching down the eastern side of the valley from Stanage in the north through Froggatt and Curbar to Gardom's Edge, which lies above Baslow. The miners needed gritstone for the great crushing-wheels that ground the lead ore; the farmers for millstones to turn their hard-produced corn into flour.

The production of wheels or rollers for the lead-crushing circles did not begin, in truth, till Arkwright had already established himself at Cromford. In Daniel Defoe's time, fifty years before, the ore was crushed by hand with a hammer or 'bucker' on a large, flat slab which was called a knockstone. Even as late as 1776 a German visitor to Derbyshire expressed surprise that this means of crushing was still in general use at the mines; it was, he said, primitive compared with the methods employed in Germany. Shortly after this, however, the horse-powered crushing circle made its appearance. A horse walking round a circular track operated a beam, one end of which was pivoted on a centre post and the other attached to a stone wheel or crusher. This ran around a circular floor of flat stones, crushing the ore that was shovelled in its path. Such a circle can be seen, amid a waste of hummocked ground, by the Odin Mine at Castleton. The wheel, made of gritstone, twelve inches thick and nearly six feet in diameter, lies at an angle, resting within its detached iron tyre. Erected in the early 1820s, this crusher ran, not on the usual circle of stones, but on a cast-iron ring that was bedded on gravel. This also can be seen, though the last man to scatter lead ore across its surface probably gave the final twist to his shovel something over a century ago.

Crushing circle, Odin Mine, Castleton.

But if the gritstone was not used for crushing-wheels until Arkwright's time, it had been trimmed into millstones since before the arrival of the Norman kings. Quarried from the face of the Derwent Edges, it had been cut into rough hexagonal blocks and then, resting on a pedestal of similar stone, had been rounded, flattened, grooved, and centre-holed by skilled craftsmen using hammers and chisels. From the slopes below the Edges, where discarded millstones now lie in their hundreds, the stones were transported to the village corn mills where, driven by the power of the local streams, they ground into flour the oats and the barley, the wheat and the rye that sprang from the curling furrows of the valley. Six to seven feet across and twelve inches deep, far too heavy to be moved on the back of a packhorse, they were coupled into pairs by a wooden axle and rolled along the twisting lanes like wheels. How their drivers braked them when descending the hills is difficult to imagine, but it must have been a procedure fraught with some danger. Defoe himself, on his visit to Chatsworth, viewed the high Edge, that 'so overlooks the house', with some trepidation. 'Should they,' he wrote, 'roll down a pair of those stones coupled with a wooden axis, as is the way of drawing them, they would infallibly give a shock to the building.' Their combined weight, too, could damage a bridge. As early as 1500 they must have been shaking the old humpbacked bridge north of Baslow church, for in that year a regulation was made that 'no one shall henceforth lead or carry any millstone over the bridge of Basselowe under pain of 6s 8d to the lord for every pair of millstones so carried.'

Some were used in windmills; John Farey, writing in 1808, recorded forty-five windmills at work in Derbyshire, a number of them, as he said, 'of considerable dimensions ... by which a good deal of the Flour of the District is ground'; but the main source of power was always the river. The Derwent and its numerous tributary streams provided abundant supplies of swift-running water, and there were stretches on all of them where the water ran even more swiftly than normal. At these 'knickpoints', as they were called, the river flow quickened because the bed contained a cross-band of harder rock which resisted the down-cutting thrust of the current. Here, ideally, weirs were constructed, mill pools fashioned, and leats excavated for leading off the water to turn both undershot and overshot wheels; and since the lord of the manor could insist that all corn grown within his boundaries must be ground at his mill and could claim as his right a proportion of the flour, almost every village possessed its own mill. Of the seventy-two water mills mentioned in the Domesday Book entries for Derbyshire, probably two-thirds were employed for grinding corn, and it has been calculated that by the time the villagers of Cromford first saw the swarthy figure of Arkwright there were, in the county, over a hundred and fifty water-powered corn mills.

The windmills have gone. Of the forty-five listed by Farey, only one remains in sufficiently good condition to make a visit worth while. This is the Cat and Fiddle Mill at Dale Abbey, near Derby. Five miles from the city on the Ilkeston road, the Cat and Fiddle, though constructed as late as 1788, is an excellent example of that earliest type of windmill known as a post mill. Built of horizontal weatherboarding, with a pitched roof and four sails, it was operated in the primitive but effective manner of all such mills. Access was by means of a wide wooden ladder hinged to the buck or body of the mill, and through this projected a heavy beam or tail pole. The miller first raised the ladder, usually by means of a lever and chain, and then, setting all his strength to the tail pole, pushed or winched the mill round on its pivot till it came into the wind.

Cat and Fiddle post mill, Dale Abbey.

One later mill survives, even closer to the Derwent. Set on rising ground, a mile to the east of the river at Heage, is a handsome tower mill recently restored by the Derbyshire County Council. Built in gritstone with a silver ogee, or semi-onion-shaped, cap, it has six sails, an unusual number, automatically brought round into the wind by the characteristic fantail, patented by Edmund Lee in 1745. This is a small vaned wheel on the back of the cap, set at right angles to the sails and connected by gearing to a winding mechanism. As the wind direction changes, it begins to spin silently, turning the cap and the sails to face the new quarter.

The water mills existed in far greater numbers, and if it is hardly reasonable to expect to find those that were listed in Domesday nine hundred years ago, yet the visitor can at least see the same mills that stood by the rivers when Celia Fiennes, Defoe, and the Honourable John Byng conducted their published excursions through the valley. Some are ruined, some disused but structurally sound. Others, though the millstones are silent, are still very much in use for the storage of fertilisers, animal foodstuffs or gamekeepers' equipment; and if the buildings, of necessity, have been reconstructed and some have suffered extensions which are visually and architecturally un-

Corn mill, Alport-by-Youlgreave.

flattering, yet they stand where they did two hundred, even five hundred years ago. A number of them, no doubt, cling to the very points where water-powered corn mills stood at the time of the Domesday Survey, the pools, weirs, and leats surviving through the centuries to serve the needs of a whole succession of similar buildings.

The one by the old bridge at Alport-by-Youlgreave has a near-idyllic setting. Here, at the meeting of the Lathkill and Bradford, set among the trees below the clear mill pool, is the weir that John Byng, passing this way in June 1790, noted as being 'a pretty cascade'. Beside the weir is the mill, its walls of limestone with gritstone quoins like many in Derbyshire. A corn mill was recorded here at Alport in 1159, and it may well have been the same one mentioned in the Domesday Book, seventy years earlier, as standing at Youlgreave. Certainly the mill stands at a break in the valley floor which coincides with a knickpoint, a natural site for taking power from the river. The breast wheel, which is all of twenty-one feet in diameter, can still be seen in position at the end of the building furthest from the weir.

The most satisfying, to those with an eye for architecture, is possibly the old mill in Chatsworth Park, just below the public car park and cattle grid at the southern approach from Beeley village. This is an eighteenth-century mill with a difference. Built at the time when 'Capability' Brown was land-scaping the gardens, it was obviously designed by the hand of an architect, not simply to grind corn, but to blend with its surroundings. This is easy to see, though a gale, in 1962, brought down a tree which caused extensive damage, so that only the shell of the building now remains. The undershot wheel, though broken, survives, and a five-foot millstone leans against one of the outer walls. The doors and windows are barred, but, peering through the grille, one can faintly discern, scratched on the walls, a range of dates and names from the eighteenth century. Their significance is doubtful, but it has been suggested that they may be connected with repairs to the mill, or even, perhaps, with changes of tenancy.

Another mill with distinct architectural features is Ivonbrook Grange Mill, at the head of the Via Gellia, behind the Hollybush Inn at the Grangemill crossroads. Dating from the middle of the eighteenth century, this was clearly in its day a most handsome structure. Solidly built in limestone, with

Chatsworth Park Corn Mill.   *Ruined machinery, Ible Mi*

quoins of gritstone and arched gritstone frames for the windows and doors, it now stands empty and there seems to be no record of its use as a mill within living memory.

Half a mile from here, descending the Via Gellia towards Cromford, are the remains of perhaps the oldest mill of all. Ible Mill is now nothing more than a crumbling ruin, but a ruin well worth investigation. Ploughing through the undergrowth, across the tumbled stones, one can climb inside what is left of the building. The waterwheel has gone, but the wrecked machinery can still be seen, overgrown with thorns and clutched by the grasping tendrils of trees. The wooden upright shaft inclines at an angle, and, looking through the tangle of brushwood that hides them, one can make out the pit-wheel and wallower, two sets of millstones and the wooden shaft that once took the drive from the waterwheel. Closer examination will reveal another very interesting feature: some of the wooden teeth on the gearing wheels have been replaced by iron, the new iron segments being nailed to the wooden wheels when the machinery was, at one time or other, reconditioned.

It is difficult to estimate the age of Ible Mill, but its layout and mechanism both reflect standard medieval practice. Fortunately, perhaps, once its working days as a corn mill were over, it was never adapted to a different use. Many mills have been, with disastrous results. The Sough Mill at Over Haddon, by Lathkill Lodge, is now used as a store; but though the setting, deep in the Lathkill Gorge, is a delightful one and the stream, in wet seasons, still foams across the weir, the sixteenth-century mill has been disfigured by additions of corrugated iron, which not only hide the structure of the building, but seem completely out of place in such idyllic surroundings.

It seems hardly surprising that the boundaries of the Peak District National Park, as one approaches them by road, should be marked by signs in the shape of millstones. Stone and water combined together by the Derwent, not merely for grinding corn, but for crushing mineral ores to make colouring matter, pulping rags for paper, and grinding and polishing the famous black marble. The waters of Bonsall Brook were used for paint manufacture; there were small paper mills on the Lathkill at Alport, the Ecclesbourne at Duffield and the Derwent at Darley Abbey; while the flow of the Wye was interrupted at Ashford to provide the power for the marble mill.

It was in 1748 that Henry Watson of Bakewell built a water-powered mill by the Kirk Dale road at Ashford-in-the-Water to saw, grind and polish the Ashford black marble. This was a form of bituminous limestone quarried from the adjacent Arrock Hill. A dark grey colour on extraction, repeated polishing turned it jet black, and in this form it had already been used for interior decoration at both Hardwick Hall and Chatsworth House. Henry Watson sold it to a much wider market. Mantelpieces, table tops, statues, vases and trinkets of multifarious shapes were cut and polished by the water-powered machinery in the marble mill at Ashford; and by the

Sough Mill, Over Haddon.

middle of the nineteenth century, when its appeal to Victorian tastes had lifted demand to a point that Henry Watson could hardly have foreseen, a considerable cottage industry had developed in the village, as black marble trinkets of various kinds were inlaid with coloured stones to produce geometrical and floral designs. When Henry Watson died in 1786, his nephew, White Watson, took over the mill and, developing his interest in the geological structure of Derbyshire, proceeded to use the Ashford black marble for a much more erudite purpose. With it he created beautiful inlays to illustrate the geological strata of the county, while at the same time developing and expanding the trade that his uncle had founded. His geological work earned him a high reputation: one which today stands perhaps even higher; but John Byng was hardly impressed by his trinkets. Inspecting some at Bakewell in 1789, he remarked that such ornaments were 'to be seen to more perfection in many shops in London', and added somewhat tersely, 'If Mr W hoped for a buyer in me, he was mistaken.' But many people did buy. The business flourished for another hundred years till, late in the nineteenth century, changes in taste brought a fall in demand. The mill was finally closed in 1905. Part of the site was later taken to divert the A6 road, and what remains is now used by the Severn-Trent Water Authority for the storage of pipes.

Apart from the soil, the four great natural resources of the valley were stone, mineral ores, water and wool, and all were, in some sense, interdependent. The farmers who ploughed the soil to produce their crops needed iron for their implements. The millers who processed those crops to make flour needed both the stone and the water for grinding. The miners who brought up the lead in their kibbles required iron for their tools, and the surface workers who processed the products of their underground labour needed stone for crushing and water for washing. Those who farmed the sheep that gave the valley its wool needed stone for their walls, their washes and pinfolds; while the cottagers who then turned the wool into cloth needed iron and water to speed two of their numerous stages of production.

Though much of the wool produced, even after the landed families assumed command of the great monastic granges, was sold outside the valley in its still raw condition, the spinning of thread and the weaving of cloth for family use was a common activity within the walls of innumerable limestone cottages. Prior to spinning, and after the wool had been washed, it had to be carded to straighten the fibres so that they lay in roughly parallel lines. This was achieved by drawing the wool between two wooden hand-boards or 'cards', as they were called, faced with leather and studded with wire. The production of such wire, like that provided for the ore-washing sieves, required iron from the slitting mills and, after that, the ingenious machinery of a wire-drawing works. Christopher Schutz's Hathersage factory and the one set up by Sir John Zouch at Makeney both served the growing market for wool-carding wire.

Once the cloth had been woven on a simple hand-loom within the cottage, it had to be fulled. The constant touch of fingers had left a residue of dirt and grease on the wool, and the cloth was of an open weave, slackly woven. Fulling, the combined process of cleaning, shrinking and thickening, was carried out by pounding the cloth in tubs of water laced with fuller's earth, a type of clay that, on immersion, fell to powder and acted as a detergent. This had been, from ancient times, a tedious task, as men had had to trample the cloth in the tubs; but in the thirteenth century fulling stocks were invented: heavy wooden hammers made to rise and fall by the power of a waterwheel and installed in what came to be known as fulling mills. There were many such mills around the Derwent Valley and, though none have survived, they must have been at work in that generation-space that saw Celia Fiennes and Daniel Defoe jogging on their horses up and down the hills. One was recorded at Hartington; another at Alport, upstream of the bridge; and three, at least, on the By-Flatt in Derby, close to The Holms where Edmund Evans established his iron-slitting mill.

Cotton, imported from the Levant and hand-spun in Lancashire, was also woven in sheds and cottages by the Derwent, and more particularly by its tributaries, the Lathkill, the Peakshole Water and the Noe. In the early eighteenth century there were cotton-weaving sheds by the river at Alport and on the Edale road at Hope, and the making of cotton cloth was wide-spread in cottage homes at Stoney Middleton and Bradwell. The sheds at Hope have now been converted into dwellings, but the visitor can identify them by the blocked-up doorways still visible in the stonework. At Bradwell there must have been a considerable number of domestic looms, for the Fox family operated a shuttle manufactory in a workshop at the bottom of Water Lane.

Though close to the water and, in places like Alport, on the river bank itself, the weaving was still pursued on the hand-loom. It was a cottage occupation or the work of some small-scale family establishment; and, fifty years before Arkwright, this was the general pattern of industries in the valley, whatever they produced and wherever chance or natural resources had located them.

There were, indeed, many of them, sprinkled about the slopes and the flat water meadows against a backcloth of crop fields and grazing sheep; but the mining of lead and the quarrying of gritstone were still individual or group occupations, apart from some minor injections of capital by London merchants at infrequent intervals; the making of nails and the spinning and weaving of wool were almost purely domestic; corn milling was manorial, an integral part of whatever remained of a feudal economy; the paint and paper works were isolated phenomena; and the ironworks were small in their ramifications and under-capitalized in comparison with those of later years: Francis Hurt was not yet born, and Edmund Evans on The Holms was merely signalling the birth of a dynasty which expanded its interests in the next hundred years to embrace copper, lead and tin, paper, corn and bricks, and a banking concern in the city of Derby.

The time was not far distant when the great lead companies would spend thousands of pounds in the driving of soughs and the provision of steam engines to work mining levels at a depth then undreamed of; when the quarrying of millstone grit would give way to limestone, and assume such proportions that it gashed and scarred whole stretches of the valley; when the working of iron would be dominated by the massive Butterley Company; and when the spinning of wool would yield place to cotton, and be housed not in sheds and the small limestone cottages, but in great textile mills like the one that still frowns upon the village of Calver.

Change was in the air. As Defoe journeyed north through the valley into Yorkshire, the London Lead prospectors were tapping the rich unexploited veins of lead on the windy heights around Winster and Wensley Dale; and, perhaps even more significant, this indefatigable traveller had already seen, by the Derwent at Derby, what he later described as 'a Curiosity of a very extraordinary Nature' and the only one of its kind in England.

'I mean,' he wrote, 'those Mills on the Derwent, which work the three capital Italian Engines for making Organzine or Thrown Silk.'

3 The First Curiosity

Here is a Curiosity of a very extraordinary Nature, and the only one of the kind in England: I mean those Mills on the Derwent, which work the three capital Italian Engines for making Organzine or Thrown Silk, which, before these Mills were erected, was purchased by the English Merchants with ready Money in Italy; by which Invention one Hand will twist as much Silk, as before could be done by Fifty, and that in a much truer and better Manner. This Engine contains 26,586 Wheels, and 96,746 Movements, which work 73,726 yards of Silk-thread, every time the Water-wheel goes round, which is three times in one Minute, and 318,504,960 Yards in one Day and Night. One Water-wheel gives Motion to all the rest of the Wheels and Movements, of which any one may be stopt separately.

Daniel Defoe: *A Tour thro' the Whole Island of Great Britain,* 3rd Edition (1742).

In 1681 the Catholic King of France, Louis XIV, urged on by his court favourite, Madame de Maintenon, began a systematic persecution of the Protestant Huguenots. They were excluded from every kind of public employment; condemned under the law, by reason of their religion, as people unfitted to hold positions of trust.

During the next four years the persecution was intensified. Edicts were issued closing Huguenot churches and Huguenot schools; it was made a penal offence for a Huguenot pastor even to preach; and when, sooner than submit, members of the community began to leave France, Louis forbade them to emigrate under legal pain of being sent to the galleys.

The Huguenots were a gifted, industrious people. In trade and industry, in technical skills, they outdistanced most of the Catholics of France. Thrifty and talented, they had already done much to make their country the wealthiest among the European states; but no skill they might possess atoned, in Louis' eyes, for the deadly fact of their heretical beliefs. He was determined to crush them into submission, even if this entailed forcible conversion and the billeting of soldiers in Huguenot homes; but there were many to whom religion meant a great deal more than either property or life, and one by one, family by family and group by group they fled from the country. Large numbers were caught and sent to the galleys, but numbers more escaped, crossing the frontiers to Holland and Brandenburg, crossing the Channel to find refuge in England.

Some of them were silk-weavers, following an occupation which, in those days, demanded a high measure of technical skill. They settled in Spitalfields, a village on the outskirts of the City of London and already a centre of some importance for the production of woollen fabrics. Here they developed an industrial community, living in pleasant, some in stately, houses, filling their neatly-kept gardens with flowers, planting mulberry trees in the rustic lanes. It was they, indeed, who founded the first gardening societies in England; but they also turned Spitalfields, by 1700, into the principal English centre of silk manufacture.

They did, however, experience some difficulties. The weaving of silken cloth required supplies of silk thread, and since, in this country, silk could not be produced in sufficient quantities, it had to be imported and spun into thread on hand-operated machines. This was a slow process; the amount so produced was insufficient to meet the weavers' demands; and to fulfil their ever-increasing requirements silk thread, known as reeled or thrown silk, had, in addition, to be imported from abroad. Some of this came from as far away as India, some from the Levant, and some indeed from France; but by far the greatest quantity was imported from Italy where, for over a hundred years, silk had been 'thrown' or spun into thread on water-powered machines: a mechanical secret jealously guarded by Italian manufacturers, who, by virtue of their monopoly, dominated the market.

In the early years of the eighteenth century, those years when Defoe was travelling the length and breadth of Great Britain, silk weaving in England achieved a position of considerable prosperity; and with the growth of Spitalfields and the continued immigration of Huguenot weavers, it became a matter almost of national importance to mechanize and power the throwing of silk.

It was out of this need to ensure adequate supplies of spun silk for the weavers, and to do so without resorting to expensive imports, that Daniel Defoe's 'Curiosity' by the Derwent came to be born.

The man who sparked off the venture was Thomas Cotchett. Little appears to be known about him, apart from the established facts that he was born at Mickleover, near Derby, in 1640, trained at Gray's Inn, and then, for some reason, set himself up as a silk reeler in London. From his very position he must have known of the problems of the Spitalfields weavers and, a man of initiative, he probably saw the chance of making a fortune if only he could power-manufacture spun silk. In 1704 he built a silk mill on the Derwent in the middle of Derby. The mill stood at the northern end of a small island in the river, known as the By-Flatt, close to the sites of the old fulling mills. It was a three-storey building, 62 feet long and 35 feet high, housing in total 8 spinning machines and 1,340 spindles. The machines were Dutch, since the mechanical details of the much more efficient Italian ones were still unknown in this country, and they were driven through shafting and gearing by a waterwheel $13\frac{1}{2}$ feet in diameter. The installation of this power supply and its transmission to the machines were the work of George Sorocold, the earliest of a number of talented Lancastrians who, in the next hundred years, by their mechanical ingenuity or business acumen, were to transform the many faces of the textile industry.

Born in the 1660s in a Lancashire area noted for the manufacture of clocks and locks, Sorocold, a man of academic background, studied at Cambridge before marrying a Derbyshire girl and settling in Derby in 1684. Three years later he was engaged on the task of rehanging the bells at All Saints Church, now Derby Cathedral; and by 1692 had constructed the town's first public waterworks, driven by a waterwheel close to the By-Flatt and pumping water through four miles of pipes. The pipes were made from the bored-out trunks of elm trees, and Sorocold later took out a patent for a water-driven boring machine for this purpose.

The Derby works continued to pump their water for close on a hundred and fifty years and, once they were erected, Sorocold found himself in growing demand. By 1700 at least a dozen towns, as far apart as Exeter and Norwich, Newcastle and Portsmouth, had similar installations for which he was responsible; but the one that earned him the highest reputation was his reconstruction of the London Bridge waterworks, an undertaking he completed the following year, powering the pumps by a waterwheel of twenty-foot diameter, and constructing, for the first time, much of his transmission mechanism out of cast iron.

He was already, therefore, a man of both local and national reputations when Cotchett invited him to work on the silk mill, the site of which was adjacent to his waterworks; but despite his undoubted mechanical genius, perhaps because Cotchett lacked the business ability to sustain a project so ambitious in its nature, the venture came to nothing. Cotchett's mill was built and, predictably, failed; and this was the point in time when Thomas Lombe and his half-brother, John, appeared on the scene.

Lombe, born in 1685, was the son of a worsted weaver of Norwich. By 1715, at the age of thirty, he had accumulated a fortune by merchanting silk in his native city and also in London. A man of ambition like Thomas Cotchett, he was equipped with a capable, inventive mind and, unlike Cotchett, an aptitude for business. This pioneer silk mill on a Derbyshire island had, during its short and unsuccessful life, attracted his attention. A specialist in silk, wide awake to the need for a powered silk-throwing industry in England, he took note of the experiment and, according to Samuel Smiles (though he adduces no evidence to support the statement), revealed his interest in more significant form by despatching his younger half-brother, John, to work as an apprentice at Cotchett's mill.

The events that followed the failure of Cotchett's business have been cloaked in legend. The often-repeated story, and repeated so often that it must have gathered elements of half-truth on the way, is that Thomas Lombe then sent his brother to Italy to disguise himself as a workman, obtain employment in a throwing-mill and make drawings of the secret Italian machines. At the end of two years, so the story goes, John returned to England with the necessary information, only to be pursued by the vengeful Italians and to meet his death at the hands of a beautiful temptress, who was sent across the Channel to beguile him with her charms and then kill him with poison.

Despite the fact that he was active in the dukedom of the Medici, the truth is probably far more prosaic. John Lombe's date of birth, quoted sometimes as 1693, is not precisely known; but he certainly died in 1722. He was younger than his brother, so at the time of his death he could not, at most, have been more than thirty-six; but there is no sound evidence to support a tale of poison, and in the early eighteenth century, at a time when the expectation of life was distinctly shorter than it is in our day, to die from some vague internal disorder at thirty-six or even at thirty was by no means unusual. As late as 1842 the average ages of death were recorded as being for mechanics, labourers and their dependants, no more than 17; for trades-men and their families 20; and for members of the professions and the gentry only 38.

There seems no doubt, on the other hand, that he made his reported expedition to Italy. He appears to have been sent to Leghorn in 1715, but precisely what his assignment was can now be only a matter of conjecture. It may be that the legend here approaches the truth, and he was indeed engaged on a subtle piece of industrial espionage; though it has been pointed out more than once that such a journey was, in its essence, unnecessary, since Vittorio Zonca had already published a book in Padua in 1607 which contained a description and drawings of the Italian machinery, and this was certainly available on the open shelves of the Bodleian Library as early as 1620. Such being the case, it might have been expected that Thomas Lombe, with his own acute interest in the silk-throwing process, would have heard of the work and indeed have seen it; and that Sorocold himself, at Emmanuel College, Cambridge, would likewise have known of and had access to it; but, since the book was in the nature of a general treatise on buildings and machinery, rather than a specialized thesis on silk manufacture, it seems more than likely that commercial circles in England in the eighteenth century may not even have known of its existence. In any case, reading a description of an unfamiliar machine and studying drawings are no real substitute for observing the actual mechanism in action. Many early drawings were so incompetent that anyone trying to copy them would soon have been in difficulties, and it remains a possibility that Thomas sent his brother to verify points that were not exactly clear, to note improvements made in the hundred years since Zonca's book had been published, or even perhaps to devise refinements which would give English manufacturers, once the Italian machines were installed, an advantage over any European rivals.

Whatever the case, John Lombe's excursion seems to have produced the results that were needed, for in 1718 Thomas obtained a patent, No. 422, for 'three sorts of engines never before made or used in Great Britain, one to wind the finest raw silk, another to spin and another to twist the finest Italian raw silk into organzine in great perfection, which has never before

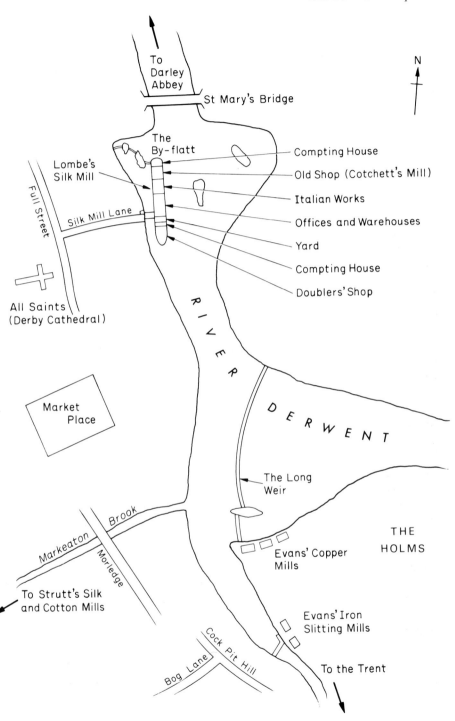

Derby.

been done in this country'; and, armed with this safeguard which guaranteed him sole use of the machines for a period not to exceed fourteen years, he took over Cotchett's mill, drew up plans to expand it, and engaged George Sorocold on the work of construction.

The task that faced Sorocold was a formidable one, and very different from the construction of waterworks, pumps and river navigations which had, up to that time, almost exclusively engaged his attention. Even his experience on Cotchett's mill could have proved of only very limited value, since the scale of Lombe's undertaking dwarfed all that had previously been achieved on the By-Flatt.

According to Rhys Jenkins, in his article on Sorocold which appeared in the *Engineer* as long ago as 1918, 'it involved the making and fitting of, what was for that time, an enormous number of small parts—toothed wheels, spindles and bearings . . . [and] to ensure that all the spindles, bearings and wheels in a machine were even moderately exact in shape and size, with the skill and appliances then available, must have been a great task.' It was calculated that the machines themselves required more than 10,000 spindles and 25,000 spinning reel bobbins, in addition to 4,793 star wheels, 9,050 twist bobbins and 45,363 winding bobbins; and these machines had to be installed in a single building and driven from a single water-powered source.

The machines were of three kinds, for winding, doubling and twisting the silk, though the doubling machines, as in Cotchett's mill, were operated by hand and required separate accommodation. The silk would arrive at the factory in processed skeins, and would be wound on to bobbins by a winding machine. It would then be doubled by hand. This entailed winding the strands from several bobbins on to a single and probably larger one. After that it would be twisted or thrown into yarn in an entirely different part of the building, the weft yarn or tram being slightly twisted, but a stronger twist applied to the warp or organzine.

It was planned to retain Cotchett's three-storey mill with its Dutch machines. This, to distinguish it from the rest of the structure, was to be known, appropriately, as The Old Shop; but running south from its walls along the narrow stretch of the By-Flatt island there was to be a new and much more extensive complex of buildings. Cotchett's mill was to be used, in part, for doubling, and it was modified by the insertion of two rows of continuous windows on the eastern side overlooking the river. Behind these the doublers were to work at their machines and, so that they could be kept under constant observation, a compting house tower was to be added at the northern end, projecting slightly from the frontage. The Italian Works or throwing mill, in which the new Italian-style machines were to be installed, was to extend from the south wall of Cotchett's mill for a further 110 feet along the river. It was to be a five-storey building, $55\frac{1}{2}$ feet high, set on 26 river arches, and lit by 140 windows; while beyond it was to be a further complex of buildings containing warehouses, sorting rooms, a carpenter's shop and offices, with a staircase tower surmounted by a belfry. Here a bridge from the mainland was to open on to a courtyard, and this yard was to separate the main mill building from the Doublers' Shop. This was to be three storeys high, 139 feet long, with continuous windows behind which the doubling machines were to be set; and since, apparently, doublers were not to be trusted to work at a reasonable speed unless they were under unbroken supervision, a second compting house or observation tower was to be added at the northern end of the shop. The whole complex was to extend for 120 yards along the island; its total floor area would be something in the region of 40,000 square feet; and the undershot waterwheel, 23 feet in diameter, was to be housed on the landward side of the Italian Works.

In conception it was massive, at least for the early eighteenth century, and it was Sorocold's task to construct it and ensure its mechanical efficiency: to link the intricate machinery to the water installations. There seems no doubt that John Lombe, who had actually seen the Italian machines at work and 'whose head was extremely well turned for the mechanics', afforded him some assistance; it was reported that while the mill was being built he set up his machines in Derby Town Hall and 'other rooms' in the neighbourhood, and carried out preliminary experiments with them; but the eventual success of the Lombe brothers' works was a triumph for Sorocold, and entitles him perhaps to be called Britain's first mechanical engineer.

It was undoubtedly his master work and, as Daniel Defoe records, it very nearly killed him:

> For going to show some gentlemen the curiosity, as he called it, of his mill, and crossing the planks which lay just above the mill-wheel; regarding, it seems, what he was to show his friends more than the place where he was, and too eager in describing things, keeping his eye rather upon what he pointed at with his fingers than what he stepped upon with his feet, he stepped awry and slipped into the river. He was so very close to the sluice which let the water out upon the wheel, and which was then pulled up, that though help was just at hand, there was no taking hold of him, till by the force of the water he was carried through, and pushed just under the large wheel, which was then going round at a great rate. The body being thus forced in between two of the plashers of the wheel, stopped the motion for a little while, till the water pushing hard to force its way, the plasher beyond him gave way and broke; upon which the wheel went again, and, like Jonah's whale, spewed him out, not upon dry land, but into that part they call the apron, and so to the mill-tail, where he was taken up, and received no hurt at all.

The mill was completed by 1722, the year of John Lombe's death and, apart from a brief period at the end of the century when machines for sawing and polishing marble were installed, it continued to be used for silk manufacture till 1890. Thomas Lombe was knighted in 1727, and when he died twelve years later, his widow sold the building to William Wilson and

The Silk Mill as it exists today.

Samuel Lloyd, who continued to use it for its original purpose. After that it passed through many different hands: travelling through Derby in the mid-nineteenth century, William Adam remarked that it was then 'in the occupation of Mr Taylor'; but it continued to stand in more or less its original form for close on two hundred years till wear and tear, fire and reconstruction, produced a substantial change in its appearance.

In 1890 part of the structure collapsed because the piles had rotted through, and twenty years later a fire destroyed the Italian Works and caused extensive damage to those parts that adjoined them. Not long after that the Doublers'

Old Silk Mill gates. Made by Robert Bakewell about 1722, and now re-erected on their original site.

Shop was demolished and the main building reconstructed in a different form as the Riverside Works, to be used by a firm of manufacturing chemists who produced among other things those long, sticky flypapers that hung in many shops, and indeed in many homes, till they were finally superseded by the aerosol spray.

Though the By-Flatt, like The Holms, is no longer an island, and the bridge has disappeared to accommodate a power station and what will eventually, it is hoped, be riverside gardens, this reconstructed mill still stands on the river bank behind the cathedral, is still known as The Silk Mill, and houses the new Museum of Industry and Technology. The structure is very different from Thomas Lombe's original; but standing by the bell tower, recognizable though altered, the visitor who possesses an imaginative eye can pursue, with some success, his own work of reconstruction. The present mill, roughly the height of the Italian Works but divided into three storeys as against five, stretches more or less the length of the old main building: the warehouses, the Works and Cotchett's Old Shop. The stone foundation arches, no longer washed by the waters of the Derwent, are probably some of those constructed by Sorocold; and the fine wrought iron gates that once guarded the bridge to the silk mill island—the work of a local craftsman, Robert Bakewell, at his shop in Oakes Yard—have recently been removed from the centre of the city to their original site.

Thomas Lombe's venture, unlike Cotchett's, proved to be quite a remarkable success, and the mill rapidly acquired a fascination for visitors; but when, in 1732, at the end of the stipulated fourteen years, Lombe applied for his patent to be extended, the patent office turned down his request. The opposition of other manufacturers, who were determined to install the Italian machines, proved far too strong, and he was paid a lump sum of £14,000 in recognition of his achievements, on the understanding that he agreed to display models of his machines in some public place. He therefore arranged for the models to be constructed, and put them on show in the Tower of London. He died in 1739, a member of the Mercers' Company and an Alderman of the City, leaving a fortune of £120,000 and desiring, in his will, that his widow should set aside some £600 to be shared among the principal workers at his mill.

Once the patent had lapsed, other men built silk mills and used his machines. The migration of the hosiery trade from London to the Midlands had already begun, creating a local demand for silk thread which had not existed in Cotchett's time; and throughout the century silk remained the staple industry of Derby. By 1770 Jedediah Strutt had two silk mills in the town, one on Markeaton Brook, and the other on the Goal Brook close to its crossing beneath the Morledge. Contemporary writers on Derbyshire recorded the progress of silk in the town. Pilkington, in 1789, detailed twelve silk mills providing work between them for 1,200 people, though it is worthy of note that William Hutton, who for a time was apprenticed in Thomas Lombe's mill, added a rider two years later to the effect that they were 'all on a diminutive scale compared with the original Derby mill.' The figures merely serve to corroborate his statement, since Lombe found employment for three hundred workers.

The Napoleonic Wars seem to have brought a decline, probably due to the difficulty of importing raw silk. Farey, writing in 1817, noted only seven silk-spinning mills; but the trade was then revived by two new developments: silk tape and ribbon weaving. By 1828 Pigot's *Commercial Directory* was listing nine 'silk throwsters' in Derby, and as late as 1840 seventeen mills spinning or weaving silk were recorded in the town, mainly in the area round Markeaton Brook.

But Lombe's ideas spread beyond Derby. By 1768 there were six mills in Stockport and 3,000 workers were employed on silk in Macclesfield, a figure which by 1830 had swollen to 10,000 with seventy factories at work in the area. Such expansion was, indeed, not always welcome. Ormerod, writing in his *History of Cheshire* about 1815, complained of Macclesfield that 'the neighbourhood has been spoilt by manufactures and is no longer fitted to be the residence of a gentleman'; but the Macclesfield silk trade had, by that time, put out its own shoots into the Peak. Mills had sprung up on the edge of the Pennines at Rainow, Wincle and Wildboarclough, and the weaving of silk as a domestic industry, probably on behalf of Macclesfield agents, had penetrated back to the Derwent Valley, reaching places as far away as Tideswell and Eyam.

Yet all this expansion was relatively slow. It occupied more than a hundred years from the time that Lombe established his mill, and the growth of the industry in the whole of that period was confined to isolated geographical pockets: Macclesfield, Stockport and their immediately adjoining areas in south Lancashire and north-west Derbyshire; Sherborne and Gillingham in Dorset; Frome and Taunton in Somerset; Malmesbury in Wiltshire; and Braintree in Essex, where the Huguenot, George Courtauld, established a factory which was later to grow into the biggest man-made fibre industry in Britain.

At the beginning of the eighteenth century silk had been one of the most profitable of commodities and, with the success of Lombe's venture, seemed set to develop as a serious rival to the traditionally wealthy wool trade of the South; but in the sixty years after Arkwright arrived at Cromford, it was dwarfed by cotton. Not that the silk manufacturers failed to learn from Lombe's example; on the contrary, those who set up their mills in Macclesfield and Stockport copied almost slavishly the buildings, mechanisms and organization at Derby; but the silk industry never had the potential for expansion that the cotton manufacturers very soon enjoyed. Raw silk supplies were not easy to obtain and were, moreover, expensive. This meant that silk fabrics were always, in essence, luxury articles, and a luxury trade provided no sound basis for developing the powers of mechanized production; the home market had little in the way of elasticity, and the chances of developing an export trade were poor in competition with silks made on the continent and further afield in the Asian countries. The cotton trade, on the other hand, could draw from what appeared to be unlimited sources of raw material; and once the Louisiana Purchase opened up vast new tracts of land in the American South, and these areas developed the mass production of cotton on a plantation system powered by negro labour, that raw material (apart from years of war and financial crisis) grew steadily cheaper. Population was increasing and there was an expanding market in Britain for cheap cotton goods, and the new machines that were to speed production and reduce its costs enabled the cotton men to tap an export market that appeared almost as limitless as their supplies of raw material.

'Cotton stockings,' wrote David Macpherson in 1785, 'have become very general for summer wear and have gained ground very much upon silk stockings, which are too thin for our climate and too expensive for common wear for people of middling circumstances.' It was on the basis of this market of immense potential inside our own shores that the cotton industry took its first confident steps, and, sixty years after Arkwright established himself at Cromford, Edward Baines in his *History of the Cotton Manufacture in Great Britain* could record that 300 million pounds of raw cotton were being imported every year, that exports were worth over £18 million, that there were 237,000 operatives employed in spinning and weaving factories, and that the number of persons supported by the manufacture was a million and a half. He wrote:

> This manufacture furnishes nearly one-half of the exports of British produce and manufactures; it supports more than one-eleventh part of the population of Great Britain; and it supplies almost every nation of the world with some portion of its clothing . . . To complete the wonder . . . it has sprung from insignificance to its present magnitude within little more than half a century; and it is still advancing with a rapidity of increase that defies all calculation of what it shall be in future ages.

This was the half-century when the silk industry, though expanding in Macclesfield, was little more than holding its own in Derby, had collapsed in Sherborne, and was petering out in Stockport, with the silk mills one by one turning over to cotton. So, although George Sorocold and Thomas and John Lombe created between them the first successful power-driven factory in Britain, and built it for the purpose of spinning silk thread; and though their mill was copied by silk manufacturers before Arkwright was old enough to know the end of a spindle from the end of a shuttle; yet the silk industry which, because of their work, had stood for a generation in the very forefront of industrial progress, failed because of its own inherent weaknesses to capitalize on their achievement, and it was left to the entrepreneurs of cotton to reproduce and develop their ideas.

But on the cotton industry, and so in the end on that worldwide change from domestic production to a factory system, the influence of the Derby mill was profound. Here, on this narrow island in the Derwent, a large number of machines had been placed within the walls of a single building and driven from a single source of power. Within those walls, too, hundreds of employees, mainly women and children, had tended the machines, called to work at fixed hours by the sound of a bell, the span of their labour dictated precisely by revolving wheels and rotating spindles, every single turn of Sorocold's wheel, as Daniel Defoe calculated, producing 73,000 yards of silk thread.

Fifty years before Arkwright built his first box-like, water-powered factory at Cromford, the Lombes had produced its archetype; and Jedediah Strutt who followed them in Derby, establishing two silk mills within a mile of the By-Flatt, consciously copied, though on a smaller scale, their building design and organization. Strutt then went into partnership with Arkwright, and between them they produced a succession of cotton mills, first of all in Derbyshire, then in Staffordshire, Lancashire, Yorkshire and Scotland, faithfully carrying with them, wherever they built, the traditions established long before in Derby. As late as 1816 the sons of Jedediah Strutt, giving evidence before the Select Committee on Children Employed in Manufactories, acknowledged that the children at their Belper and Milford mills worked twelve hours a day, six hours before and six after dinner, including time allowed for breakfast and tea. 'This,' they went on to say, pleading their case by reference to the Lombes, 'has been the invariable practice at the original silk mill in Derby [and] in this neighbourhood for more than 100 years.'

The silk mills at Stockport, copies of that at Derby, became, one by one, factories for spinning cotton. The Park Mill was the first to change in 1783, Carrs' two years later and others by 1790, providing a pattern, throughout the next fifty years, for the thousand or so cotton mills erected in Lancashire; while, even before the demise of the silk trade in Stockport, Arkwright had extended his interests north of the Mersey by constructing his spinning mill at Birkacre, near Chorley.

The first Sir Robert Peel, whose father founded the great firm of calico printers and who, in 1787, erected a cotton-spinning mill at Burton-on-Trent, freely admitted his debt to Arkwright. 'We all looked up to him,' he said, 'and imitated his mode of building . . . Our buildings were copied from the models of his works.'

From the spinning of cotton, the Derby tradition, fostered by Strutt and transmitted by him to Arkwright, spread still further, penetrating into the worsted and other textile industries. Mills for worsted manufacture, modelled on those of Arkwright, began to spring up in the Midlands, Lancashire, the West Riding and Devon. John Marshall in Leeds and the Dakeynes at Darley Dale adopted the Arkwright techniques and organization when they set up their flax mills; and eventually, with the advent of mule spinning, the woollen industry of the West Riding also succumbed, the pattern extending itself, after 1850, to Titus Salt's great alpaca mills at Saltaire, near Bradford, and Lister's adjacent Manningham Mills, producing velvet and plush.

Sorocold and the Lombes had pioneered on their island a completely new method of industrial production, based on a revolutionary form of building, a single source of power and a mechanical discipline. By that stroke of invention, they determined the pattern of the textile factory, its physical structure and internal organization, for the next two hundred years.

Standing today by the Silk Mill in Derby and touching the rough weathered stone of the arches, while the sounds of the city beat in one's ears and the traffic flows at speed across the new concrete bridges that now span the river, it is difficult to escape the feeling that here, on this narrow strip of land by the Derwent, some vital part of our modern world was born.

The curiosity became the commonplace.

That, in itself, provides the measure of their achievement:

> Thomas Lombe, mercer;
> John Lombe, silk mechanic;
> George Sorocold, engineer.

Original foundation arches for Lombe's Silk Mill, Derby. Built by George Sorocold, c. 1718.

The Valley in the Process of Transformation.

4 The Man from the North

. . . a man who has done more honour to the country than any man I know, not excepting our great military characters.

Sir Robert Peel, speaking of Arkwright: *Minutes of Evidence taken before the Select Committee of the Children employed in the Manufactories of the United Kingdom, 1816.*

It is agreed by all who know him that he is a Tyrant and more absolute than a Bashaw . . . If he had been a man of sense and reason he would not have lost his patent.

Letter from Matthew Boulton to James Watt, concerning Arkwright, 7 August 1781.

A hundred and thirty years before Thomas Lombe established his silk mill, a young country parson, so the story goes, found himself in love.

> He paid addresses to a young woman in his neighbourhood, to whom, for some cause, his attentions were not agreeable; or, as it has been with more probability conjectured, she affected to treat him with negligence to ascertain her power over his affections; whenever he paid his visits she always took care to be busily employed in knitting, and would pay no attentions to his addresses; and pursued this conduct to so harsh an extent and for so long a period, that the lover became disgusted; and he vowed to devote his future leisure, instead of dancing attendance on a capricious woman . . . to devising an invention that should effectually supersede her favourite employment of knitting. He succeeded, and in vain did she (afterwards) try to reclaim his attentions.

The parson was William Lee of Calverton, near Nottingham; the invention was the stocking frame; and the story, embroidered no doubt after more than a century of varied repetition, was written down in this form in 1831 by Gravener Henson, himself a knitter, in his *Civil, Political and Mechanical History of the Framework Knitters.*

Like the legend that surrounds the death of John Lombe, this delightful tale of the birth of an ingenious industrial machine needs to be treated with considerable reserve; yet it may well contain at least a germ of the truth. Whether or not the Reverend Lee produced his invention as a result of persistently frustrated love, most versions of the story concede that what kindled his passion for invention was the sight of a woman laboriously knitting stockings by hand.

The result was a complex piece of mechanism, containing three and a half thousand different components, the basic principle of which was not to be bettered for two hundred years; a machine which commenced its life in 1589 in a Midland village fifteen miles from the Derwent, travelled to

France and then back to London, to return from there to the district of its birth after an exile of almost a century and a half.

It was the growing presence of the stocking frame in and around Derby in the early eighteenth century that provided Thomas Lombe with his chance of success: a chance that Cotchett, twenty years earlier, had never enjoyed. It was the predominance of this machine in the Nottingham area by 1768 that was instrumental in persuading Arkwright to travel the hundred miles southward from Preston and so seek his fortune in a town where hosiers were clamouring for thread; but the irony remains that William Lee, like so many men of genius whose inventions have multiplied the wealth of others, died a poor man, almost certainly frustrated, possibly embittered and, except by his relatives and a handful of workmen, utterly unsung.

He first taught his brothers to use the frame, and he and they worked together, making stockings in Calverton. Meanwhile he applied to Elizabeth I for a patent, but, having seen the machine, she refused to grant one, some say because she thought it would bring distress to the hand-knitters, others, more cynical, alleging that she saw no virtue in a machine devised merely to knit poor-quality woollen stockings rather than fashionable hose from spun silk.

After this initial disappointment Lee seems to have successfully adapted his frame to use silk as well as wool, but James I also denied him a patent, so in 1603, with his brothers and a number of trained local workmen, he took nine of his frames to France, where briefly, according to Edward Baines, he won the support of King Henry IV and set up at Rouen a small stocking manufactory. The King, however, soon died and his patronage with him; and Lee, reduced to poverty, breathed his last in Paris in 1610.

His brother James, apparently, then came back to England, bringing most of the frames with him and selling them in London before returning to Calverton. Small in numbers though they were, they proved to be the basis of a framework knitting industry that grew in the capital, slowly at first and then more rapidly as the century progressed. London was the nation's centre of fashion; the Spitalfields silk market lay close at hand; and the industry had so developed by 1663 that the master knitters were granted a charter and incorporated as the London Company of Framework Knitters. As a chartered company they laid down a number of protective regulations, specifying certain standards of work, empowering their representatives to destroy unsatisfactory products and fine the knitter concerned, limiting the number of apprentices a master might employ, and placing other restrictions on the operation of the trade.

For a time they were successful; the London trade flourished; by 1727 there were two and a half thousand frames at work in the capital; but the demand for cheaper stockings, that David Macpherson noted in 1785, was already making itself felt at the expense of the luxury silk trade of London, and this increasing demand produced an entirely new type of master, the hosier. Frames were adapted to knit cotton yarn; they became more complicated and therefore more expensive, too expensive for the independent craftsman to afford. To replace him as a master came the capitalist hosier, often with no previous experience of the trade, who owned not a handful of frames but hundreds, hired them out to stockingers and, supplying the raw material, paid them for delivering the finished stockings to his warehouse. These men with an eye to profits, fighting to survive in what was becoming a competitive market, had no regard for standards of quality or the limits placed on apprentice employment. They set their faces against the Chartered Company, developed a pool of illegal labour, and when, in 1728, in a historic test case, the Nottingham magistrates refused to recognize that the ordinances of the London Company were valid in their town, more and more of the hosiers began to shift their business centres to the Midlands. By 1812 the number of frames at work in London had sunk to a hundred, and there were reputed to be 25,000 in the provinces, the greater proportion in the counties of Nottinghamshire, Leicestershire and Derbyshire. Nottingham developed cotton hose as its speciality, Leicester clung to woollen, and Derby, with its numerous silk-throwing mills, concentrated on silk. By 1750 the London trade was dying, and the Framework Knitters' Company virtually extinct.

This eighteenth-century migration of the hosiery industry from London to the Midlands brought William Lee's stocking frame back once more to Calverton, and with it that distinctive combination of dwelling house and workshop, the framework knitter's or stockinger's cottage. The frame was intricate to operate, and the knitter, who used both his hands and his feet, needed the best of the light for his work. A family would at first rent a single frame, then perhaps a couple, but at the height of the domestic industry's prosperity there were families accommodating three or four frames. No doubt in many cases such frames were housed in existing rooms; but, where a better quality trade became well established, cottages were built with a continuous window running the length of the frontage, either under the eaves or on the ground floor; while some, instead, had a purpose-built workshop in the form of an annexe, or even a completely separate structure, usually double-storeyed with space for the frames on the upper level where the windows were set, and a flight of outside steps which the knitters had to climb.

Calverton and other towns and villages in Nottinghamshire—Woodborough, Stapleford and Sutton Bonington among them—still possess a number of framework knitters' cottages, standing in isolation or clustered in terraces; and they still survive up and down the Derwent Valley, relics of an age when cotton supplanted silk on the banks of the river, and when the families of lead miners and spinning-mill operatives knitted behind their windows on frames rented from the master hosiers of Matlock and Belper.

Framework knitter's workshop, The Dale, Bonsall.

The industry was widespread in the village of Bonsall, north-west of Cromford. In 1844, 143 frames were counted at work there; and some half-dozen shops can still be seen today. A visitor, climbing up the slope of the Dale, can find, on the left-hand side of the road, a small limestone workshop, quoined in gritstone, with a long frame window in the upper storey and the familiar flight of stone steps for access. A single stone above the lintel of the ground-floor door bears the date of its construction, 1737. A later example, with a chimney of brick, stands in an elevated position by Bonsall Cross. It was used as an outpost of the Matlock hosier, Crowder Johnson, and continued to operate till after the end of the First World War. On Holloway Road at Duffield there is a good example of the single-storey annexe built on to a cottage; but the finest stockinger's house in the Derwent Valley, possibly perhaps in the whole of Derbyshire, is in the main street at Crich, opposite the lane that runs down to Fritchley. Here a three-storey stone-built house in a terrace has had a row of eight windows, each with nine small panes, inserted below the eaves to give light to an elongated top-floor workroom.

These workshops in the Valley, with their attendant master hosiers, were merely, however, a logical extension, to the west and north, of the

Stockinger's house, Crich.

greater cotton hosiery industry of Nottingham; and as the numbers of frames multiplied, in and around the town, after the magistrates' decision of 1728, the Nottingham hosiers found themselves continually frustrated by the shortage of yarn or, to be more precise, yarn of a suitable quality for their frames. The first machine-made cotton stockings, produced in the town in

1730, used cotton thread spun in India, but such Indian yarn was no long-term answer to the demands of a growing textile industry; it was expensive to import, needed four or five doublings and, even then, was awkward to knit on a frame. Lancashire yarn was no more satisfactory; spun for the making of fustian, a cloth of linen warp and cotton weft, it was too irregular in texture; and when the Nottingham hosiers, in desperation, attempted to establish a local spinning industry to satisfy their needs, they once again ran into serious problems. Prior to the growth of hosiery manufacture, the town had been a centre for the making of worsted, a woollen cloth using the long fibres of wool, as distinct from ordinary woollens which used the short fibres. The spinners of Nottingham, trained for many years to spin with long fibres, found the short-fibred cotton too difficult to handle, and the hosiers had, once more, to resort to Indian yarn, which made their products too expensive for the mass market they were attempting to cultivate and capture.

They were, moreover, faced with competition from Gloucestershire. The West Country spinners, unlike those at Nottingham, were skilled at handling the short-fibred wool, since this was the type that grew on their local sheep. They adapted themselves to spinning cotton with much greater ease, and the town of Tewkesbury began to produce large numbers of cotton stockings, which were of poorer quality than those of the Nottingham hosiers, but considerably cheaper. With these they penetrated markets in the Midlands; the sales of Nottingham-knitted stockings declined, and the Midland hosiers faced the possibility that, unless they could somehow secure supplies of home-spun cotton of a satisfactory texture for use on their frames, they would lose their potentially profitable market and might indeed be forced to abandon manufacture.

This was the situation when Richard Arkwright, in the month of April, 1768, set out from Preston to take his newly-invented spinning frame to Nottingham.

Whoever undertakes to write Arkwright's biography is likely to saddle himself with a thankless, if an intriguing, task.

There remains so little of certainty to work on. Details of the first thirty-five years of his life are sparse, and perhaps not surprisingly, since he lived at that time in comparative obscurity; the facts that have been authenticated are meagre to the point of barely existing at all; even his son, the younger Richard, could assemble very few, and he began to make enquiries only seven years after his father had died. In addition to this lack of early information, the business records which could have illustrated his later, successful years have practically all vanished, some perhaps destroyed in the disastrous fire at Cromford in November 1890; and the little of his personal correspondence to survive is limited to a handful of letters, spanning a period of eighteen years, to his daughter Susannah, to an attorney at Wirksworth, and to Josiah Wedgwood and Jedediah Strutt. R. S. Fitton and A. P. Wadsworth, in their classic business study of the Strutts and the Arkwrights, were forced to admit the paucity of concrete evidence. Arkwright, they conceded, was 'one of the biographical enigmas of the eighteenth century'; and failing the emergence of some, as yet undiscovered, collection of documents, he seems certain to remain so.

The views of his contemporaries are curiously conflicting. The first Sir Robert Peel described him as 'a man who has done more honour to the country than any man I know'; but whoever it was who wrote his obituary notice in the *Gentleman's Magazine* damned him with irony and the faintest of praise as 'if not a great, a very useful character'. Josiah Wedgwood, the illustrious potter, expressed the view that he was 'a very sensible intelligent man', but Matthew Boulton and his partner, James Watt, were of a different opinion: Boulton castigated him as 'a Tyrant and more absolute than a Bashaw', and declared in letters to Watt that he was by no means a man of sense and reason and scarcely indeed a 'civilised being'; while Watt, in return, implied that he considered Arkwright's lack of modesty and assumptions of knowledge as hardly the attributes of a man of understanding.

The breezy, energetic, but sincere London merchant, Samuel Salte, called him 'a happy mechanic'; yet Jedediah Strutt who, as his partner, probably knew him better as a business associate than anyone else, and who appears to have been a somewhat melancholy, introspective man, referred to him indirectly as 'perverse' and 'ill-natured'. Thomas Ridgway, who founded a bleaching firm in Bolton and knew him when he lived there in earlier days, said that he was sober, industrious and clever and 'might probably have done better could he have Stooped to the vulgar, but his spirit was much superior to it'; John Byng, on the other hand, taking note of his market and castle at Cromford, preferred to say that he was 'cunning' and implied that his style in building was typical of the nouveau riche: vulgar, tasteless, and reminiscent of the slums of 'Marybone' and Clapham.

In June 1790 some doggerel verses, reputedly written by an old woman of Cromford and pasted on the door of the Greyhound Inn, thanked him 'for all favours done'; but the *Gentleman's Magazine* went out of its way to express an entirely contrary opinion: 'Sir Richard, we are informed, with the qualities necessary for the accumulation of wealth, possessed, to an eminent degree, the art of keeping it. His economy and frugality bordered very nearly on parsimony.'

Indeed, the only two descriptions of Arkwright that tally are those of Thomas Carlyle and Joseph Wright of Derby. He was, wrote Carlyle, a 'plain, almost gross, bag-cheeked, pot-bellied Lancashire man, with an air of painful reflection, yet also of copious free digestion'. This was precisely the same man that Joseph Wright painted in 1790, a fact not to be perceived with any great amazement, since Arkwright had already been dead for three years when Carlyle was born, and the writer, presumably, had to rely for his physical description on the artist's famous canvas. It was no wonder that William Nicholson, making his first tentative biographical enquiries a few years after time had carried Arkwright away, found it hard to decide whether he was, after all, a 'superior genius' or merely a 'cunning schemer and collector of other men's inventions, supporting them by borrowed capital and never afterwards feeling or showing any emotion of gratitude to the one or the other'.

Sir Richard Arkwright, by Joseph Wright of Derby.

Such opinions, to say the least, are of considerable variety; and given a second, less than cursory, glance, they perhaps reveal more of their authors than of Arkwright. Some of them certainly need to be weighed against the circumstances that prompted their utterance; the prejudices, fears or plain lack of knowledge among those who expressed them.

Strutt, for instance, was too close an associate to pass a reasonably objective judgment; Wedgwood and Salte too far removed to be knowledgeable; while Peel and John Byng, Boulton and Watt all had their personal axes to grind, and Arkwright's character was the revolving stone against which they chose to sharpen their blades.

Peel's assessment was given in the course of his evidence to a Commons Committee enquiring into children's conditions of work. His attention had been drawn by members of the Committee to an epidemic at his Radcliffe factory, and doubts were being cast on the effectiveness of his ventilation system. He was under attack, and his response was to say that such ventilation had been good enough for Arkwright, and Arkwright was a man who had done the country exceptional honour. 'Our buildings,' he said, 'were copied from the models of his works'. That was very true; but the impression remains that Peel was, to use a modernism, 'passing the buck', and to strengthen his case was crediting Arkwright with perhaps too much in the way of honour, and too little of sheer economic expedience.

Matthew Boulton had been affronted. Arkwright had spoken scathingly of his India Reels, metal parts for winding silk, which he was then manufacturing and selling at a price to the East India Company. He could, he said, 'make a thing for that purpose to answer as well for a shilling apiece'. Having delivered himself of this masterpiece of tact, he proceeded, undeterred by any shred of remorse, to further provocation. He sued a Lancashire spinner, Colonel Mordaunt, for open infringement of one of his patents: an act which the imperious Boulton condemned as unreasonable. When he lost the case, and his carding patent was in consequence invalidated, he refused moreover to give up the struggle. Boulton was outraged. To his way of thinking, Arkwright had already done more than enough damage. By his lack of common sense and his refusal to compromise, he was placing in jeopardy not merely the rest of his own precious patents, but other people's as well; and for Boulton and Watt, clinging desperately to their steam engine patent in the face of mounting criticism, this provoked a dangerous situation indeed. 'I fear for our own,' Watt wrote to Boulton; 'I fear we shall be served with the same sauce for the good of the public'.

His own private exasperation with Arkwright was hardly calculated to make the dour, introverted, melancholic Watt more tolerant than Boulton over what he clearly felt to be an act of folly. Arkwright had apparently been instructing him on improvements to the steam engine, a lesson which, no doubt, the genius of steam had found difficult to stomach.

Byng was an aristocrat, and disinclined to look with favour on a man who had risen swiftly from the 'rabble of artisans'; added to which it had been a wet night in Cromford and 'blew a storm the whole day', meteorological facts which could well have proved sufficient to sour the very aspect of Arkwright's castle. Even Thomas Ridgway can hardly be classed as an unbiased witness, though he passed his opinion seven years after Arkwright had died. It was offered in response to a letter from Arkwright's son, seeking information about the early years of his famous father. Replying to such a civil request from a near relative, it would have been difficult for any man to write ill of the dead.

All opinions are bound, to some extent, to be subjective, and these of his contemporaries are no exception; but among them and others, the fruits of later, probably more mature reflection, there is a consensus. Arkwright, it appears, was aggressive, hard-headed, domineering and irascible; he was ambitious, both materially and socially; self-confident and boastful, never admitting his indebtedness to others; semi-literate and yet mechanically ingenious; industrious and shrewd, expecting to find similar qualities in others and treating them accordingly; fair to his employees if they worked hard on his behalf, but ruthless if they wasted his time and money; a man who could drive a good bargain, wide awake to the profitable realization that money spent on his workers' welfare would return to him doubled in the parallel forms of industrial peace and increased production; determined to have his way, and, accustomed to success, a bad loser on the rare occasions when he failed.

Such a man, though inevitably a difficult associate, had the energy, driving force, and day-to-day self-discipline to scale heights the less gifted or the more inhibited viewed with despair. Arkwright's wealth and success aroused the envy, from time to time, of his fellow manufacturers, but in times of crisis, to the end of his life, they always turned to him as their natural leader; and if, as some say, he appropriated, without compunction, other men's ideas, it was his own mechanical and commercial contributions that turned them from dreams into rattling machines to spin cotton and money.

Carlyle, for all his rancid words about a 'bag-cheeked, pot-bellied Lancashire man', still acknowledged his worth. 'O reader,' he continued, 'what a historical phenomenon is that bag-cheeked, pot-bellied, much enduring, much inventing barber! French Revolutions were a-brewing: to resist the same in any measure imperial Kaisers were impotent without the cotton and cloth of England; and it was this man that had to give England the power of cotton.'

Richard Arkwright had his faults; he was, perhaps, a compendium of all those allied to self-interest and self-esteem; but Peel was right, in a sense, when he said that his fellow Lancastrian had done the country honour.

Arkwright did more than that. He drove Britain at speed into the nineteenth century, and, for the thirteenth child of a family with only limited resources, that was no mean achievement.

Born in 1732 in the small town of Preston, he was apprenticed to a barber, and became a 'lather boy'. At the age of eighteen, having finished his training, he moved to Bolton, where he found employment with a maker of wigs, named Edward Pollit. Pollit soon died, but Arkwright appears to have carried on the business on behalf of his widow till 1755, when he married a girl called Patience Holt and set up on his own as a barber and wig-maker. According to Thomas Ridgway, he worked 'with most indefatigable industry and with some success' and 'was always thought clever in his peruke making business and very capital in Bleeding and toothdrawing'. The marriage seems to have been happy, but after the birth of their son, Richard, the following December, Patience sickened and died. This was a blow, but he continued to grind away at his business, shaving his customers for a penny a time, and experimenting, in his shop below the level of the street, with a fast dye for wigs. In this he succeeded and appears to have prospered, in spite of the asthma that frequently assailed him. In 1761 he improved his prospects by marrying again, this time to a woman named Margaret Biggins, who came from Leigh, near Warrington. She brought a little money into the marriage, and with this he was able to buy a shop in a better situation, and expand his interests further by taking a public house. This, however, despite numerous alterations which cost him more than he could rightly afford, proved to be a failure, and eventually he sold both the shop and the tavern and began to concentrate exclusively on the manufacture of wigs, employing a journeyman to help him and travelling to markets and fairs in the Peak to buy women's hair.

He had already, while working as a barber, displayed an unusual interest in mechanics. 'It was perceived,' wrote Thomas Ridgway, 'in his common conversation, which often turned on subjects of that kind. I well remember we had often great fun with a Clock he put up in his shop, which had all the appearance of being worked by the smoke of the chimney and we have caused a many to believe it was so.' The trimming of hair and the shaving of beards lent themselves to much desultory conversation, and Arkwright, no doubt, was well acquainted with the problems that, at that time, faced the Lancashire weavers. Thirty years previously, John Kay of Bury had invented the flying shuttle, a device attached to the loom by which the weaver could jerk the shuttle from side to side; and though it was never widely adopted till his son, Robert Kay, in 1760, added his own invention of the drop box for mechanically selecting shuttles holding different coloured yarns, yet the weavers had, for years, been starved of thread. The shuttle had enabled them not merely to weave a wider cloth than the traditional six-foot broadcloth, but to weave it much faster; and the spinners, still working on their single-thread hand wheels, had been unable to supply yarn in sufficient quantities. James Hargreaves' spinning jenny, which first saw the light in 1764, had, though still a hand-operated machine, solved the problem of speed; but the thread it produced was often of an unsatisfactory strength, and susceptible to breakage when used as warps on a loom. From talking to his customers, Arkwright must have been aware of the need for a powered machine to spin strong and even thread for the warps; and, being Richard Arkwright, he must also have realized that an invention of this kind could yield its author a handsome fortune.

His marriage to Margaret Biggins led him, on occasions, to Warrington and Leigh, and into meetings with two men, both from that area, who were to play a considerable part in the development of his ideas. They were Thomas Highs, a reed maker, who lived in Leigh, and a second and entirely different John Kay, who made clocks in Warrington.

It is at this point that Arkwright's career enters the realm of debate. Much has been deduced, from insubstantial evidence and with conflicting results, concerning his relationship with these two men. No-one knows for certain what passed between them, but it seems likely that Highs had at least tried to make a new spinning machine and had persuaded Kay to help in the difficult and intricate work of its construction. It also seems likely that, once constructed, the machine had either failed to work or had failed to produce the right texture of thread; and that Highs and Kay had despaired of a solution some time before Arkwright arrived on the scene. There appears to be little doubt, whatever the stage their experiments had reached, that he talked to Kay, and gleaned enough information about the machine to convince himself that it was capable of further development. He therefore turned his mind to devising improvements, and recruited Kay to help him. Thomas Highs was ignored.

According to some accounts, Arkwright then devoted so much of his time to perfecting the machine that his business affairs suffered, his wife complained and he left her because, at length, in an understandable tantrum, she smashed one of his models. Certainly by the January of 1768 he and Kay were in Preston. They had prevailed on John Smalley, a Preston publican, and David Thornley, a Liverpool merchant, to back them financially; had rented rooms at seven guineas a year in the schoolmaster's house by the parish church—now Arkwright House, recently restored as a Heritage Centre—and were working on the prototype of the roller-spinning frame. Not that they were indiscreet enough to make the news public; they apparently told their landlord that they were 'making a machine to find out the longitude', and the strange noises emanating from their workshop parlour encouraged two passers-by to liken the sound to the devil tuning his bagpipes, a belief in the supernatural that was doubtless prompted by the comparative proximity of Pendle Hill, the home of Lancashire witches.

The partners were soon successful. Within the space of another three months they had built a machine, presumably derived from Highs' original idea, to spin cotton through rollers. There were four pairs of rollers. The first gripped the cotton, which then passed to each succeeding pair. These, rotating at progressively faster speeds, attenuated the strand, and a turning spindle added the twist. Highs had probably worked on the basic idea, which was no more his than Arkwright's, since John Wyatt and Lewis Paul had pioneered a method of spinning by rollers thirty years before; but Arkwright's contributions, which transformed the machine from a failure into an ingenious success, were possibly, first of all, to alter the distances between the sets of rollers and recalculate their speeds, and then to attach an additional weight to the top roller of each pair. This may sound simple, but it was no easy task and called for considerable expertise. To achieve a reliable method of spinning, the rollers had to be spaced precisely. The distances between them had to equal the average length of the staples; a greater separation and the thread would come apart; a lesser separation meant that it would snap. The relative speeds were also critical, and the weight on the rollers had to be correct. The fact that Arkwright succeeded where others had failed is a tribute to his perception and mechanical ingenuity. His machine achieved a tighter grip by the rollers, an ideal tension on the fibres between them, and a smoother and more effective spinning of the yarn.

The spinning frame was a reality, but Arkwright had already made up his mind to leave Preston. In the March of that year, 1768, the anger of unemployed spinners in Lancashire had erupted against the growing number of jennies. Hargreaves' house in Blackburn had been attacked and burnt down, and jennies in the town had been wilfully destroyed. Shortly after this, in fear of his life, Hargreaves had secretly fled from Lancashire; and the astute Arkwright had no intention of offering the spinners an opportunity to vent their frustration on him and his frame. Lancashire was clearly an unhealthy county for spinning-machine inventors. Hargreaves had taken refuge in Nottingham, and he decided to follow him before the existence of the frame became public knowledge. The Midland hosiers were desperate for thread; there was money available in Nottingham to finance a man who could prove his ability to spin the right kind of yarn by mechanical means; and the town possessed a colony of highly-skilled framesmiths, whose assistance would be vital in constructing his machines. So, a month after Hargreaves' abrupt departure, Arkwright, accompanied by Kay and Smalley, followed him to Nottingham.

Once arrived there, he applied for a patent 'for a new Piece of Machinery never before found out, practised, or used, for the Making of Weft or Yarn from Cotton, Flax and Wool'; and this was granted, after some initial delay, on 15 July 1769, Smalley signing as a witness. The delay may have been due to a shortage of money. Certainly there are signs that Kay and Arkwright quarrelled, and that Smalley's resources were beginning to run out. Arkwright then approached the Nottingham bankers, Ichabod and John Wright, and, with their assistance, he and Smalley rented a site between Woolpack Lane and Hockley and established a small mill, hardly bigger than a workshop but soon to be expanded, driving their frames by the power of horses harnessed to a horizontal driving wheel. After a somewhat shaky start, the mill seems to have flourished and hosiers began to buy Arkwright's yarn; but progress was apparently disappointing to the Wrights, who withdrew their support, recommending him instead to two wealthy hosiers, customers of theirs, Samuel Need of Nottingham and Jedediah Strutt, who by that time had established two silk mills in Derby. It was with their financial backing and with them as his partners that, two years later, in 1771, Arkwright extended his activities to the Derwent Valley and built his first mill at Cromford.

The reasons why he chose Cromford as the site for the first of his water-powered mills have been, of recent years, constantly debated. One stimulus to such debate is that no records exist of his correspondence with Need and Strutt, and the only surviving reference to the intended move is an indirect one, in a letter to Strutt as late as 1772, implying that Need was sceptical of its success.

Need's agreement was vital. He was wealthier than Strutt at this particular time, with a hosiery warehouse in Low Pavement at Nottingham, and a house at Arnold outside the town. When he died in London in 1781, he was reputed to be an immensely rich man. He was probably supplying the bulk of the money for Arkwright's venture, which was likely to entail a considerable risk, dependent as it was on a new technique of water-powered frame spinning and notoriously difficult road communications with the Nottingham market and the ports of London, Hull and Liverpool which supplied the raw cotton. It was his desire, it seems, to concentrate resources on developing the promise of the Nottingham mill, and Arkwright's success in securing his support for the projected move could well have owed much to Strutt's tactful persuasion.

What was in Arkwright's mind can only be conjectured from knowledge of his character. His was a restless ambition, and eighteen months of steady progress at Nottingham may have made him impatient to expand his business. Such expansion, however, if the new spinning machinery were to be used to full advantage, required a much larger scale of operation and a change of power technique; and for such a change Nottingham lacked the necessary facilities. Horses were quite unsuitable; they were expensive to maintain; and Arkwright clearly believed that water power was the answer. A ten horsepower waterwheel could prove more efficient and considerably cheaper than half a dozen horses, and the technical possibilities of roller-spinning cotton by such a form of power had already been explored some thirty years before by Wyatt and Paul in their small, but financially unsuccessful, factory at Northampton; while Jedediah Strutt was not only familiar with Lombe's silk mill on the Derwent, he was himself the owner of two water-powered silk-throwing mills on its Derby tributaries.

The trouble was that the Trent, in the Nottingham area, was too sluggish a river to harness successfully without expensive installations. Cromford, on the other hand, could provide the swift current of Bonsall Brook, flowing from the Griffe Grange Valley by Scarthin Nick along the line of what was to become the Via Gellia, and, in addition, the considerable outfall from the Cromford Sough, the underground tunnel, a hundred years old, that drained the Dove Gang mines in the Wirksworth lead field. Both of these water sources were used by Arkwright, and it seems almost certain that he knew of their existence since, according to Stephen Glover, writing in his *History of the County of Derby* in 1829, his travels in search of hair had led him to base his activities on Wirksworth some time prior to 1768. Added to which there was a site immediately available in Cromford: a corn mill site, adjacent to the water-powered lead-smelting mills run by the Lascelles family at Cromford Bridge.

He may have realized, too, that the lead mining industry in the area was contracting, and this promised, at least initially, a supply of cheap labour in the form of lead miners' wives and children: labour, moreover, that would certainly be unorganized compared with that available in a town such as Nottingham, where, a few years later, the houses of the master spinners were attacked and their workshops burnt down. For this reason the very remoteness of Cromford from busy industrial centres and their attendant unrest may well have been an added recommendation, especially since he was developing new techniques and experimenting with new machines for which secrecy was essential.

The pirating of Kay's shuttle and Hargreaves' jenny was common knowledge, and Strutt would certainly have told him of his own experience of spies, following the invention of his Derby Rib knitting machine in 1759. The machines, as a precaution, had been placed in a room lit only by sky-lights, but men had climbed on the roof to look down at the frames. In his letter of March 1772 to Strutt, Arkwright was clearly obsessed with secrecy. 'Desire ward,' he wrote, 'to send those other Locks and allso Some sorts of Hangins for the sashes he and you may think best and some good Latches and Catches for the out doors and a few for the inner ons allso and a Large Knoker or a Bell to First door. I am Determind for the feuter to Let no persons in to Look at the wor[k]s except spining.' For a man so obsessed, the very isolation of the village of Cromford must have been an advantage.

It is possible, also, that he was becoming progressively disenchanted with Nottingham. His ambitions were social, as well as being industrial, com-mercial and financial. Indeed, it might be said of him with some edge of truth that, semi-literate as he was, all his other ambitions were but rungs of a ladder by means of which he was determined to climb to social eminence. Gravener Henson, repeating the legends that abounded in Nottingham concerning Arkwright, tells of his craving to become a member of the gentry, to live in a mansion and ride in a carriage, all of which desires he fulfilled in his lifetime; but social progress, as he must have discovered quite early, was difficult to achieve in Nottingham, run as the town was by a

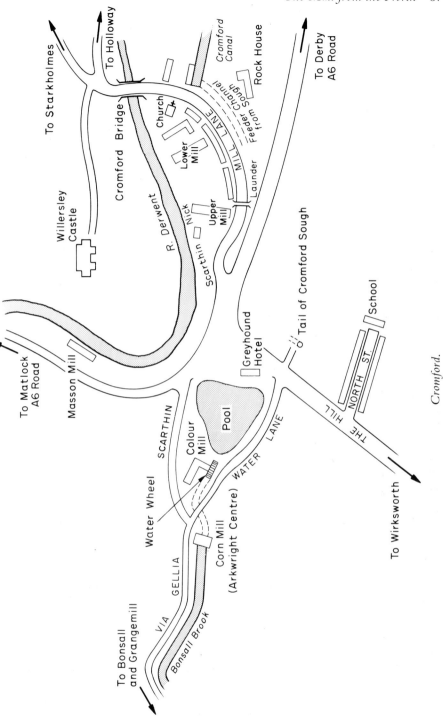

Cromford.

closed Corporation, the members of which were elected for life and which was dominated by Nonconformist tradesmen drawn from the congregations of the three main Dissenting Chapels in the district. Arkwright was no Dissenter. The only way he could have entered the local establishment was by buying a place, and he was not yet rich enough to afford such a luxury. Cromford, on the contrary, promised the chance of easier acceptance. The gentry of the area owed their social positions, not to Dissent, but to wealth accumulated from the lead mining industry; and a mile to the north lay Matlock Bath, developing as a spa and already attracting visitors from that level of society to which Arkwright intended, by hook or crook, to climb.

It could have been a combination of all these factors—its water power, its promise of a labour supply, its very isolation, and the opportunities it offered for social advancement—that drew Arkwright to Cromford; but the most likely explanation, when all the many points of debate have been counted, is that it was Cromford water, and the small, manageable, available site which attracted him. He had some financial backing, but not a large amount of capital. He was looking for a site which would provide him with a little, but not too much, development space; which possessed a reliable water supply; and which was not too far distant from the recognized centres of the hosiery trade. The Cromford corn mill site fulfilled all these conditions at a time when water power was in demand and at a premium.

But, whatever his motives, the results of his move were positive enough. With the arrival of this dynamic and ruthless man, this quiet, remote community of lead miners and framework knitters was to suffer a convulsion, the shock-waves of which were to penetrate swiftly the length and breadth of Britain.

On the first day of August 1771 Arkwright, Smalley, Need and Strutt leased, at an annual rent of £14,

> All that river stream or brook, called Bonsall Brook, situated and being within the liberty of Cromford . . . together with the stream of water issuing and running from Cromford Sough in Cromford aforesaid into the said Bonsall Brook with full liberty and power to divert, turn and carry the said brook, stream and water down the south side of the highway in Cromford aforesaid and under or over the same highway; and also all that piece or parcel of ground in Cromford aforesaid lying between Bonsall Brook and the intended new cut and extending in length from the turnpike road leading to Matlock Bath . . . to erect and build . . . one or more mill or mills for spinning, winding or throwing silk, worsted, cotton, linen or other materials and also such and so many water wheels, warehouses, shops, smithies etc., banks, dams, goits, shuttles and other conveniences.

This gave them the land they needed to construct their factory, and the water rights required to provide it with power.

Once the lease was signed, they wasted no time. Purchasing a house known as Steephill Grange, they demolished it for stone; and, probably using the local calamine, roasted and mixed with quicklime, to produce a hard mortar, set their builders to work. By December there were signs that the fabric of the mill was nearing completion, for the partners were advertising in the *Derby Mercury* for 'two journey men Clock-Makers, or others that understands Tooth and Pinion well: Also a Smith that can forge and file.—Likewise two Wood Turners that have been accustomed to Wheel-making, Spoke-turning, etc.': a sure indication that progress had reached the point where machinery was being constructed and installed; and in his letter to Strutt the following March, Arkwright implied that, though the building still lacked 'Latches and Catches', at least some experimental spinning had commenced. 'I Cant think of stoping this Con[c]ern hear,' he wrote, 'as that at nottingm. is [not] or Ever will be aney thing in comparison to this.'

The mill, Cromford Upper Mill, was built without any architectural extravagance. It was merely a functional, barrack-like shell, five storeys high; but for Arkwright it represented a considerable advance, for the frames housed within it were powered by an undershot or low-breast waterwheel.

A legend has developed that he purposely chose to build the mill here at Cromford because he knew that, at this point, a spring of warm water flowed into the Derwent, ensuring that, even in the hardest of weather, the river never froze; but, while Matlock Bath certainly had its warm springs, the terms of the lease make it quite apparent that the partners had no intention of using the Derwent. The warm water legend, if it has any application at all, must refer to the outfall from Cromford Sough, which was used, in

Cromford Upper Mill.

conjunction with Bonsall Brook, as the source of power; the combined waters of the brook and the sough being carried to the wheel along a ground level channel. The power the sough produced, and the vital part it played in driving the mill machinery, can be deduced from the fact that, in 1791, the Cromford Canal Company calculated the average flow from the sough to be $71\frac{1}{2}$ tons of water per minute, while that of the brook was only $5\frac{3}{5}$.

Though detailed evidence of progress is lacking, the mill appears to have prospered, and in its early stages Need's connections with the Nottingham hosiers must have proved a valuable asset to Arkwright. If he was frustrated at all at this time, it was probably by the inability of his yarn to penetrate the fashion hose and lace net market for which Nottingham was noted. In this field, a finer yarn was required, which only became available in quantity when, in 1779, Samuel Crompton invented his mule. But, if frame yarn proved unsuitable for fashion specialities—though it was infinitely superior to that spun on jennies—it was ideally suited for the warp of calico or pure cotton cloth. Because of the powerful influence of the woollen industry, there had, for more than half a century, been a virtual prohibition on the sale and manufacture of printed calicoes, and unprinted ones had been subject to a double excise duty; though after 1736 the duty had been reduced for Lancashire fustians, half-cotton materials that used a flax warp. The fact that Hargreaves' jenny was unable to produce a yarn of sufficient strength for calico warps had induced the Lancashire manufacturers to stay with their fustians, but Arkwright and Strutt realized that their stronger machine-spun twist could answer all the requirements. If jenny thread were used for the weft, and the hardier frame-spun thread for the warps, then calico

Bonsall Brook.

manufacture could well develop into a national asset and a massively profitable market for the partners' yarn. It was in pursuit of this outlet that, in 1774, they submitted a petition to the House of Commons in the name of 'Richard Arkwright and Company of Nottingham, Spinners of Cotton, and Manufacturers of British White Stuffs'. The petition was successful; the manufacture of white calico was granted official blessing, subject to the condition that it should be marked with blue threads and stamped 'British Manufactury'; the excise duty on printed cottons was reduced; and the profitability of the Cromford mill virtually assured.

Meanwhile, inside the mill, further mechanical experiments were in progress. The spinning frame produced a satisfactory yarn, but, for the yarn to be continuous, Arkwright's machine needed to be furnished with roving —loosely twisted strands of cotton which were, in turn, made from carded sliver, a fatter untwisted sort of cotton rope. In simple terms, if the frame was to function at maximum efficiency, the processes which prepared the cotton for spinning required also to be mechanized. The answer was provided in Arkwright's second patent—that for his key invention, the rotary carding engine, with its lap device to feed in the fibres, and a crank and comb to remove the carded cotton in a continuous sliver. The patent for this invention, taken out in April 1775, covered no less than ten different machines, among them devices for opening and cleaning the cotton, drawing the fibres, and simultaneously twisting and winding the sliver on to a bobbin. Arkwright claimed in his patent application that he 'had brought to perfection Certain Instruments or Machines which would be of Public Utility in Preparing Silk, Cotton, Flax and Wool for Spinning'. This was, perhaps, an exaggerated claim: some of his devices were never employed; others were perfected by later inventors; but he had at least devised a series of machines which, working as a production line beneath a single roof, could convert raw cotton into cotton thread. By breaking down the complex business of spinning into a series of operations, each of which could be, and was in later years, successfully mechanized, he had pointed the way for others to follow. This was, without doubt, his greatest technological achievement; and a remarkable one for a self-taught mechanic. Coupled with his invention of the spinning frame, it was instrumental in transforming the manufacture of textiles from a domestic into a factory industry.

By 1776 he was ready to expand his own manufacture. He had, in seven years, transformed himself from a ragged inventor, touting for money, into a wealthy mill-owner who could 'set up his Carriage' and provide his daughter, Susannah, with 'genteel riding dresses'. There were profits available now for expansion, and he and his partners set in hand the construction of a second mill at Cromford. This, the Lower Mill, was larger than the first. It was seven storeys high and powered, like the first, by the waters of Bonsall Brook and the Cromford Sough, which passed from the first mill to turn two wheels, fifteen feet in diameter, sunk in a wheelpit twenty feet deep beneath the middle of the building. From the depth of the pit, these were certainly overshot or high-breast wheels.

The erection of the mill proceeded through the summer and seems to have been completed by early September, for the *Derby Mercury*, on the nineteenth of the month, reported that Arkwright and Company had provided a feast for more than two hundred workers engaged on its construction. They were, so the correspondent wrote, 'regaled with a large Quantity of Strong Beer, etc., yet the Day was spent with the greatest Harmony imaginable'. From the time of its completion, the size of Arkwright's work-force showed a rapid increase. William Bray, the first of many tourists to comment on the Cromford mills, reported that, in 1777, they employed 'about 200 persons, chiefly children'; but by 1783, according to Pilkington, the number had risen to 800. Six years later Arkwright was recruiting 'poor people' from Winster, four miles across the moors; while Byng, the same year, estimated the labour force at 1,150.

This number would include not merely those employed at the Upper and Lower Mills, but at the third of Arkwright's factories at Cromford. Masson Mill, between the village and Matlock Bath, was completed in 1784, close to the site where, twelve years earlier, Robert Shore of Snitterton and George White of Winster had established a paper mill, drawing their water power from the Derwent. Arkwright, by this time, was virtually a millionaire. The aggressive self-confidence of early days was now buttressed, and perhaps to some extent tempered, by the massive depth of his financial resources: he was wealthy enough, despite a characteristic explosion of wrath, to ride a legal storm in the following year which resulted in the cancellation of his patents; and this, his new mill, named after the close in which it was constructed, revealed all the signs of increased prosperity. The first two mills had been austere and forbidding, reminiscent of prison blocks, with their grey stone walls and rows of small-paned windows. Masson was different. It was built of red brick, edged with stone quoins, and the projecting frontage carried a cluster of Venetian windows and a decorative cupola surmounted by a weathervane. It was the first and only one of Arkwright's mills to use the Derwent for power, and this also, perhaps, displayed a new assurance. In the course of thirteen years he had used Bonsall Brook and the Cromford Sough, the Cress Brook, the Wye, the Ecclesbourne and the Dove, but had fought shy of taming what Defoe had described as a 'fury of a river'. He had, it may be, good reason to fear the Derwent; in 1785, his nearest neighbour, Peter Nightingale of Lea, lost his mill in a flood, and fourteen years later the swollen waters swept away Calver Bridge and damaged the cotton mill built by the hosiers, Gardom and Pares; but here, at last, at Masson, at a point in the gorge where a series of rapids increased the speed of the flow, the river was channelled through a succession of impressive water installations to power the new mill. The unusual down-curved construction of the weir

Masson Mill today.

may have been a sign that Arkwright was still mistrustful of the waters, but William Adam, viewing the scene from the top of Cat Tor in 1851, found a grandeur in the harmony of river and mill. 'Immediately below to the left,' he wrote, 'the river loses its quiet and peaceful character, breaking in fury over the Weir and foaming amongst the dark fragments under it—and close by, the Mill mingles the din of its heavy machinery with the roar of the fall.'

By 1791 Arkwright had completed his building at Cromford. Samuel Need had died a full decade before, 'advanced in Years and after a very long Illness', and following his death the partnership had been dissolved. Smalley had already been pensioned off to Wales, and, once Need was gone, Strutt and Arkwright decided to part. Strutt retained his interests at Belper and Milford, Arkwright those at Cromford, and from that time forward he was able to mould the village, and the life of the village, to suit his own plans.

Between 1785 and 1791 he extended his original complex of buildings by adding a battery of warehouses, which stretched from the Upper Mill a hundred yards east towards Cromford Bridge, and also what may have been the fourth of his mills or merely an extension linked to the Lower Mill at first floor level; but there was more to Arkwright's Cromford than factory buildings, weirs and dams and storage facilities; he created there deliberately, with no local or central government assistance, an industrial community, a kind of patriarchal factory village, over which he presided with a benevolent feudalism characteristic of a lord of the manor.

Down-curved weir, Masson Mill.

His mills stood in virtual isolation, severed from the townships of Derby and Nottingham by unmade roads that twisted for miles up and down steep hills and over desolate moors; and since, to his credit, he steadfastly refused to take advantage of the parish apprenticeship system, he was forced, once the limited local labour ran out, to attract and hold workers by providing not merely favourable working conditions, but housing, public services and social welfare on a scale hitherto unattempted except by the greater landowning families.

He built what John Farey, in 1815, described as 'numbers of neat and comfortable Cottages' along the pleasant stretch of North Street and on both sides of the road that climbs steeply to Wirksworth. He provided an inn, the Greyhound, to accommodate travellers, to preside over the market, for which he obtained a charter in 1790, and to act as a social centre for the expanding community.

Towards the end of his life he began to build a church, and, on rising ground beyond the River Derwent, a mansion fit for the master of Cromford. Willersley Castle was reputed to have cost him £20,000, but he never had the satisfaction of living inside it, for in 1791, when the final touches were being applied to the interior, a workman's carelessness in using a lamp started a fire which gutted the building. Within twelve months, and well before the repairs were completed, Arkwright was dead, and it was left to his son to finish the house and take up residence there.

John Byng paid a visit to Willersley Castle on that June morning in 1790 when 'it blew a storm the whole day', and he damned it as 'an effort of inconvenient ill taste'. Modern critics, among them Sir Nikolaus Pevsner, have been kinder to Willersley, but Byng's assessment was scornful:

> The ceilings are of gew-gaw fret work; the small circular staircase . . . is so dark and narrow, that people cannot pass each other; I ask'd a workman if there was a library?—Yes, answer'd he, at the foot of the stairs. Its dimensions are 15 feet square (a small counting house) and having the perpendicular lime stone rock within 4 yards, it is too dark to read or write in without a candle! . . . What confinement! At Clapham they can produce nothing equal to this, where ground is sold by the yard.

Nor was he more impressed by its outward appearance. 'It is the house of an overseer surveying the works, not of a gentleman wishing for retirement and quiet. But light come, light go, Sir Rd has honourably made his great fortune; and so let him still live in a great cotton mill!'

Willersley Castle, Cromford.

Rock House, Cromford.

Byng's wish never found its fulfilment. Arkwright died, as he had lived, at Rock House on the cliff above his barrack-like mills. His later life had been a mixture of frustrations and achievements. In 1785 a group of master-spinners from Lancashire and Derbyshire, who had flagrantly infringed his patent rights by equipping their mills with water spinning-frames, brought an action against him to have the patents invalidated. They resurrected Thomas Highs and his friend, John Kay, who both swore in court to making a spinning machine identical with Arkwright's two years before his patent had been granted; and despite much eloquent pleading from Arkwright's counsel, who predictably questioned Highs' unaccountable silence for sixteen years, the jury found for the plaintiffs and the patents were cancelled.

Arkwright swore to make the 'Manchester rascals' pay. This, of course, proved impossible, but his fortunes were, by this time, so solidly based that they seem to have been but little affected by the loss; and, in the years that remained, he was to receive compensation of a very different kind. In 1786 he was knighted, and the following year was appointed High Sheriff of the County of Derby. His social ambitions were almost wholly achieved. He was accepted at last as a member of the gentry, his mansion was being built and he rode around his domain in what the *Manchester Mercury* described as a 'very elegant and fashionable' carriage drawn by a team of the finest greys.

His funeral was equally impressive. J. P. Malcolm wrote in the *Gentleman's Magazine* that, as the cortege passed the High Tor on its way to Matlock Church:

> The road was now nearly impassable from the crowds of people and carriages ... The ceremony was conducted with much pomp, and, as nearly as I can remember, was thus: A coach and four with the clergy; another with the pall-bearers; the hearse, covered with escutcheons ... then the horse of the deceased, led by a servant; the relations, and about fifteen or twenty carriages, closed the procession, which was perhaps half a mile in length. The evening was gloomy, and the solemn stillness that reigned was only interrupted by the rumbling of the carriages and the gentle murmurs of the river; and as they passed, the echo of the Torr gently returned the sound.

The later history of the Cromford mills was one of varying fortunes. In 1785 Arkwright began to re-organize his system of water power, exercising the rights conferred by the lease 'to divert, turn and carry' Bonsall Brook and the Cromford Sough along different channels. He dispensed with the ground-level water course that had powered the wheel of the Upper Mill, replaced the undershot by an overshot wheel, and carried the sough water along a higher channel and across the road to the mill in a wooden launder. This was replaced in 1821 by a cast-iron trough, but Arkwright's initial reorganization, which entailed linking the sough with the Greyhound dam by an underground channel, produced flooding in several of the Wirksworth lead mines and resulted in a long-drawn-out legal case. This ended in favour

Warehouses, entrance gate and water launder, Cromford.

Greyhound Pool, Cromford.

of the sough proprietors. Arkwright was ordered to pay, first for repairs to the damaged sough, and then an annual rent of £20 for the privilege of taking water for his mills.

This was the beginning of a protracted battle to retain sufficient water power from Cromford Sough to drive the Upper and Lower Mills: a battle finally lost by Richard Arkwright junior in 1837, when a new sough, the Meerbrook, cut to drain the lower levels of the mines, diverted most of the water. The Upper Mill ceased production in 1846, to become successively a brewery, a laundry, and finally in 1921 a colour works, operated first by the Cromford Colour Company and then by Burrell Colours till 1979, when it was purchased for preservation by the Arkwright Society. The Lower Mill, after standing empty for some time, was leased to a hosiery firm as a warehouse, only to be destroyed by fire in November 1890. Fanned by a breeze, the flames enveloped the building, and within three hours the roof and walls had fallen in. 'The destruction of any part of the mill,' wrote the *Derby Mercury*, 'is a circumstance greatly to be regretted, yet Derbyshire people will be pleased that two out of three blocks of buildings remain to identify Cromford with Sir Richard Arkwright.' Fire had, however, not completed its work, for in 1930 the Upper Mill, in a similar way, lost its top two storeys.

Masson Mill had a happier fate. Production here was unaffected by the loss of water from the sough, and in 1898 the premises were sold by Frederick Arkwright to the English Sewing Cotton Company. In the next thirteen years new buildings were added to north and south of the original block; in the 1920s water turbines were introduced to replace the wheels; and the mill is still in use for textiles today.

In 1636 Thomas Hobbes, the philosopher, listed his Seven Wonders of the Peak. In their early days Arkwright's cotton-spinning mills were very much an additional wonder, and tourists visiting the spas at Buxton and Matlock would turn aside deliberately, in spite of the calamitous state of the roads, to stand and stare at these gaunt, sullen structures with their rows of windows. Erasmus Darwin extolled them in verse; Joseph Wright immortalized them in paint, and even John Byng, who was swift to complain that the vales had lost their beauties and every rural sound was 'sunk in the clamours of cotton works', described them as magnificent. 'These cotton mills,' he wrote, 'seven stories high, and fill'd with inhabitants, remind me of a first rate man of war; and when they are lighted up, on a dark night, look most luminously beautiful.'

In those days they were something altogether unique: hundreds of flickering pinpoints of light in the age-old darkness of the Derwent Valley; the first of their kind; buildings shuddering with a power that promised a new future to the villagers of Cromford. But that future never came. If Arkwright had tossed aside his roller-spinning frames and equipped his mills with the newly-invented mules; if Cromford had been closer to the port of Liverpool and its warehouses stacked with supplies of raw cotton, nearer to the markets and the fertile centres of cotton technology, this little township on the banks of the Derwent might have spread and sprawled and multiplied in ugliness as Manchester did. But Arkwright was stiff-necked, Cromford too remote. After seventy years of life the waterwheels ceased to turn, the flickering lights were extinguished, and the people of the village turned back to their lead mines, their parcels of land, to the grinding of paint and the quarrying of stone. Other men built their replicas of Arkwright's mills, but they built them in Lancashire, Yorkshire and Scotland; they copied his organization, his business methods; created, like Robert Owen, industrial communities based on his original conception at Cromford; but the village where the massive revolution began has remained, for almost two hundred years, cocooned as he left it: the site of the first successful water-powered mills for the spinning of cotton, the place where the concept of industrial welfare in a closed community, so dear to the evangelical spirit of the age, found its first full expression.

In Cromford today very little seems different from what it must have been two centuries ago. True, the limestone lorries clatter past the Greyhound and cars full of tourists block the A6 junction to Matlock Bath, but behind the shops in the market place the sough still emits a trickle of water; Bonsall Brook flows gently towards the mill pool; the Upper Mill and its warehouses, bleak as the shell of some long-disused gaol, still lour upon the lane that runs down to the bridge, their recent activity only disclosed by the pigment spilling green round the entrance gate; Masson still throbs, its red brick glowing, its Venetian windows and cupola recently restored by English Sewing and the Arkwright Society, reconstructions worthy of a society dedicated to conservation and a firm that still proudly displays on its mill the legend 'Sir Richard Arkwright & Co.'; and beyond the Derwent, Willersley Castle, now a Methodist guest house, still hides behind the trees that Sir Richard's son planted, and its lawns and gardens that Adam so much admired sweep down to the river and the foaming weir. Perhaps, as Byng implied, it was never a Chatsworth; but to linger in the Well, looking up through the spiral staircase to the sky, is to savour the feeling that this was the very way that Arkwright climbed, not only in his house, but also in his life.

To walk in Cromford today is to walk with shadows, and shadows that fade and change and fade away again according to the time, the season and the weather. To stand in the empty market place by the Greyhound as the night ebbs away and the dawn light of autumn shows itself red through the mists above the river is to dream oneself back into the eighteenth century, to watch the candles flicker into life behind windows high on the Wirksworth hill, to hear the bell clang from the flat roof of Masson, and to see the shades gather: women and children streaming down the slope, knuckling the sleep from their half-open eyes, and passing through them and climbing more slowly and wearily, those whose twelve-hour shift has ended, at last, with the coming of the day. To climb the heights above Masson on a spring afternoon is to stand with William Adam, see the flood waters breaking white across the weir, and listen, as he did, to the song of the river and the sound of the mill; and to take the same path of a winter evening is to share with John Byng that luminous beauty as the darkness of the gorge shrouds the deep red brick, the mill loses shape and its rows of windows spring into light, reflected from the water like the lamp-lit ports of a black man-o'-war afloat on the Derwent.

But the shadow that even now dominates Cromford is cast, as it was two hundred years ago, by a pompous, self-opinionated, asthmatic old man, who stumps out of Rock House, clambers into his carriage, swings at speed past the mills that were the heart of his empire and disappears in the dust of an unmade road up the slope towards Wirksworth.

The products of his mills, in this twentieth century, may well be diverse; through their gates may come paint, man-made fibres and tape; but Sir Richard is still about his business of cotton, and those who live in Cromford and know Cromford's story wake in the small hours and listen in the silence that breeds imagination for the sound of his carriage wheels on the hill.

5   The Rumbling Stream

When soothing darkness spreads
O'er hill and vale ...
Then, in full many a region, once like this
The assured domain of calm simplicity
And pensive quiet, an unnatural light
Prepared for never-resting labour's eyes
Breaks from a many-windowed fabric huge;
... the rumbling stream,
That turns the multitude of dizzy wheels,
Glares, like a troubled spirit, in its bed,
Among the rock below ...

William Wordsworth: *The Excursion*, Book VIII (1814).

Where Derwent guides his dusky floods
Through vaulted mountains and a nights of woods
The nymph "Gossypia" treads the silver sod
And warms with rosy smiles the wat'ry God;
His pond'rous oars to slender spindles turns
And pours o'er mossy wheels his foaming urns ...

Erasmus Darwin: *The Botanic Garden* (1789–91).

Now the waters of the Derwent and its tributary streams, used for hundreds of years to turn grindstones in the corn mills, to power the rise and fall of hammers for the fulling of cloth and the forging of metal, and to operate the bellows that blasted air into furnaces, were harnessed to drive the frames and the mules for spinning cotton.

By 1789 there were some twenty mills in the valley, spinning cotton by power; and by the turn of the century this number had swollen to more than thirty. They were based inevitably, in their structure and organization, on Arkwright's original mills at Cromford: simple in design, stark in appearance, constructed like boxes partitioned into separate compartments or floors to accommodate machines and the people whose work, night and day, was to tend them. Rectangular in shape, normally of gritstone, they varied in size from three to half a dozen storeys in height, their wooden floors supported by wooden beams on cast-iron columns. Their roofs were low-pitched, their windows multi-paned and positioned identically on each of the floors; and both ends of the structure might boast a projecting buttress-tower, rising through the storeys, and housing perhaps a spiral stair and a lavatory block. In later years the more elaborate would mingle limestone and brick in their gritstone walls; would have pediments, bell-turrets and probably a clock; the windows and doorways might assume a more handsome

Cast-iron columns and brick arches, North Mill, Belper, 1804.

Georgian appearance and, because of the distressing tendency of wooden-framed mills to erupt into uncontrollable flame, the wooden internal framework might well be sheathed in metal, and later replaced by cast-iron beams and ceilings of tile or plaster and hollow-pot supported on brick arches springing from the columns.

At the end of the century the great majority of them were still powered by waterwheels; and those which, by that time, had installed a steam engine were probably using steam as nothing more than ancillary power, employing it, in some cases, merely to pump the water from the tail-race back against the flow to the storage pool. Waterwheels were at first of the undershot type, but a dozen years before Arkwright's first mill was built, the engineer, John Smeaton, had conducted a series of experiments on the relative efficiency of overshot, as against undershot, wheels. His findings, presented to the Royal Society, had shown that an overshot wheel was twice as efficient; and, because of this, once the pattern of the water-powered textile mill had been established in the valley, mill-owners, in the same way as Arkwright at Cromford, either altered their mechanism or constructed new mills to incorporate the more effective overshot wheels. In this way, and by constructing dams in steep valleys, they extracted increasing amounts of power, not merely from the Derwent, but from smaller streams whose flow, at a superficial glance, was too weak to power more than a diminutive mill. When Thomas Tempest, at the close of the eighteenth century, acquired the Peckwash paper mill on the Derwent, his water lease endowed him with the right to extract 800 horsepower from the river; the eight-mile course of the undistinguished River Ecclesbourne provided, at one time, sufficient power to drive nine separate mills; and at Two Dales, near Darley Dale, Edward and James Dakeyne harnessed the waters of the tiny Sydnope Brook to power their flax-spinning mill by constructing three dams, stepped one above the other, and enclosed by the walls of a steeply-climbing valley. By this means they secured, for their water-pressure engine, a head of nearly a hundred feet of water.

Of the cotton mills, a number were constructed by Arkwright; others by hosiers, metal manufacturers, landowners or groups of enterprising merchants who operated under licences granted at his pleasure; while a few, understandably in view of his extortionate royalty demands, were built, equipped and run in outright defiance of his spinning-frame patent.

In addition to spawning factories in Lancashire, Yorkshire, Staffordshire and Worcestershire, and extending his interests into Scotland by a partnership with David Dale at New Lanark, Arkwright sprinkled his mills across the Derwent Valley. In 1777 he leased a stretch of land by the River Wye at Bakewell from Philip Gell of Hopton, who was later to drive a road from Carsington to Cromford and call it Via Gellia. On this land, which he leased for a term of fifty years, he built Lumford Mill and installed his son as manager; but here, as at Cromford, the provision of power led him into trouble. The terms of the lease took no consideration of two important facts: that the water rights on the Wye upstream from the mill were owned by the Duke of Devonshire, and those downstream by the Duke of Rutland. Nor, so it appears, did Arkwright consider these two powerful members of the British aristocracy worthy of consultation. It may be, indeed, that he purposely chose to ignore them, for the Duke of Rutland was known to be hostile to the presence of manufacturers upon his estates, and, according to all the evidence, the Duke of Devonshire's attitude was hardly more friendly. Whatever the case, he pressed ahead with his work on the water installations without any attempt to secure permission, changing the course of the river and constructing his dams and ponds by extracting gravel, stone and soil from land belonging to the Rutland estate. The Duke of Devonshire complained of interference with his fishing, but Rutland went further. He sued Arkwright for trespass, alleging not merely encroachment on his land, but diversion of the Wye from its 'ancient course' to his corn mill downstream. Arkwright had to back down. He admitted the trespass, paid the Duke compensation and agreed to lease the water for forty-two years at a nominal rent of £10 a year.

Thereafter the mill appears to have prospered. It is perhaps significant that when Richard Arkwright junior, who doubled his father's capital by diverting it into banking, decided to sell most of his cotton-spinning interests, he retained the mill at Bakewell along with those at Cromford; and while sentiment may have played some little part, since he in turn passed the mill on to his sons, the younger Arkwright was cast in his father's mould: he was too astute a man of business to cling to a mill that was a depreciating asset. Such evidence as exists points to the fact that Lumford was a highly profitable concern. The *Gentleman's Magazine* reported in August 1792 that it was bringing in £20,000 a year.

In its heyday it gave employment to some 350 workers, mainly, as at Cromford, women and children; but the local resources of labour seem, from the outset, to have proved insufficient, for, as soon as the mill was opened, 'good-natured girls' were imported from Manchester. They were probably still being recruited in June 1790 when Byng, then at Bakewell, 'took a walk to Mr. Arkwright's great cotton mill—and wo'ld have enter'd it, but entrance was denied', the reason being, so he wrote, 'that I sho'd disturb the girls!'

The mill was eventually sold in 1860 to the seventh Duke of Devonshire, who leased it as a cotton mill. Burnt down eight years later and then rebuilt, it was still spinning cotton in the mid-1890s when it was said to have housed nearly twelve thousand spindles. In 1898 the site was taken over by the Dujardin-Planté Company, who used it for seventy years to manufacture electric storage batteries, and during most of that time it was powered by the two massive high-breast wheels, installed in 1827 and 1852 to replace the original undershot wheel. These two cast-iron wheels, 25 feet and 21 feet in diameter, continued to turn under pressure of water from the Ashford Dam till 7 January 1955, when a gear segment of the older wheel broke and jammed. They were then, at last, after more than a hundred years of almost continuous working, replaced by a horizontal water turbine.

The same year that he signed the lease of land at Bakewell, Arkwright also leased from Gell the site and premises of a corn mill at Wirksworth; and two

Haarlem Mill, Wirksworth.

years later he opened negotiations with John Baker, a hosier, for more land at Cressbrook in the valley of the Wye at the junction of Millers Dale and Ravensdale.

In this dramatic setting, amid scenery that Adam described as 'wild and magnificent', Baker had established a peppermint distillery, using as raw material the wild mint that grew on the slopes of the valley. Arkwright replaced it by a cotton-spinning mill, three storeys high and powered, it would seem, by water from the Cress Brook, impounded in a pond, channelled beneath the road and down to the wheel, and then discharged into the Wye.

It was a short-lived venture, fraught with disaster. On 15 November 1785, the mill suffered the fate reserved for so many of these early wooden-framed buildings, equipped as they were with wooden machinery, devoid of dust-extraction and lit by candles. It was burnt to the ground, with its adjoining cottages and, according to the *Derby Mercury*, cost the lives of two small boys who, while watching the blaze, accidentally fell into the pond and were drowned. Arkwright then appears to have abandoned the site, sub-leasing it to Barker Bossley, the brother of Alexander Bossley, his attorney at Bakewell. Bossley rebuilt the mill and probably acquired the lease or purchased the land in 1792 when Richard Arkwright junior commenced his policy of retrenchment; but a quarter of a century later the site was developed out of all recognition by William Newton, and Bossley's mill became an insignificant part of a much larger complex, overshadowed by the majestic Georgian structure which, even today, still dominates the valley.

The lack of records in connection with the Wirksworth mill made it difficult for a time to determine which of two existing buildings was Arkwright's work. The Speedwell and Haarlem Mills lie close together beside the Derby road at Millers Green in the valley of the Ecclesbourne, but the terms of the lease now make it clear that Haarlem was Arkwright's, and Speedwell the work of John Dalley, a local merchant, who had his own connections with the Nottingham hosiers. Certainly Haarlem, a four-storey building of stone and brick, bears all the hallmarks of an early Arkwright mill; and since the premises were sub-leased in 1792, at a time when Arkwright junior was divesting himself of his cotton-spinning interests, this change of ownership may possibly be significant.

The name Haarlem, still emblazoned on the end of the mill by the road, was a later addition. During the cotton depression which preceded the end of the Napoleonic War, the mill was converted to the weaving of tape by the firm of Madeley, Hackett and Riley, who in 1806 had established the Haarlem Tape Works at Derby. They transferred the name, and Haarlem the mill has remained ever since. In 1879 the Wheatcroft family, who had themselves commenced a family tape-weaving business at the Speedwell Mill, expanded into Haarlem and later concentrated their activities there. The mill, though no longer in the possession of the Wheatcroft family, continues even now to produce narrow fabrics, while Speedwell, in the hands of Modern Plan Insulation Ltd, has become a centre for cavity wall and roof insulation.

These outposts of Arkwright's empire in the valley seem to reflect today the inevitable disintegration of a pioneering enterprise, overtaken by its more progressive competitors and eventually, and all too wisely, sold into dispersion. Practically nothing remains of his Lumford Mill, save perhaps the small stone building that flanks the A6 road and Messrs Fearnehough's industrial knife-blade factory; and even this may be a somewhat later addition, though it was probably built before 1799. The old mill at Cressbrook, almost certainly Bossley's rather than Arkwright's, decays among the outbuildings clustered round Newton's magnificent mill. Only Haarlem, now established as Arkwright's work, remains alive and entire; its metal-braced walls, though this could well be an optical illusion, seeming to have a singular outward curve that testifies to age and a weight of machinery. On a bleak winter day, when the clouds hang like smoke over Millers Green, Haarlem reflects that same grimness of feature, that same brooding spirit that Arkwright built into his Cromford mills.

While Arkwright's widespread empire was developing, his partner, Jedediah Strutt, was constructing his own, further down the valley, at Belper and Milford.

The son of a farmer and maltster, Strutt was born in 1726 at South Normanton, near Alfreton, a village community based on agriculture and, to a lesser extent, on framework knitting. South Normanton contained a Presbyterian core and the Strutt family was dedicated to Dissent, an influence that dominated Jedediah's life. At the age of fourteen he was apprenticed to a wheelwright in the village of Findern, a Nonconformist stronghold four miles south-west of Derby, and it was there that he met an energetic and capable girl called Elizabeth Woollat, whom he married in September 1755. Shortly before this, probably at the time when he was still a journeyman-wheelwright, one of his uncles died and left him the stock on his farm at Blackwell. Jedediah thereupon migrated to Blackwell and turned his hand to farming, using some of his horses, according to local tradition, to carry coal from the pits at Denby to Belper and Derby. Just how profitable a sideline this proved to be is impossible to determine, but Elizabeth was a woman of some drive and determination, and it was probably with her encouragement that he embarked on the venture and set out soon after to turn his mechanical aptitude to profit.

With the help of a neighbour, a Mr Roper of Locko, he began to work on the problem of adapting William Lee's stocking frame, a century and a half after its invention at Calverton, to knit ribbed hosiery; and by 1758 had succeeded in producing an ingenious attachment with a separate set of needles operating vertically to make a rib stitch. Early the following year he took out a patent for 'a machine to manufacture ribbed stockings', the Derby Rib machine as it came to be called, and it was on the joint ownership of this patent with his brother-in-law, William Woollat, and the support of Samuel Need, with whom he went into partnership, that his fortune was based. He moved to Derby, established a hosiery business with an agent in

London, and by 1769, when Arkwright appeared on the scene from Nottingham, was, at the age of forty-three, a well-established and prosperous hosier, buying silk twice a year at the East India Company's sales, spinning it in his silk mill, putting out the thread to cottages to be knitted, and selling the finished goods, for the most part, to London merchants.

It would be difficult to find a greater contrast between partners than that which existed between Arkwright and Strutt. Arkwright was an extrovert, coarse and domineering, with unlimited ambition and abounding self-confidence; Strutt was sensitive, solemn and withdrawn: a man whose ambitions were real enough, but circumscribed by what he believed to be possible, considering the fact that he was, as he said, 'a Tradesman'. It was typical of Arkwright that he built Willersley Castle, and spent £3,000 in clearing the rock to provide an eminence that overlooked Cromford; typical of Strutt that the house marked out as his probable home stood, neat, dignified and unostentatious, in the main street at Milford.

He had a reputation for probity that perhaps Arkwright lacked. Just as legends multiplied with the years about Thomas Highs' part in the invention of the spinning frame, so they gathered, too, around the Derby Rib machine; but, however much both may be lacking in truth, the difference between them is, in itself, revealing. According to James Pilkington, a 'rude and imperfect idea' of the rib machine 'had been furnished by a common workman, named Roper'—Mr Roper of Locko, who was employed by William Woollat. Gravener Henson later took up the tale. This Roper, he wrote, 'though an ingenious fellow, was indolent in his habits, and loved ale and company better than intense scheming, and was consequently inadequate to the task which he had to encounter; he however made several specimens, which he produced with much exaltation to his pot companions at Locko, who having more wisdom advised him to display them to his master'. Roper took their advice and showed them to Woollat; Woollat consulted Strutt who, so the legend goes, sold one of his horses for the sum of £5 and paid the money to Roper in exchange for his machine, later developing it, with the help of Woollat, into the device that was patented in 1759. The parallel with Highs and the spinning frame is inescapable; but whereas legend has a habit of magnifying the vices and virtues of its subjects, it also has an uncanny knack of reflecting the popular conceptions of character. Of Richard Arkwright it never so much as whispered that, even at the height of his wealth and success, he ever paid a single farthing to Highs.

In Jedediah Strutt there were quirks of character, human failings that a man like Arkwright, failing to understand them, would assuredly, at least in secret, have dismissed as nothing but bumbling inadequacies. No record survives of the way in which Arkwright courted his wives, but he would probably have found it very difficult indeed to show patience with Jedediah's protracted courtship of Elizabeth Woollat. In the words of Messrs Fitton and Wadsworth, 'he fluttered round the candle like a moth for seven years before he could make up his mind'; and, having at last reached the point of decision, subjected the young lady to a letter of almost a thousand words, full of alliterations and flights of poetic fancy, buried among which, in a sentence that occupied a quarter of the letter, was his long-delayed declaration of intent: 'I am ready to be all you cou'd wish me to be, if you Lov'd me, and which is all I wish, your Husband.'

Jedediah Strutt, by Joseph Wright.

The penny-a-time barber turned cotton millionaire would have found it equally difficult to understand how a man could possibly confess to his son, as Jedediah did, his own, often painful, lack of assurance. Whether Richard Arkwright ever felt himself inadequate, no-one will ever know; if he did, the acknowledgement, likely enough, never dropped from his lips; but in 1774 Jedediah wrote a letter of social guidance to his eldest son, William. 'If I woud,' he wrote, 'I cannot describe to you the awkward figure one makes, the confusion and the imbarrassment one is thrown into on certain occasions from the want of not knowing how to behave, and the Want of assurance to put what one does know into practice.'

It is hard to imagine Arkwright even harbouring such thoughts. It is quite impossible to believe, in view of his insatiable social ambitions, that he would ever have used to the younger Richard the words that Strutt used to William elsewhere in the letter. 'I need not tell you,' he wrote, assuming without question that no mere wheelwright could even aspire to the ranks of the nobility, 'that you are not to be a Nobleman nor prime minister, but you may possibly be a Tradesman of some emminence.' Such circumscribed ambition would never have done for Arkwright; and yet it is one of the stranger ironies of history that in 1856, when his grandson, still living in the great house at Willersley, was nothing more than plain Mr Peter Arkwright, Jedediah's grandson, Edward Strutt, was created Baron Belper. One cannot help feeling that Sir Richard, like the queen, would not have been amused.

But Strutt's life, too, had its minor ironies. Not long before his death, he composed his epitaph:

Here rests in Peace J S—Who, without Fortune, Family or friends raisd to himself a fortune, family and Name in the World—Without having wit had a good share of plain Common Sense—Without much genius enjoyd the more Substantial blessing of a Sound understanding—With but little personal pride despisd a mean or base Action—With no Ostentation for Religious Tenets and Ceremonies he led a life of honesty and Virtue—and not knowing what woud befall him after death, he dyed resignd in full Confidence that if there be a future State of retribution it will be to reward the Virtuous and the good
This I think is my true Character   J Strutt

When he died, he was buried in a vault under the Unitarian Chapel in Field Row at Belper, and a tablet was inscribed:

Jedediah Strutt
The Founder of this Chapel
Died A.D. 1797, aged 70 years

Perhaps, after long reflection, being Jedediah, he might have approved.

In 1773 Belper was a village of five hundred people: a colony of nailers and framework knitters, whose irregular settlements clustered round the old cobbled market place. It was four years later, when Arkwright's second mill was rising at Cromford, that Strutt began to build on the east bank of the Derwent at Belper Bridge. Four years after that he bought from Walter Mather of Derby the old forge site at Makeney, by Milford Bridge, which was advertised for sale in the *Manchester Mercury* as 'New Mills and Mackenay Forges in the Parish of Duffield and County of Derby, most beautifully and conveniantly situated upon each side of the River Derwent'. New Mills or Milford, a mile and three quarters south of Belper, was then a settlement of eight houses, and there, on the western side of the river, Strutt also set in hand the building of a mill. Belper was in production by 1778, Milford possibly by 1782, and as the great double complex continued to grow, the two places were transformed. Milford became an appreciable village, with factory houses to east and west of the river, the mill by 1818 employing seven hundred people. Belper by 1811 had expanded to become the second largest town in the county, and thirty years later had a population of close on ten thousand. Its streets were lit by gas, and two thousand workers passed daily in and out of the six great mills that fringed the Ashbourne road.

In all, over a period of forty years, Strutt and his sons built eight mills at Belper: the Old Mill, two North Mills, the West, South, Reeling, Junction and Round Mills; and at Milford, over a slightly longer period, the Old

Old Forge site and Lower Weir, Makeney—Milford.

Mill together with its East and South Wing extensions, a Bleaching Mill, a Warehouse, a Mechanics' Shop and a Dye House. In the course of that time, Belper became to some extent a Strutt company town, Milford a Strutt village; and William, Jedediah's eldest son, while the younger Richard Arkwright was withdrawing from cotton to multiply his wealth as a money-lender to the aristocracy, extended cotton's debt to his remarkable family by pioneering new techniques of construction that produced in his lifetime the fire-resistant mill.

William, the first of five children born to Jedediah and Elizabeth Strutt, inherited his father's mechanical ability. His own son, writing in 1831, soon after his father's death, maintained that he invented a self-acting mule forty years before Richard Roberts took out his patent in 1830; 'but we believe,' he wrote, 'that the inferior workmanship of that day prevented the success of an invention which all the skill and improvement in the construction of machinery in the present day has barely accomplished'. In that same year, the President of the Royal Society, which elected him a Fellow in 1817, named him as 'the author of those great improvements in the construction of stoves, and in the economical generation and distribution of heat, which have of late years been so extensively and so usefully introduced in the warming and ventilation of hospitals and public buildings.'

But there was more to William Strutt than mere mechanical genius. He was an architect of the highest distinction, responsible for many of Derby's bridges and that showpiece of nineteenth-century medicine, the Derby Infirmary. A close friend of Erasmus Darwin and Jeremy Bentham, he was one of the joint founders, and President for twenty-eight years, of the famous Derby Philosophical Society, which counted among its members not only Darwin, but Matthew Boulton, James Watt, Joseph Priestley and Josiah Wedgwood. It was largely owing to him that the mills at Belper and Milford were, at the time of his death, possibly the best equipped in the country; but his soundest claim to fame rests on his designs for fire-resistant mills, and their construction, according to his specifications, on the banks of the Derwent.

Fire was the bane of the early timber-framed cotton mill. Wood, oil, grease and cotton dust in quantity combined to produce conditions for flash-fires that spread with incredible speed and destroyed the whole fabric; and even if they started slowly and smouldered among the cotton, they were difficult to detect, might break into flame in the middle of the night, and, since many of the early mills were sited in lonely areas to take advantage of water power, and fire-fighting knowledge and equipment were primitive, the results were, more often than not, equally disastrous. The catalogue of catastrophe is evidence enough: Arkwright's Nottingham mill was lost in 1781, the first mill at Cressbrook in 1785, and Thomas Evans' Boar's Head Mill at Darley Abbey three years later; then came Christopher Kirk's at Bamford in 1791, Gardom and Pares' at Calver in 1802, and the North Mill

William Strutt, F.R.S., by Joseph Wright.

at Belper the following year; plus the destruction of Litton in 1874 and the Lower Mill at Cromford in 1890. The problem was a pressing one for factory owners even as early as 1791, and in the spring of that year the most advanced industrial building of the time, the Albion Flour Mills in London, equipped by John Rennie and powered by two double-acting Boulton and Watt steam engines, was burnt to the ground. The destruction of this magnificent six-storey building, admired by engineers such as Telford and Smeaton, probably did more to stimulate experiment than any cotton mill fire in a remote part of Derbyshire; but it was nonetheless from Derbyshire, from the Derwent Valley and from William Strutt that the eventual solution of the problem came.

Hollow earthenware pot, with lid.

Strutt had already shown interest, as early as 1789, in the use of cast iron for bridge construction, and in 1792, the year after the fire at the Albion Mills, he began to build a calico mill at Derby and the Warehouse at Milford. Both these buildings, and the West Mill at Belper completed in 1795, were constructed to avoid the exposure of naked timber, and, as such, they represent an intermediate stage between the timber-framed mills and those completely iron-framed. The columns or stanchions inside the buildings were made of cast iron, and springing from them to support the brick-tile and gypsum plaster floors were arches of brick. The beams were of Baltic fir cased in thin sheet iron, and on the topmost floors, where weight was also an important factor, the arches were of hollow earthenware pots, resembling loose-lidded plant pots, encased in plaster. The columns were made by Ebenezer Smith at the Griffin Foundry in Chesterfield; while the earthenware pots, which served the double purpose of lightening the weight on the timber beams and reducing thrust on the walls, were produced at the Peak Pottery at West Hallam, six miles east of Belper.

In 1796, the year after the West Mill was opened at Belper, Charles Bage, a friend and correspondent of William Strutt, probably inspired by the work already done and assisted by Strutt's advice and technical expertise, carried the evolution of the fire-resistant factory one stage further. At Ditherington, on the edge of Shrewsbury, he built a five-storey flax mill with both columns and beams of cast iron, thus creating the first iron-framed building in the world; and when, providentially perhaps, in 1803, Jedediah's timber-framed North Mill at Belper was destroyed by what the *Derby Mercury* described as 'a most tremendous fire', William rebuilt it, iron-framed throughout, after the pattern of the Ditherington Mill. He later built the Reeling Mill and South Mill in similar fashion on the Belper Bridge site, and also the extensions to the Old Mill at Milford.

The mill complex at Belper, occupying both sides of the Ashbourne road, became so extensive that it was connected by a covered bridge spanning the roadway. This was loopholed for defence against Luddites, Strutt probably remembering the destruction by rioters in 1779 of Arkwright's Chorley mill and his subsequent arming of Cromford with 'Fifteen hundred Stand of small Arms . . . a great Battery of Cannon' and 'upwards of 500 Spears . . . fixt in Poles of between 2 and 3 Yards long'. The loopholes were never used, though, in the disturbed state of the Midlands at that time, they were a sensible precaution.

It was at much the same time that Strutt added to the complex the peculiar Round Building, an octagonal, stone-built mill which probably derived from a mixture of theories emanating from his own mind and that of his friend, the philosopher, Jeremy Bentham. Bentham conceived what he

Interior, North Mill, Belper. Showing William Strutt's fireproof construction of cast-iron columns with transverse brick arches springing from the connecting, hidden cast-iron beams.

Loop-hole, from the interior.   *One of the loop-holes on the bridge approach, North Mill, Belpe*

described as a 'simple idea in Architecture': a building of eight segments, in which an overlooker, surveying the whole from a central well, could maintain a close watch on everything that happened. The idea was particularly suited, he said, to prisons, but it might be extended to factories, madhouses, hospitals and schools. Whether William Strutt believed, like the Lombes, that his workers would benefit from constant supervision seems doubtful indeed, for the Strutts, at least in the context of the early nineteenth century, were model employers; but the very design could well have appealed to his fire-resistant instincts, especially since the mill may have been built for scutching, a process of mechanical beating which opened the cotton fibres and facilitated cleaning, and which, at that time, was a recurrent source of fire.

It is one of the overwhelming tragedies of industrial archaeology that, in the course of the last twenty years, the Strutt mills have, one by one, disappeared: those at Belper demolished to make way for a new West Mill and a modern synthetic processing plant; those at Milford as part of a widening scheme for the A6 road. It is sad enough that the Round Mill had to be sacrificed, for this was a unique industrial building; but the loss of the Milford Mills in 1964 was particularly grievous, since only here, on this close-knit site in the narrowest part of the Lower Derwent Valley, was it possible to see the three separate stages in the evolution of the fire-resistant mill: the timber-framed Old Mill, the Warehouse with its cast-iron columns and timber beams, and the later iron-framed extensions.

At Milford, little now remains. The one surviving monument of value, the Old Dye House, built in 1832, was demolished two years ago; but Belper has been more fortunate. Though five of William Strutt's six great mills have gone, his classic North Mill remains, now lovingly preserved by English Sewing, still connected to the modern complex on the west by the loopholed bridge that spans the Ashbourne road. To ascend in the hoist, climb to the attic storey at the top of the mill, and then walk down floor by floor, through the forest of cast-iron stanchions and beams, to the basement cave where those stanchions are bedded in massive stone piers and the stupendous empty wheel pit echoes to a whisper, is to feel in the dank subterranean darkness the shudder of power that must have run through the walls when the waters of the Derwent turned the great wheel, and the shafting set in motion the thousands of spindles.

Attic, North Mill, Belper. Formerly the schoolroom set aside by the Strutts for the education of the children of their employees.

North Mill, Belper, 1804.

Stone piers, basement, North Mill, Belper.

Arkwright and Strutt dominated cotton-spinning in the valley. By the close of the eighteenth century they owned more than a third of all the mills in operation, but, fired by their obvious financial success, men of other interests, farmers and hosiers, lead smelters and ironfounders, turned to the spinning of cotton as an apparently foolproof method of multiplying such capital as they happened to possess. By the time that Waterloo brought Napoleon's exile to the South Atlantic, down the stretch of the Derwent from Bamford and Calver to Darley Abbey and Wilne, and on its tributary streams and brooks, the Noe, Wye and Ecclesbourne, Lea, Bentley and Sydnope, the morning mists of the valley were gathering around a host of gaunt gritstone buildings powered by their storage dams, weirs and waterwheels.

Until 1785, when Arkwright's patents were cancelled, those who ventured to divert their money into cotton had to take out a licence or, ignoring the patents, equip their mills with spinning-frames and risk legal action. It is impossible now to say, with any precision, who were the pirates and who the licensed spinners of cotton; but Gardom and Pares at Calver, at least for a time, operated under licence and found it very costly.

It was in 1778 that two Midland hosiers, John Gardom of Bakewell and John Pares of Leicester, probably in association with a London banker, James Heygate, leased from Thomas Eyre of Hassop a corn mill site at Calver, and there, on the turnpike to Wardlow Mires and Manchester, set to work to establish a cotton-spinning mill. By 1785 it was a three-storey building, but over a period of three years at the end of the century, the enterprise was plagued by successive disasters. In 1799 the Derwent, in summer flood, washed away Calver Bridge and took part of the mill with it; and this first trail of havoc had scarcely been repaired when a fire broke out and burnt the structure to the ground. Undaunted, the partners reconstructed the mill on more ambitious lines, raising walls of gritstone, three feet thick, to a height of six storeys, with a large central pediment, and staircase turrets at either end at the rear.

The new mill went into production in 1804. By 1830 it employed two hundred workers, and waggons were regularly delivering raw cotton along the turnpike from Manchester and returning north with loads of spun yarn, though the original trade with the Leicester hosiers, stemming no doubt from the Pares connection, was still retained in quantity. In 1833 the weir on the Derwent at Froggatt Bridge was enlarged and a new goit constructed to lead the flow of water round the front of the mill to a new stone wheel-house. This held two wheels, 24 feet in diameter and 17 feet wide, which produced between them 160 horsepower.

In the late nineteenth century the mill had a succession of different owners, and cotton-spinning ceased at last in 1923. Virtually unused for the dozen years preceding the Second World War, it was pressed into service during the war years as a storage depot, and the yard, on the site of the first mill pool, was adapted to hold a plant for crushing and washing fluorspar to be

Wheelhouse interior at Calver Mill.

used in the making of steel at Sheffield. By 1947 the magnificent old mill was a scene of stagnation and progressive decay. The waterwheels had gone for scrap, mud and gravel from the spar plant had silted up the yard and the meadow by the river, and the grounds were overrun with briar and nettle. It was at this time that the mill was bought by W. & G. Sissons, a long-established Sheffield firm engaged in the manufacture of stainless steel. In the course of thirty years they have given new life to one of the oldest cotton-spinning sites in the valley. The mill now, once again, works to full capacity, producing stainless steel holloware; the manager's house is now the company offices, the grounds have been landscaped, the whole of the main block has been re-roofed, and unsafe floors replaced to take the heavy metal presses. The external fabric has been carefully preserved, and those who drive the A623 from Baslow to Wardlow Mires can still see Calver Mill, gaunt and sombre, perhaps almost brutal, yet impressive in its dignity, rising above the village as it did when the news of Napoleon's defeat filtered at last into the Derbyshire hills. Within the old wheelhouse the water still thunders through the two great arches, stultifying speech; and down in the village

Calver Mill, from the rear.

they recall another time and a different war, remembering the morning, not so long ago, when they woke to see the swastika flying from the top of Gardom's old mill. Unbeknown to millions of television viewers who followed the series based on Pat Reid's account of the prisoners-of-war held in Colditz Castle, they were seeing, in part, not the walls of Schloss Colditz, nor some studio mock-up, but the gritstone of Calver. When the prisoners escaped across the roof of the fortress, it was sometimes across the mill's reconstituted roof; and when they looked down on the Sanctum Sanctorum, the inner courtyard of the castle, they were, on occasion, looking down on a yard spread with plastic cobbles, where, thirty years before, a plant had ground spar from the Derbyshire lead mines to use as a flux for making the very steel that helped to relegate Colditz to nothing more than a grim and forbidding memory.

When Gardom and Pares first started to spin their cotton at Calver, they paid initial premiums of £7,000 for the use of Arkwright's patents, and contracted in addition to pay an annual royalty of a further £1,000. This, in 1778, was a very considerable sum of money; and it was no wonder that some of the entrepreneurs who established the early mills determined to forge ahead without permits from Arkwright, sooner than pay such exorbitant sums. One such was Peter Nightingale, lead merchant and smelter and neighbour to Arkwright at Lea, near Cromford. He set up his mill in 1784 close to the road from Holloway to Cromford, powered it by the waters of the Lea Brook that flowed, at this point, into the River Derwent, and advertised for workers in the *Derby Mercury*, promising houses for large families and employment for the children. Arkwright, who subsequently purchased from Nightingale the manor of Cromford, sued him the following year for infringement of patents and won his case, though five months later the Lancashire pirates, predictably alarmed, had the case re-opened by a writ of *scire facias*, resurrected Thomas Highs and had the patents revoked. Nightingale's mill was later sold to a hosier, Thomas Smedley, whose son John founded the first great hydropathic establishment at Matlock, which became, in the Second World War, a school of military intelligence and is now the headquarters of Derbyshire County Council. The mill was converted to the spinning of worsted and the combing of wool and, though the spine of it survives almost intact, it stands now amid the much larger Smedley complex, progressively expanded over a period of a hundred and ninety years.

Others of the cotton mills constructed at this period in the Derwent Valley do however remain, mostly disused or now manufacturing very different products. Christopher Kirk's mill at Bamford, built in 1780 and, according to Pilkington, on 'a construction very different from that at Cromford', can still be approached by a lane that cuts off left from the road climbing up through the village to Yorkshire Bridge. It is now in the hands of the Carbolite Company, who produce electric furnaces and laboratory equipment. The straight weir still powers turbines which generate electricity.

The mill built by William Stretton and J. L. and Joseph Thacker at Wilne on the Derwent in 1781 has been, for the last twenty years, a fireworks factory and gunpowder store. Access is forbidden under the Explosives Act, but the mill can be seen by taking the lane to Church Wilne from the cross-roads at Draycott. Samuel Unwin's two mills at Tansley are now used for storage by a joinery firm, the Top Mill still preserving its three-arched stone conduit which carried the water from a dam to the wheel site; while the Ladygrove Mill at Two Dales, near Darley Dale, originally built by a grazier, Abraham Flint, and later expanded by Edward and James Dakeyne into a flax-spinning mill is now used by a firm making cattle and poultry foods. It was here that the Dakeyne brothers built their series of beautiful, mirror-like dams up the steep Sydnope Valley, and, to cope with the 96-foot head of water so induced, patented in 1830 their water-pressure disc engine.

Perhaps the most remarkable survival, in view of its setting, is the four-storey mill on the River Noe in the Vale of Edale, half a mile east of Edale village. Here, in this lonely spot, difficult of access, Nicholas Cresswell, a freeholder on the moorland pastures, and three Manchester cotton carders, James Harrison, Robert Blackwell and Joseph Fletcher, combined in 1795 to build a cotton-spinning mill on the site of what had been a corn mill and tannery. Labour was, inevitably, in such an isolated place, difficult to recruit. Workers brought in from the towns were accommodated in cottages on the road by the mill, and in bunk beds in the attic of a nearby house, still known as Skinners Hall, as it was when the site was in use as a tannery; but most of the women walked each day from Castleton, two miles away, tramping, in the absence of any direct road, over the thousand-foot high saddle in the hills at Hollins Cross: the old coffin-track that was used when the dead of Edale were carried for burial at Castleton church, the nearest consecrated ground until 1633, when the village of Edale acquired a church of its own.

Despite its isolation, the mill continued to spin cotton till forty years ago. Thereafter, for a time, its fate paralleled Calver's. It was used for storage and then stood empty for years, a pattern of neglect, the land around it run to seed in a tangle of thorns. Its restoration of recent years has not been due, like Calver's, to any revival of industrial interest, but rather to that increasing retreat from the cities which tempts businessmen from Sheffield to buy houses or weekend cottages in the Peak. Part of the interior has been turned into flats, and though the walls have been pierced at ground-floor level to provide parking space for cars, the work has been cunningly and tastefully contrived to match the older stonework. Those visitors to Edale who take the trouble to turn aside down the short track that leads to the yard of the mill can, as a result, see a close approximation to the gaunt old building which, for days and nights on end, when the winter blizzards closed down on the Dale, provided not merely a place of work, but also a dormitory for the women of Castleton.

Edale Mill.

Boar's Head Mill, Darley Abbey.

If Edale is the most remarkable survival, perhaps the most evocative is the mill and industrial community established by the Evanses two miles north of Derby. Approaching the city on the A6 from Belper, one reaches a round-about where the Ripley road branches in from the left. Taking neither of the two main exits, but what appears to be a minor road lying between them, a visitor to the valley can, as it were, step back, in less than half a mile, into the eighteenth century. Here is Darley Abbey, where in 1783 Thomas Evans, the owner (since his father's death in 1746) of lead mines at Bonsall and the iron-slitting mills on The Holms at Derby, built with his sons, Walter and William, a cotton-spinning mill and named it after the crest on his family's coat-of-arms, the Boar's Head Mill.

In addition to his interests in lead, iron and copper, Evans had established a bank in Derby in 1771. Arkwright was one of its early customers, and it was he who persuaded Thomas, then sixty years old, to build and operate a mill under licence from him. While it was under construction, Arkwright was a partner, and later on William Strutt and his sister, Elizabeth, may have had shares; but eventually the mill and its many extensions became purely and simply an Evans concern, multiplying the family's already substantial wealth to a point where, when Thomas Evans died in 1814, his estate was valued at over £800,000.

The six-storey mill was built on the eastern bank of the Derwent, and powered by water channelled through the wheelhouse from a diagonal weir nearly six feet high and 360 feet long. By the end of 1783 it was already in production, only to be destroyed precisely five years later in a massive conflagration from which the fire-fighters could salvage nothing but the wheel. Circumspectly insured, as Jedediah's North Mill at Belper was not, it was rebuilt in the course of the next twelve months. William Strutt's fire-resistant methods of construction were not developed at that time, but Evans took the precaution of nailing thousands of foot-square sheets of tin on the wooden beams to prevent, as best he could, any repetition of the disaster.

By 1830 the work force numbered more than five hundred, and on the rising ground to the west of the river, connected to the mill by a toll bridge above the weir, the Evanses constructed a factory village: rows of pleasant, three-storey cottages: West Row, North Row, Brick and Lavender Rows, with their intervening squares. Already, by 1795, there were more than sixty cottages, and by 1830 nearly two hundred, regularly lime-washed by a team of painters who worked through the village from end to end and then started afresh.

The older parts of the village were classified as a Conservation Area in June 1970, the mill is now leased to a number of different firms, and to walk down Old Lane to the bank of the river is to pass, so it seems, through an artificial time-lock and stand in a peaceful eighteenth-century refuge, not four hundred yards from the rumbling traffic of the main Derby road. The water still tumbles over the weir, and the iron-railed tollbridge spans the river to the solid brick mill; while behind, on the slope, rise the rows of Evans cottages, the multi-paned windows meticulously painted, the squares now landscaped with trees, lawns and bushes, and the cobblestones restored. Apart from parked cars, silent witnesses to the fact that Darley Abbey is now in the twentieth century, one could well imagine that, somewhere on Brick Row or Lavender Row, the never-ceasing painters were still dipping brushes in their buckets of lime, gossiping perhaps to girls in plaid shawls: the Evans badge of comfort, distributed free to the women who came to work at their mill.

Calver, Edale and Darley Abbey are places the visitor ought not to miss; but, above all, those who drive through the valley should climb up from

Ashford to Monsal Head, Hernstone Lane End as it was called in turnpike days, and then twist down the dale to see the grandeur that William Newton left behind him at Cressbrook.

Newton was born at Cockey Farm, Abney, on the moors above Tideswell, in December 1750. His father was a country carpenter and the family was poor, but William was more than usually gifted. He showed a skill in the craft of carpentry that attracted the attention of genteel and wealthy families in the neighbourhood, who employed him, from time to time, to work in their houses. He thus acquired not merely a technical reputation, but access to books, and became fired with an ambition to make himself a poet. He began to write verses, which claimed the admiration of Anna Seward, the poetess, known in her day as the Swan of Lichfield. She wrote to the *Gentleman's Magazine*, enclosing one of his sonnets dedicated to her, which the editor, perhaps because of her patronage, elected to publish.

Meanwhile Newton's talent for carpentry had earned him an even more exalted patron. In 1780 the Duke of Devonshire, then building (from the profits of his copper mines at Ecton) the Crescent at Buxton, appointed him head carpenter; and at much the same time Arkwright employed him to construct the machinery at his Cressbrook mill, paying him a salary of £50 a year. By 1785 the Crescent was completed, and in that same year the mill was burnt down. The fire, unfortunately, also destroyed his cottage and everything he possessed, and it was largely due to Anna Seward, who lent him money, that he survived till Barker Bossley bought the site from Arkwright. Bossley offered him a partnership, provided he could find £200. He borrowed £50 from Miss Seward and the rest, so runs the legend, from another impressionable feminine admirer. By 1790 he was worth £1,000, and a quarter of a century later, still dabbling in verse, could afford to build the magnificent mill which now dominates the valley of the Wye at Cressbrook.

Set on the valley floor between steeply climbing heights, it was a four-storey Georgian structure in dressed limestone, twelve bays in length, with a hipped roof and bell tower, and a central pediment, surmounted by a clock, that broke forward from the front and rear elevations. Inside, its cast-iron columns supported wooden beams, and it was powered by two large waterwheels fed by the Wye from a pool cut out of the massive limestone walls of the gorge upstream. William Adam, visiting some thirty years later, was suitably impressed. The mill pool he described as a 'beautiful lake'. Here, he wrote, 'enclosed on all sides by some of the highest ground in Derbyshire . . . the lofty perpendicular limestone walls which invest it on either side, form but the basis of towering hills which start from their summit.' The mill itself, he continued, is 'a wonderful structure in such a position, for we seem here shut in on all sides, apparently far, very far from the great world. It is indeed a romantic spot.'

To see Newton's mill, even today, is to approve of Adam's words. Of all the water-powered mills for the spinning of cotton built in this pioneer

Cressbrook Mill.

period in the valley, Cressbrook is by far the most rewarding, not merely architecturally, but also in its setting. Yet its tragedy lies in its very situation. Accessible only by steep and narrow lanes, amid what Adam described as 'truly Alpine scenery' in an 'unfrequented pass', it lies nowadays beyond the reach of any really profitable industrial development. Since its closure as a cotton mill in 1965, it has progressively decayed. Its windows have been broken, holes have appeared to pit the slate roof, and the clock, wound for long by a local resident, has lost its power to strike or even to move its now-paralysed fingers. Scheduled as a building of historical and architectural importance, the exterior is now under a preservation order, and a local builder, fired no doubt by the example of Edale, has planning permission to convert a part of the interior to flats.

The mill has already been re-roofed, and hope exists that the fabric may yet be fully restored. That hope must, at all costs, be kept alive, since it means the preservation of one of the richest of the valley's industrial monuments. It would be sad indeed, though balm to his and Anna Seward's poetical vanities, if the only memorial that remained to William Newton were his gravestone set in the churchyard at Tideswell, which styles him, not the builder of Cressbrook Mill, but The Minstrel of the Peak.

Newton's Cressbrook, set like a country mansion in the cleft of the Wye, was the ultimate achievement; yet, in spite of his work, in spite of Peter Nightingale and Thomas Evans, in spite of the two Johns, Gardom and Pares, and the host of other, equally enterprising men whose mills began to rise along the banks of the rivers and streams and brooks, the cotton world of the Derwent was commanded by the Arkwrights and their partners, the Strutts.

Double weir and site of Strutts' Mills, Milford.

Arkwright was the pioneer. He provided the initial, the necessary thrust; but the Strutts, in more measured and leisurely fashion, may, across the years, have made the greater contribution. They revolutionized the construction of the textile mill, their factories were better equipped than Arkwright's, their water controls and power mechanisms far more ambitious. Jedediah, perhaps because of his familiarity with Sorocold's work in Derby, never seems to have had that fear of the Derwent that, one suspects, was always present in Arkwright's mind. The double weir at Milford and the Horseshoe Weir at Belper, which produced a vast lake of twenty-two acres, were quite remarkable feats of engineering. The Belper weir, at one time, powered eleven wheels.

They also, in the generation after Arkwright's death, developed and expanded, at Belper and Milford, the social provisions that he had pioneered on behalf of his workers. Their housing at Belper—Long Row and The Clusters; William, George and Joseph Streets, named after Jedediah's three sons—was superior to Arkwright's. They provided gas for the town, heating and artificial lighting in their mills, and meat, grain, vegetables, milk, butter and eggs from their farms at Wyver, Black Brook on the Ashbourne road, and Moscow Farm at Milford, built in 1812, the year of Napoleon's disastrous retreat.

The Strutts attained nobility, the Arkwrights did not, but another hundred years have produced their own ironic form of compensation. Amid the great complex at Belper Bridge, which Jedediah Strutt, in all probability, financed on his own, and almost in the shadow of his son's great achievement, the fire-resistant mill, there is a sign that carries the same legend as Masson. It reads quite simply: 'Sir Richard Arkwright & Co.'

There is no mention of Strutt.

6 New Foundations

New foundations are always laying, new buildings always raising, highways repairing, churches and public buildings erecting, fires and other calamities happening, fortunes of families taking different turns, new trades are every day erected, new projects enterprised, new designs laid; so that as long as England is a trading, improving nation, no perfect description either of the place, the people, or the conditions and state of things can be given.

Daniel Defoe: *A Tour thro' the Whole Island of Great Britain*, Volume II (1725).

So the transformation of the Derwent commenced. The cotton mills rose, in the words of Sir Arthur Bryant, 'like giant wraiths on the wild Matlock hills'; but this scattering of gritstone, while it brought a change to the aspect of the valley, was only the beginning.

This growth of a factory-based cotton-spinning industry up and down the river and on the banks of the streams and brooks that linked with its waters was happening at a time when, in other parts of Britain, equally significant developments were in progress. In 1709, in a narrow gorge of the Shropshire Severn at Coalbrookdale, a Quaker brass merchant from Bristol, Abraham Darby, had succeeded for the first time in smelting iron in a coke-fired furnace; and though the use of coke, in place of the traditional charcoal fuel, was slow to spread and was restricted for many years to the production of cast iron, the raw material of Darby's foundry, the invention of the reverberatory puddling furnace by Henry Cort later in the century extended its use to wrought iron manufacture. Moreover, when Arkwright arrived at Cromford, the steam pumping engines of the Devonshire blacksmith, Thomas Newcomen, had already been at work for a full fifty years; and by the time his second mill was rising in the village, James Watt, first at Falkirk and then in partnership with Matthew Boulton in Birmingham, was already working on the series of technical improvements that were to transform Newcomen's crude invention into an efficient source of power for the driving of machinery. James Brindley, from Tunstead, high above the valley of the Derbyshire Wye, had completed a life's work of cutting canals; Thomas Telford, John Rennie and John Macadam were learning the skills that would enable them to cover the face of Britain with harbours and waterways, roads and bridges; while, in the very year that Arkwright died at Rock House, William Murdock, an employee of Boulton and Watt in the Cornish tin-mining town of Redruth, lit his office with coal gas; and, in that same town, a young man by the name of Richard Trevithick was preparing to develop more of Murdock's ideas, and, by experiments on high-pressure steam and locomotives, to chart out a course for George Stephenson, twenty years later, to follow.

This national outburst of energy was, in its own way, self-generating, since its progress was dependent on a series of factors that were themselves interdependent. The needs of one industry could only be fulfilled by developments in another. Problems that were posed in one field of progress produced answers from a second, and these answers in their turn generated more problems and produced more solutions. Factories needed stone and timber for their construction, and these required the working of quarries and sawmills. The shell of a factory had to be equipped with machines and power resources to drive them. Waterwheels and, in later years, steam engines provided the power, but waterwheels needed both iron and timber and steam engines, coal and iron and brass. Brass needed copper, and to mine coal and copper meant deeper-sunk shafts and the need to pump water from flooded levels; while to smelt iron with coke required coal for coking and an increased blast. Steam pumps and blowing-engines pumped out the water and blew the furnace fires, but demanded in their turn more coal, iron and brass. The factories, to expand, needed raw materials in increasing quantities and markets for their products, and the provision of these required roads, canals and railways to ease transportation; while roads, canals and railways needed stone for embankments, cuttings and ballast; heavier and more precise forgings of iron for bridges, locks and aqueducts, plateways and edgerails, engines and waggons; and processed coal in expanding tonnage to fuel the fireboxes of steam locomotives.

The result of all this interlocked activity was an age of economic growth which has come to be known as the Industrial Revolution; though, as many historians have already pointed out, the word 'revolution' is perhaps a misnomer. It implies a sudden and violent occurrence, whereas this great change, which transformed a medieval agrarian economy into one based on modern industrial techniques and, in so doing, altered the face of the country and the lives of its people, was of slow development and, for the most part, peaceful. It was evolutionary, rather than revolutionary. Like a string of packhorses it started haltingly, gathered in course of time the momentum of a stage coach and then accelerated to the speed of a railway train.

Professor W. W. Rostow, in a recent analysis of economic growth, designated this period of high acceleration as the period of 'take-off'. In Britain, he said, it covered the twenty years after 1783: those years when growth became the normal condition, when investment rose, new industries expanded and profits were re-invested, stimulating the demand for other manufactures and supporting services to ensure their distribution. The leading sector in this 'take-off' was, he claimed, the cotton textile industry; and, assuming this to be true, then it can also be claimed with some degree of substance that the Derwent Valley pioneered this expansion. Certainly in cotton textiles, both chronologically and geographically, it was the leading sector. The twenty years that followed 1783 encompassed much of the work of Richard Arkwright and Jedediah and William Strutt; and indeed, by the

Derwent, the 'take-off' may well have commenced even earlier, for, by 1783, Arkwright and Strutt were already spinning cotton in eight separate mills.

Their achievements, pre-ordaining an economic pattern that was followed in other and distant parts of Britain, stimulated a host of ancillary industries and the services to support them, covering the valley, once the home of sheep and Defoe's 'subterranean wretches', the lead miners, with iron foundries, smelters and rolling-mills; factories producing machine-tools and wire; quarries and brickworks; bleaching and bobbin-making establishments; gasworks, potteries and manufactories of tape. Main roads were turnpiked; canals were cut to link the Derwent with the Severn, the Trent and the Mersey; George Stephenson drove the railway northwards by the river towards Sheffield and Manchester; and new industries proliferated until, within a century of Arkwright's death, the valley was producing articles as varied in their nature as telescopes and candles, paint and lace, hats and cheese, besom brooms and boots, pearl buttons and bottles of mineral water.

Even before the railways stimulated a massive increase in demand, iron was required in the form of castings for a variety of machinery, and it was certainly, in part, to profit from this requirement that, in 1780, Francis Hurt not only extended and developed his ironworks at Alderwasley, but, in the same year established another at Morley Park, near Heage. On the high ground above Belper, whose nailers he already supplied with bar iron and where Jedediah Strutt had recently built the first of his cotton-spinning mills, he erected a coke-fired blast furnace, the earliest in Derbyshire, and added a second in 1818. Thirty-five feet high and built of sandstone with gritstone reinforcements on the forepart arches, the furnaces were set against the shoulder of a ridge to make it easier to charge them from above, and at the height of their productive capacity were turning out 1,400 tons of pig iron a year.

With their steam blowing engines, banks of coke ovens, pig beds, foundries and 3,000 yards of connecting waggonways, they must have presented to the wondering villagers of Heage not merely the hope of constant employment for hundreds of men, but a veritable panorama of hell. Once the iron ore and limestone were tipped from the ridge into the circular charging holes of the furnaces, and the blast was introduced from a battery of engines that produced between them a hundred horsepower, the earth must have shaken around Heage village and belched smoke and flame as if from the crater of some Derbyshire volcano. To Francis Hurt, ensconced in his Georgian mansion across the valley at Alderwasley, the glow in the night sky above Morley Park must have proved an infinite source of satisfaction, not to mention pride; but for those who heard and saw from the closeness of Heage it must have seemed, as the Black Country seemed to James Nasmyth, that 'the horizon was a glowing belt of fire, making even the stars look pale and feeble'.

Leased later by the Hurts, like the works at Alderwasley, to John and Charles Mold, who dealt extensively in coal as well as in iron, the foundries broadened the range of their products year by year, supplying among a wide variety of castings the seven-ton casing for the first Dakeyne brothers' water-pressure engine installed at their flax mill in Darley Dale, and 500 five-inch diameter pipes to carry the gas from the Strutts' gasholder at Milford to the hosiery warehouse of Ward, Brettle and Ward in the main street at Belper.

The steam engines blasted cold air into the furnaces for the final time in 1874, and since then nature has slowly but inexorably reclaimed the site. The stubs of the massive sandstone towers now stand on their own, isolated ruins amid a flat expanse of agricultural land. The coke ovens, pig beds, foundries and tramways have all disappeared; crops ripen, stock grazes where once the iron waggons, loaded with coal and ore and limestone, rumbled and clanked along plateways to the furnaces. James Nasmyth, himself a mechanical engineer and inventor of the steam hammer, but also the son of a Scottish portrait painter, remarked of the Black Country that in those 'ghastly grey' regions, Vulcan could be said to have driven out Ceres. 'In some places,' he wrote, 'I heard a sort of chirruping sound, as of some forlorn bird haunting the ruins of the old farmsteads'. But it was 'a vile delusion. It proceeded from the shrill creaking of the coal-winding chains, which were placed in small

Morley Park blast furnaces, Heage.

tunnels beneath the hedgeless road'. A hundred and fifty years ago, when the Morley Park furnaces, one or the other, were in continuous blast, birds must have shunned, in a similar way, the sky above Heage. Now the larks sing again in the sunlight of spring, but the great stone towers that parched and killed the grass, reduced trees to blackened skeletons and drove the lark and lapwing from the sulphurous sky, stand silent, deserted, a century dead, and more anachronistic than the pyramids whose shape they so closely resemble.

There were foundries too at Milford, where the Strutts produced ironwork, possibly for their waterwheels; at Dale Abbey, near Ilkeston, where a coke-fired blast furnace smelted the iron that for eighteen years was cast for machine parts, boilers and cylinders and square and round stoves for heating the cotton mills; and on The Holms at Derby, where the Evans' slitting-mill still continued to turn out rods and bars of iron; but the expansion of the industry within the valley was dominated, as cotton-spinning was by Strutt and Arkwright, by the Butterley Ironworks.

It was in 1790 that Benjamin Outram and Francis Beresford established a company to mine coal and ironstone on the Butterley Hall estate, and built an ironworks on the line of the Cromford Canal at Ripley to produce pig-iron and multiple types of casting. Beresford was a member of a long-established Derbyshire landed family and a joint promoter, with Richard Arkwright and others, of the Cromford Canal, which was then under construction to provide an outlet from Cromford through the Erewash Valley to the Trent and the North Sea, and by the Midlands canal system to Manchester and the Lancashire hinterland. Outram was a surveyor, mechanical engineer and pioneer of the early waggonways that linked canals to their customers, the coal mines, quarries, factories and ironworks, and at that time was acting as assistant engineer on the Cromford project. Clearly they were both aware of the financial possibilities of siting a new ironworks close to a new canal in an area where the raw materials of their industry were available.

The following year they expanded their partnership, bringing in to join them first William Jessop, the canal's chief engineer, and then John Wright, the Nottingham banker. Jessop was then approaching the peak of his career as a builder of canals, and Wright, the grandson of Ichabod Wright, the Baltic iron merchant and banker who had helped finance Arkwright, was betrothed and later married to Beresford's daughter.

The ironworks, Benjamin Outram and Co., rapidly prospered under the impact of the French Revolutionary War which broke out two years later, in 1793; and by 1796 the single coke blast furnace erected at Ripley was producing nearly a thousand tons of pig-iron a year. In the next twenty years this production was increased to some 4,500 tons by the addition of two other furnaces at Ripley and a second works at Codnor Park, with two further blast furnaces and a puddling forge for making wrought iron.

During the short but acute depression that followed the end of the Napoleonic Wars there was a pause in expansion, and at three o'clock on a wet June morning in 1817 some sixty to a hundred of the Pentrich 'revolutionaries' appeared at the doors of the foundry yard by the old hexagonal works office armed with guns and spears, scythes and pitchforks, in a farcical and completely abortive attempt to take over the plant. If not excusable, the attempt was at least understandable, since, in the Ripley district, with the coal trade contracting, iron prices falling, and considerable unemployment, economic conditions were all too conducive to violent protest; but the following year there were signs that the slump was relaxing its grip. Expansion was resumed, and the firm, known since Outram's death in 1805 as the Butterley Company, entered on a period of remarkable growth.

Guided by Jessop's son, the younger William, the company extended its already wide ownership of limestone quarries, collieries and mineral deposits; a third furnace was constructed at Codnor Park; by 1827 Butterley was employing 1,500 men; and it was estimated three years later that the company was the largest owner of coal in the East Midlands area and the second largest producer of iron. Sir Richard Phillips, who made a tour of the United Kingdom in 1828, left a vivid description of what he saw at Codnor Park. He wrote:

> It is the kingdom of Vulcan, and to describe it requires a poet with a genius for the sublime, like Homer and Milton. Conceive a space as large as Lincoln's Inn Fields, covered with extended fires and smoke, with the rumbling of blasting engines, the thumping of welding hammers, and scores of men carrying about masses of iron at a white heat—imagine furnaces of melted iron with their narrow doors, from which light flows with sensible momentum, and blinds those who dare to look upon the liquid lakes within—behold sets of revolving wheels, one of them 24 feet in diameter, weighing 20 tons, yet whirling 72 times in a minute, and see the connection of this balance and regulator,—view twenty kinds of apparatus, alive as it were, and with Cyclops moving among them, and you have before you this vast Derbyshire iron works.

Between 1790 and 1830 the firm produced a variety of cast-iron goods which almost defies analysis: structural ironwork for docks and bridges and canals; pipes for gas and waterworks; winding and pumping engines, steam locomotives and a multitude of rails; machine castings, lock mechanisms and, as was recorded in the company's books, even 'a heater for a tea urn'. For Telford's Caledonian Canal they provided lock gates and machinery, rails for the temporary tramways, and two steam dredgers designed by William Jessop; for the Ecton copper mines a steam winding engine and an ore-crushing machine. They produced rails for waggonways at Bugsworth, Swanwick, Brinsley, Fairfield, Beggarlee, Pinxton, Belvoir, Offham Hill, Caldon Low and the London Docks; and built two complete lines, the Croydon, Merstham and Godstone Iron Railway and the Cromford and High Peak. For the latter they supplied virtually every single piece of equipment: rails and waggons; bricks, beams for bridgework and cast-iron window frames; winding machinery for the inclined planes and eight stationary steam engines, one of which still remains, greased, oiled, polished and glowing with vigour in its solid stone engine house at Middleton Top.

The company's engineers always seemed to stand in the forefront of progress. Cort's puddling and rolling processes were introduced at Codnor Park in 1818, and Neilson's hot blast was at work at Ripley six years after its invention in 1829. On 18 June 1835, Mr Joseph Glynn wrote a letter to the editor of the *Mechanics Magazine*. 'The Butterley Company,' he confided, 'have six blast-furnaces, of which four are now in work. The whole of these furnaces are blown with heated air'.

It was a member of the company, Sir John Alleyne, who, by patenting the mechanical traverser in 1861, invented a better method of handling plate and bar iron through the rolls of a mill. He also designed a reversing rolling mill; and in the following year, 1862, perfected a revolutionary method of forge-welding: an entirely new technique that made possible the construction of the roof of St Pancras station, which, on its completion in 1867, was, at 240 feet, the longest free metal span in the world.

But perhaps the most unusual Butterley product was the Walking Locomotive of William Brunton. Brunton, a Scotsman, born in Dalkeith in 1777, started work in the fitting shops at New Lanark mills, and from there moved to Boulton and Watt at Soho where he became superintendent of the engine manufactory. In 1808 he was appointed engineer to the Butterley Company, and four years later designed his locomotive. This, perhaps the most extraordinary steam-propelled vehicle ever conceived, rested on four wheels, but was propelled by jointed legs or 'ski-sticks' at the rear, actuated by steam. Tested on the Butterley Gang Road, the limestone railway connecting Crich Quarries with the Cromford Canal, it performed so well, at $2\frac{1}{2}$ m.p.h., that a second one was built for Newbottle Colliery in County Durham. This, however, exploded disastrously in 1815, killing eleven people, and the project was abandoned.

In 1863 it was reported that Butterley was rolling the largest masses of iron then made, and the firm continued to prosper into the twentieth century, latterly producing wrought-iron rod for the making of anchor chains. The Codnor Park works was closed down and dismantled in 1965, but the original site is still in operation as the Butterley Engineering Co. Ltd.; and motorists driving along the A61 from Alfreton to Derby, as they approach the sharp left-hand bend where the hill climbs to Ripley, can still see the old road sloping down to the yard, and the hexagonal office where, a century and a half ago, George Goodwin, the company's agent, stood in the fretful drizzle of rain and defied the men of Pentrich, telling them to disperse or they would all be hanged.

Three of them were, the following November, on Nun's Green in front of the Derby Gaol.

The iron industry in the valley also nurtured its craftsmen and artists: men like James Fox and Andrew Handyside.

Fox, who set up an engineering works on the Derwent at Derby in 1785, started as a butler at Foxhall Lodge in Staffordshire in the service of the Reverend Thomas Gisborne, and his emergence as a skilled mechanical engineer was due, at least in part, to Gisborne's patronage. Samuel Smiles, writing in 1863, had no doubts at all about the role that the reverend gentleman played:

> Though a situation of this kind might not seem by any means favourable for the display of mechanical ability, yet the butler's instinct for handicraft was so strong that it could not be repressed; and his master not only encouraged him in the handling of tools in his leisure hours, but had so genuine an admiration of his skill, as well as his excellent qualities of character, that he eventually furnished him with the means of beginning business on his own account.

Fox established his business at a most propitious time. The cotton, silk, lace and hosiery industries were expanding in the Derby and Nottingham areas, and in addition to receiving commissions from Arkwright and Strutt, he soon became a specialist in lace machinery and the manufacture of lathes. The firm, in course of time, extended its catalogue of products, turning out a series of cast-iron articles as varied as kitchen ranges, garden rollers and even railings for tombs. According to John Farey, steam engines were also manufactured at the works. Certainly when John George Bodmer, the Swiss inventor of spinning machinery, visited the plant in 1817, an engine was under construction for a steamboat to work the Trent; but Fox's great achievements were the invention of new machines and the production of large machine-tools of more advanced design than those which were advertised by his numerous competitors. He was variously credited with devising machines for cutting screws and gears, a self-acting lathe, a planing machine and an engine for cutting cog wheels; and though it may be impossible to prove, among a multitude of claimants, that Fox was indeed their original inventor, it remains on record that in 1806 he exported to Russia a condensing steam engine, two screw-cutting lathes and a machine for cutting and dividing wheels. His reputation as a skilled mechanical engineer stood very high indeed, and he provides perhaps the classic example of a man who devised and built his own machine-tools to equip his own workshop, and then discovered that he could sell them at a profit to a world-wide market.

If Fox was the inventive craftsman, Handyside was the artist. A Scotsman, born in Glasgow, he took over the Britannia Foundry in Duke Street, Derby, in 1848. The foundry, built thirty years before by Weatherhead and Glover, had always specialized in ornamental cast iron. Handyside not only maintained this tradition and achieved within it a high degree of artistry, he also developed other lines of production and concentrated on producing cast and wrought iron of a tensile strength greater than any before achieved. When his irons were tested at Woolwich in 1854, they proved to be the strongest of fifty different samples examined, and Handyside wrought iron had a guaranteed ultimate tensile strength of 20–23 tons per square inch, as against the usual 17 tons.

While turning out the normal products of an ironworks, such as cast–iron beams for bridges, Handyside developed his own specialities: water cranes for railways; cast–iron window frames; post office pillar boxes; pergolas, vases and fountains for gardens; and lamp standards to carry the new gas lighting. The pillar boxes were supplied at various prices from £7 to £12, complete with a lock and a canvas bag; water cranes cost £28 to £35; and window frames were selling in 1873 at 10 to 16 shillings a hundredweight. These last were fine examples of the iron founder's art, and the firm published a handbook displaying fifteen hundred different patterns.

The list of Handyside's structural work in iron makes impressive reading: the Central Stations at Manchester and Liverpool; St Enoch's at Glasgow; the Albert Suspension Bridge across the Thames at Chelsea; the pier in Bombay harbour; innumerable bridges and railway stations in Russia, Japan, Africa, South America, Canada and India; and perhaps most remarkable, in view of the fact that it was supplied to a steelmaker, a 40 foot high ornamental conservatory with a 21 foot diameter dome for Sir Henry Bessemer's house in London. Thoroughness was the hallmark of Handyside's methods. The cast and wrought iron bridge built to carry the Great Northern Railway over the Derwent at Derby, though finally erected almost on the doorstep of the Duke Street foundry, was first built in the works yard and tested by running six locomotives across it; and even seven years after Handyside's death, when the firm supplied the unique Barton Swing Aqueduct for the Manchester Ship Canal, this too was first erected and revolved at the works.

After 1900 the business declined. Handyside had died in 1887 at the age of eighty-one, and those who succeeded him failed, for some unaccountable reason, to keep abreast of developments. The Britannia Foundry, the source of so much delicate cast-iron tracery and so many monumental transport structures, was demolished to provide the site for a housing estate, and all that remains to signify where it once stood is a sign that bears the name 'Handyside Street'.

But if the works has disappeared, the evidence of Handyside's artistry remains. It reveals itself in numberless cast-iron window frames in mills and workers' cottages; in lamp standards, such as one in the Wardwick at Derby, which still bear the stamp 'A. Handyside & Co. Ltd.'; and, above all, in the magnificent railway bridge that spans Friargate deep in the heart of the city. Friargate was, in the 1860s, perhaps the most beautiful of all Derby's streets. In 1869, such was the local pride in this thoroughfare, that the people of the town subscribed to the planting of plane trees to enhance it. So, when, seven years later, the Great Northern Railway cut through it from side to side, the *Derby Mercury* was quick to put into print what many of those subscribers inevitably felt: that the best street in the town had been 'hopelessly disfigured', especially since a number of buildings had been demolished and the roadway lowered to pass beneath a bridge. But Handyside, commissioned to build that bridge, produced a work of art. The gentle arch was constructed from five huge castings, and the balustrades and spandrels adorned with cast-iron tracery of intricate and most delicate design: a tribute not merely to the local moulding sands, but the skill of the company's moulders and patternmakers. It is one of the finer ironies of industrial history in the Derwent Valley that the Friargate bridge, so maligned in the course of its two-year construction a century ago, should now, once again, be an object of the fiercest civic debate, and its threatened demolition be reviled as nothing short of wanton desecration.

Described as the most elaborately ornamental railway bridge ever constructed, it ought to be preserved, if only as a monument to the skills that once flourished in the city of Derby. To remove it intact to a different site— and this has been suggested—would require handling as delicate as the tracery

Handyside's Friargate Bridge, Derby.

that contributes so much to its beauty; but an age which has saved the Abu Simbel temples from the waters of the Nile and transported London Bridge across the Atlantic must surely possess the technical expertise to conserve Andrew Handyside's masterpiece of iron.

Outram and Jessop; Beresford, Hurt and Wright; Fox and Handyside: these are the names that spring into mind in connection with iron on the banks of the Derwent; but even the anonymous nailers of Belper shared, if only briefly, in the general expansion. The development of waggonways as spurs to the canals presented them, it seems, with a new and totally unexpected trade. It was the practice, in those days, to lay cast-iron rails across heavy stone sleepers. Into these sleepers two holes were drilled to take oaken plugs, and the rails were secured by driving spikes of iron deep into the plugs. The Belper workers were well equipped to make these weighty spiked nails, and it appears very probable that those that were used in 1795 on the Little Eaton Gang Road, an extension from the Derby Canal as far as Denby, were of their manufacture. Certainly the Belper trade seems to have maintained itself in spite of competition for labour from the Strutts: according to Bagshaw's *History, Gazetteer and Directory of Derbyshire* published in 1846, there were still in the town at that time some four hundred workers engaged in making common nails, while a further two hundred

Detail from spandrels, Friargate Bridge.

and fifty specialized in horse nails. But whatever renewed prosperity the nailers' shops enjoyed was destined to be merely temporary. The invention of machinery for producing common nails was already making their hand-work far too slow and costly, and though the manufacture of horse nails succumbed to mechanization only later in the century, the threat from this source was already looming over the Belper smithies. By 1900 machine-made wire nails had virtually ousted the hand-beaten product, and the nailers' shops had one by one closed their doors; though, even today, there are, among the oldest inhabitants of the town, those who speak, perhaps with misplaced nostalgia, of 'Tommy Roundheads' and 'Flatheads', two types of nails that were regularly produced.

The drawing of wire, established at Hathersage in 1566 by Christopher Schutz, also enjoyed a resurgence of activity, not merely because of the need for wire nails, but to manufacture needles for stocking-knitting frames. A number of new firms were established in the village to provide for the demands of the growing Midlands hosiery industry. Robert Cocker set up his Atlas Works on the site of the present Catholic school, and powered it by the waters of the Hood Brook, another of the Derwent's tributary streams; Robert and David Cook, in 1811, transferred their needle manufactory from Red-ditch and built the Barnfield Works, also on Hood Brook: an imposing gritstone structure with an entrance arch, a clock, and a courtyard at the rear, which still stands, though disused, just below the junction of the Grindleford road; while Samuel Fox, later the owner of steelworks in Sheffield, served his apprenticeship at the Atlas Works, started his own business for making umbrella frames, and is reputed to have ridden daily to and from his home at Bradwell, five miles away, on a boneshaker bicycle.

It was a tragedy that this new-found prosperity at Hathersage was ac-companied by a massive mortality among the workers. 'Grinders' disease', a form of silicosis caused by the spraying of metal particles and stone dust from the grinding wheels, was first investigated in 1843 by Dr G. Calvert Holland. He discovered that, throughout the country, the life expectancy of a needle grinder was no more than ten years, and that sixteen per cent of those who entered the trade in their teens died in their twenties. Of Hathersage he wrote: 'The new hands are young men from seventeen to twenty years of age, rough and uncultivated from the plough: and in those manufactories where ventilation is not secured, they are dead before the age of thirty, perhaps after two or three years of suffering.' Later in the century, wet-grinding was introduced, the wheels running in water to eliminate dust; but too late to save a generation of Hathersage grinders from this killing disease.

Out of this growing demand for iron, fortunes were smelted and cast beside the river, but the greatest bonanza of the late eighteenth century occurred not in iron, but in the mining of copper. Fifteen miles to the west of the

Barnfield Works, Hathersage.

Derwent, in the Manifold Valley, lay Ecton Hill, a whale-backed anticline of limestone and shale, twelve hundred feet high. The presence of copper as a localized deposit in the heart of this hill was probably known as early as 1622 when Gerard Malynes recorded seeing 'excellant copper ore' from 'some mines in Staffordshire . . . which absolutely is the best ore that ever was found in England'; and though he made no mention of Ecton itself, there were certainly miners at work on the hill before the Civil War. Whether they were mining for lead or for copper is still a matter of debate, but copper seems to have been worked from 1660 onwards, and this working continued in desultory fashion, partly under lease from the Dukes of Devonshire, who owned the land and the mineral rights in conjunction with the Burgoynes, and partly by the Devonshire family themselves until Michaelmas 1760 when the last lease expired.

Doubtless encouraged by rumours of rich pipes of ore beneath the surface of the hill, the fourth Duke then decided to work the mines on his own account. It was a profitable decision for, between then and 1817, Ecton yielded up 66,000 tons of high-grade copper ore worth £852,000, and the fifth Duke made a profit of £335,000 or roughly £6,000 a year, smelting the ore at his own plant at Whiston, ten miles to the south. The numerous shafts and adits cut into Ecton Hill represented, in truth, one of the richest individual copper mines in Britain, producing, on its own, 12 per cent of the total output of all the Cornish mines; and despite the fact that the shafts were sunk to a depth of 1,300 feet a few yards from the River Manifold and 800 feet below it, the problem of flooding, which plagued lead mines half a dozen miles away, proved virtually non-existent. A small, four horse-power water-bucket engine was sufficient, for many years, to cope with the normal influx of water.

In 1769 the traveller, William Efford, visited the mine and wrote a description of conditions inside the hill for the *Gentleman's Magazine*, recording his impressions in such vivid detail that they have, not unnaturally, been quoted ever since.

> Such a horrid gloom, such rattling of waggons, noise of workmen boring of rocks under your feet, such explosions in blasting and such a dreadful gulph to descend, present a scene of terror, that few people, not versed in mining, care to pass through. From the platform the descent is about 160 yards, through different lodgments, by ladders, lobs, and cross-pieces of timber let into rock, to the place of action, where a new scene, ten thousand times more astonishing than that above, presents itself: a place as horrible to view, as imagination can conceive. On the passage down, the constant blasting of the rocks, ten times louder than the loudest thunder, seems to roll and shake the whole body of the mountain. When at the bottom, strangers are obliged to take shelter in a niche cut in the rock, to avoid the effects of blasting the rocks, as the miners generally give a salute of a half dozen blasts, in quick succession, by way of welcome to those diabolical mansions. At the bottom of this amazing work, the monstrous cavern of vacuum above, the glimmering light of candles, and nasty suffocating smell of sulphur and gunpowder all conspire to increase your surprise, and heighten your apprehensions ... In descending from the principle lodgment, you pass thirty ladders, some half broken, others not half staved; in some places by half-cut notches, or steps in the rock, in others you must almost slide on your breech, and often in imminent danger of tumbling topsey-turvey into the Mine.

Seventeen years after Efford's visit, when ore production was reaching its peak at 4,000 tons a year, more than four hundred workers were employed at the mine and in the smelting works at Whiston in the Churnet Valley.

This was the time when John Byng, on his travels, paused at Ecton Hill and saw 'the many children employ'd in the laborious pounding of the stone', for which they could, if they were lucky, 'gain 6d per day'. But the prosperous days of the mine were limited. Only a few years later, as the miners dug deeper, the huge mass of ore was found to shrink away to a tithe of what it had been, and by 1800 the bonanza was over. The sixth Duke ceased his operations in 1825, and though the ore was still worked for the rest of the century by groups of adventurers and limited liability companies, the once-great mine, in the time of its heyday an English Golconda, finally closed in 1891.

The fifth Duke's profits were made despite the fact that his mining agent, Robert Shore of Snitterton, at a first attempt embezzled £1,000, and eleven years later a further £5,000. Abruptly dismissed, his assets were sold off to meet the debts, which may account for the purchase of his paper mill at Masson by Richard Arkwright. Not that the money was anything more than a trifle to the Duke, since his profits amounted to almost a third of a million pounds, a proportion of which, so tradition asserts, he spent on the construction of The Crescent at Buxton.

The immense amount of ore scooped out of the hill is perhaps best revealed by a reference to Ecton in 1883 by a mining engineer, Mr W. Ninness. Writing in the *Mining Journal* in November that year, he described how, within the hill, there was 'a point, called the Great Opening, where if a good stone thrower was to stand in its centre it would be impossible for him to hit the sides or roof of this artificial cavern with a stone, the distance being too great'; and it had already been said, though with what degree of truth it is difficult to ascertain, that Joseph Paxton, standing in one of the crystal-lined cavities, had been inspired by the sight to plan both the Great Conservatory at Chatsworth and later his remarkable Crystal Palace.

But the Derwent Valley had more solid connections with the Ecton Mine than a tenuous strand of thought that led to the largest glasshouse in the world. Even before the fourth Duke decided to exploit the vertical pipe-vaults of copper in the hill, John Gilbert-Cooper of Locko Park, who worked them under lease for twenty-one years, smelted the copper at his works at Denby, the ore being carried on the backs of packhorses by way of Newhaven and then across the Derwent; and though Gilbert-Cooper's lease expired in 1760, copper from Ecton continued to be processed at the Denby smelter till 1769, when the fifth Duke opened his own works at Whiston.

Most of the finished copper ingots from the Ecton Mine were sold for brass production, but the fifth Duke also had a contract with the navy to provide copper sheathing for the hulls of wooden ships: a new form of protection against the boring worm. Copper for this purpose was sent to Derby and rolled into sheets at the Evans' rolling mills on the island of The Holms, over three hundred tons being treated in this way in the course of two years, 1777 and 1778.

Ecton Hill, general view.

Quantities of lead were also mined at Ecton, and smelted on the spot in a specially constructed cupola. The pigs so produced were also carried by road to Derby, again by way of Newhaven, the returning packhorse trains probably picking up fire bricks at Friden for use in the Whiston smelting works. Once the Cromford Canal was opened in 1792, the lead trade with Derby was discontinued. The pigs were then transported to Cromford Wharf, and along the canal as far as Langley Mill. From there they passed along the Erewash Canal and the River Trent to Gainsborough, making for the great lead market at Hull. In the following quarter of a century 1,132 tons of lead found their way along this route.

The course of the Manifold from Ilam northwards to Wettonmill is one of outstanding natural beauty, but the traveller winding still further up-stream along the road through the gorge comes, of a sudden, on a different landscape. North of Swainsley Farm the road opens out on the scene of desolation, the dead dereliction that is now Ecton Hill. The smelt houses and dressing floors, the inclined tracks that were used for winding the ore up the face of the slope, have all disappeared; but the hill remains a ravaged abandoned waste with, at its foot, the black hole of Clayton Adit boring deep into the caves at its water-filled core. Conservationists lament, even today, the destruction of this once-idyllic stretch of the Manifold; but perhaps there are, to be measured against its loss, a few not inconsiderable compensations. The copper wrenched out of the heart of this hill went to make the brass of innumerable steam engines, lovingly polished by devoted engineers; rolled into sheets, it ensured to Jervis, Howe and Nelson the efficient fighting ships to scatter Napoleon's ambitions to the waves; its profits provided the magnificent sweep of The Crescent at Buxton; and the vision created by its vaulted caverns may well have inspired what Thackeray once described as the 'blazing arch' of the Crystal Palace.

Ecton lay beyond the fringe of the Derwent Valley, but within the valley itself hillsides of green beauty around Hathersage and Crich were rent by the quarrying of limestone and gritstone, and then left abandoned to gape like open wounds on the landscape.

Limestone was cut into blocks for building, crushed into flux for the iron-smelting furnaces and burnt down in kilns to provide much-needed agricultural lime; and from 1791, when the Butterley partners bought land there for quarrying, Crich was its most prolific source of supply.

It was in April that year that Outram and Beresford, to ensure a local supply of stone for their Butterley furnaces, purchased the land that became Hilts Quarry, erected five kilns on the line of the Cromford Canal at Bull Bridge, and connected quarry and kilns by a horse-operated waggonway. Limestone was hacked from the side of the hill, loaded into waggons which were spragged to brake them, hauled by horses down the track, descending three hundred feet in little more than a mile, and discharged into boats by mechanical tipplers from the wharf at Bull Bridge. Most of the stone was transported from there to Ripley for use as a flux to facilitate the smelting process at Butterley, but the returning barges brought coal for firing the kilns on the wharf, since the surplus stone was burnt and sold as lime to farmers, who used carts to collect it from the many landing places along the canal.

From 1805, the year of Trafalgar, until 1819 the installations were leased to the firm of Edward Banks, but apart from this brief period the quarry, kilns and waggonway were operated continuously by the Butterley Company until 1933. The scale of their workings was, however, small when set against those of George Stephenson's firm—the Clay Cross Company.

Crich provided an island of limestone in the midst of a predominantly gritstone area, with rich coal seams less than ten miles away. Stephenson first visited the area in 1835 to conduct a survey for the extension of the North Midland Railway from Derby to Leeds, and returned two years later to supervise its construction. It was while excavations were in progress for the Clay Cross tunnel, seven miles north of Crich, that the coal seams were discovered; and Stephenson was well aware of their potential profitability.

'The strength of Britain,' he said (according to Samuel Smiles), 'lies in her iron and coal beds; and the locomotive is destined, above all other agencies, to bring it forth. The Lord Chancellor now sits upon a bag of wool; but wool has long ceased to be emblematical of the staple commodity of England. He ought rather to sit upon a bag of coals.' He accordingly took leases on the Clay Cross estate, moved to Tapton House on the edge of Chesterfield, and commenced extensive mining of the coal deposits.

The North Midland extension was officially opened in May 1840, and the following year his mining concern, later to be known as the Clay Cross Company, took further leases of land at Brimington, Newbold and Tapton itself. As the mining continued, Stephenson's eyes turned southwards to Crich. Here was limestone in plenty. Quarried and burnt in kilns for agricultural fertiliser, it could consume, probably at considerable profit, the small coal and slack from Clay Cross colliery which otherwise might prove difficult to sell. He proceeded, therefore, to lease the Cliff Quarry, north of the village and a mile from Hilts, constructed eight kilns at Ambergate to the west of Bull Bridge on the line of the railway, and laid his own waggon-way down the side of the Amber Valley, ending in what came to be known as 'The Steep', a 550-yard self-acting incline, which took the loaded waggons down a one-in-five slope to their discharging bays at the Ambergate kilns.

Cliff Quarry, now the Tramway Museum, Crich.

The complex was then expanded. By the autumn of 1841, the eight kilns had become twenty, and 'the works,' in the words of Samuel Smiles, 'were on a scale such as had not before been attempted by any private individual engaged in a similar trade.' The curving bank of kilns, each 35 feet deep, 11 feet in diameter and with cones a further 20 feet high, must have dominated the confluence of the rivers above Ambergate; and, flaming from its twenty cones in the darkness, must have seemed like a row of gigantic black candles burning along the floor of the valley. At the peak of its production the plant was turning out 60,000 tons of lime a year, and it continued to flame for more than a century till the Clean Air Act and the closure of Wingfield Manor colliery, the major source of coal, led to its abandonment in 1965. The quarry and the waggonway had been closed eight years earlier, on 24 May 1957.

Hilts Quarry is now nothing more than a tip, but the ruins of the Butterley kilns at Bull Bridge, bright with a riot of yellow gorse and heather, still survive below the Cromford Canal embankment; and while Stephenson's massive Ambergate kilns were demolished in 1966 to make way for a modern gas-processing plant, his quarry at Crich has taken to itself a new lease of life. Acquired in 1959 by the Tramway Museum Society, it is now the site of a girder-rail tram track that stretches north-west along the quarry floor for three-quarters of a mile; and where the mineral waggons loaded their limestone for transportation down the hill to the kilns, tramcars from places as far removed as Glasgow and Prague, Blackpool and Johannesburg grind round the curves, with a stamping of bells, below the rugged grey face of the limestone cliff.

Because it was strong, because it could be dressed with comparative ease, and, despite its austere appearance, hinted at more internal warmth than did limestone, gritstone was always in considerable demand for domestic building; and even where a cottage was limestone-walled, gritstone was often used for window frames and door jambs, lintels and quoins to strengthen the structure. It was also required for flagstones and setts, pumping engine foundations, crushing stones and grindstones, and, once the railway age arrived, for bridges, viaducts and retaining walls for embankments and cuttings. Millstone Edge and Bole Hill, high above Hathersage, provided millions of tons through extensive quarrying that continued well into the twentieth century and left as its scars jagged walls of rock, if not of Alpine proportions, at least, in miniature, reminiscent of their intensity.

Nowadays these walls appear less obtrusive than the long grey gashes of old limestone quarries, possibly because there are natural gritstone edges running down the eastern fringe of the valley, and these man-made extensions have, since their abandonment, blended with the rest and become an accepted part of the landscape. The steep-falling edge of the Millstone Quarry certainly possesses, when viewed from a distance, an impressive grandeur, while to stand beneath its face is to experience a sensation akin to awe; and to walk below the edge of the Bole Hill Quarries amid glades of silver birch and to glimpse from time to time a crimson-crowned woodpecker tapping at the bark is to wonder at the speed with which nature reclaims the places man has ravaged. But to appreciate the weight of stone blasted from the side of this now-reclaimed hill, the visitor must stand beneath the towering wall of the Derwent Dam, over a thousand feet long and a hundred feet high. For this massive wall, holding back the waters of the upper Derwent Valley, and for that of Howden Dam, a mile and a half upstream, Bole Hill provided between 1901 and 1916 one and a quarter million tons of stone.

Limestone and gritstone comprised, in quantity, the bulk of stone exported from the valley, but perhaps the most fascinating trade in stone was in Bakewell chert, which was trundled in waggons along the newly-made turnpikes to the Staffordshire potteries. Chert is a siliceous rock occurring in the limestone, particularly in the area of Bakewell, Great Longstone and Ashford-in-the-Water; and, largely due to the experiments of Josiah Wedgwood, it came to be used in the form of runners and pavers for grinding flints to powder. Such powdered flints, when mixed with water, produced a clay-like substance which gave a whiter body to the pots, and, if mingled with lead sulphide, resulted in a brilliant cream-coloured glaze. They had therefore long been used in the Staffordshire potteries, and the flints ground in mills between blue granite grindstones.

Wedgwood, however, was disturbed by the inconsistent colour of his ware and suspected it might be due to some impurity that passed from the grinding stones into the powdered flint. With typical thoroughness he carried out a series of experiments at Etruria, proved that he was right and also satisfied himself that, if the granite stones were replaced by chert, the inconsistency of colour would disappear. According to papers in the Wedgwood Museum, he therefore recommended in 1772 'the use of Derbyshire Chert in place of blue Granites or Boulders as we call them, it answers very well and avoids the black specks in our body'; and, addressing a meeting of the Club of Potters at Hanley, he went on to declare, 'We shall abolish grinding it [the flint] with coloured Granite and make trials of a stone called Chert which is found in abundance near Bakewell, Derbyshire'.

Thereafter chert was quarried at the Holme Bank Quarry above Holme Hall, and transported along the newly-constructed turnpike from Hassop, through Kirk Dale and Monyash, to Newcastle in Staffordshire. 'The Day to Day Accounts of Robert Thornhill (1740–1820) of Great Longstone' record that John Hayne, a carrier, of Hardings Booth, Longnor, moved hundreds of tons of the stone along this route, returning no doubt with crates of pottery and loads of farm produce collected from the villages through which he had to pass.

The Holme Bank Chert Mine, so called from the tunnelling method used in extraction, continued in business till 1961; and a reporter from the *Derbyshire Advertiser*, visiting the mine in 1892, found it to be in a flourishing state. He wrote:

> The chert runs in veins between the rocks of limestone, which is allowed to remain above, and thus the depth of the cutting depends upon the height of the chert to be removed. The distance from the entrance to the spot where the men were at work . . . is over a quarter of a mile. A line of rails is laid down throughout, and over this the chert stones are conveyed on trucks drawn by small ponies. A horse 15 or 16 hands high would have no chance of passing through the crevices where, even bending as low as I could, my headgear got crushed . . . The men, numbering about 40 hands, were at work in a rather open place, well lighted up with candles. I had a hearty reception all round, and was very cheerfully initiated into the mysteries of chert getting so far as my ability to grasp things would permit on so short a visit. The sounds of bar, sledge-hammer etc were to be heard on all sides, mingled with laughter and conversation now and then. A large block of the chert, which would weigh about 20 tons, was blown down shortly before my arrival. Men were engaged cutting it into smaller blocks prior to removal. I was informed that occasionally blocks of 100 tons are got down. Powder is the principal thing in use, and occasionally dynamite. There are almost innumerable roads and turnings in this extensive mine. Many are not now in use, but the whole length, I gathered from what I saw and heard, would amount to several miles. The material, which is used in the manufacture of white ware, is now in great demand.

Although 'very large orders' were being dealt with from Scotland, the demand was mainly then, as it had been at the end of the eighteenth century, from the Staffordshire potters; but while Wedgwood and his fellow manufacturers around Burslem were graduating from slipware to creamware and jasper, the Derwent Valley was itself developing an equally distinguished range of potteries.

The industry had long-standing connections with the valley, for sixteen hundred years ago, at Hazelwood, a mile to the south-west of Belper, jars and cooking pots were manufactured to supply Roman garrisons in Northern Britain. The kilns were probably situated close to a point where the ancient track of the Portway forded the river, and distribution of their products appears to have been organized with military efficiency, for examples of these grey–buff, gritty-fabric jars have been traced as far afield as the mile-castles and forts on Hadrian's Wall.

There were medieval potteries at Dale Abbey, Crich and Burley Hill, south of Duffield on the west bank of the river; and by the later years of the eighteenth century at Wirksworth, Friden and West Hallam, near Belper. The Peak Pottery at West Hallam was the main supplier of the earthenware pots that were used, from time to time, to reduce weight and thrust in William Strutt's fire-resistant mills; and a single kiln on this site continued to fire teapots till 1945. This lone bottle kiln, now under a preservation order, still stands amid the ruins of its workshops and storehouses

Peak Pottery, West Hallam.

where the road running north from West Hallam village meets the High Lane connecting Ilkeston and Belper. There is always an aesthetic satisfaction to be gained from the gentle rotundity of an old bottle kiln, but to be able to step inside, as one can do here, and look up the curving, dwindling brickwork to the single circular light hole at the top is to experience a totally unique sensation, as if the world, while still spinning, were standing still in time.

There is no evidence that the mystical interior of this kiln produced anything but unpretentious earthenware utensils, but four miles away at Denby, Joseph Bourne was about to establish the pottery which has since achieved, in much the same field, a world-wide reputation. His father, William Bourne, originally from Eastwood, had already constructed a pottery at Belper, but Joseph, discovering, about 1808, valuable deposits of earthenware clay at Little Ryefield in Denby, set up there a separate branch of the firm. The family continued to operate the Belper kilns until 1819, transporting coal and clay from the Denby area by means of a waggon-way; but in that year production was concentrated on the site of the new deposits, turning out, even as early as the mid-nineteenth century, 'those brown glossy jugs, jars and numberless little toys', as William Adam described them, which were 'made and sent all over the kingdom'. They were eventually distributed all round the world.

But Bourne's Denby Pottery, illustrious as it became, had to take second place to the china works at Derby, founded by William Duesbury in 1755 on the east bank of the Derwent by old St Mary's Bridge. Duesbury, born in Cannock in 1725, had, by 1770, so expanded his business that he owned extensive sale-rooms in London and was sufficiently wealthy to purchase the Bow and Chelsea works, transferring to Derby much of their plant and the best of their employees. He and his son were wise enough not merely to choose their artists with discretion, but to allow them full freedom to exercise their genius. Men such as Billingsley, Boreman and William Pegg did not disappoint them. Billingsley's rose borders, Boreman's centre-pieces of Derbyshire views, and Pegg's floral designs for dishes and vases proved invaluable in establishing the firm's reputation, despite the fact that Pegg, a somewhat eccentric Quaker, grew to believe that his was a sinful art, turned his back on the painting of thistles and snapdragons, and buried himself in a small huckster's shop close to the works.

The exquisite porcelain produced by these and other artists was already known, in 1773, by the name of Crown Derby, when George III gave royal permission for Duesbury's wares to be marked with a crown; and from 1890, by grace of Queen Victoria, the firm took to itself the title of the Royal Crown Derby Porcelain Company. Its products have carried the name of the city, and carried it with pride, to people who would stare in complete bewilderment at a mention of Lombe or Sorocold or Handyside. To millions of collectors, the rich and the not so rich, widely dispersed across the face of the earth, the very word 'Derby' is synonymous with porcelain.

Iron and copper, stone and clay all played their parts in conjunction with cotton in this age of industrial expansion in the valley; but such expansion was continually creating fresh requirements, and the pattern of interlocking growth fresh demands, which could only be met either by extending old-established manufactures or developing new ones. To meet the needs of the proliferating factories, sawmills were established at Ashford-in-the-Water, at Bradwell and on the line of the Bonsall Brook; bobbin mills and bleaching plants at Fritchley and Tansley; brickworks at Derby, Friden and Wirksworth; and gasworks at Milford, Belper and Bakewell; while the growing influx of tourists, as the railways were driven further north through the valley, was recognized at Eyam by Joseph and Walter Wain, who established in the village a bottling plant to provide refreshment in the form of mineral waters.

An ever-growing need was for quantities of paper as business transactions, legal documents and packaging requirements multiplied. Here was an industry that, since the time of Queen Anne, had been expanding rapidly throughout the country and improving its techniques. Already, by 1720, home production had reached a point where it could satisfy two-thirds of

English demands, and merchants who had once made a profitable living from importing paper were noting a progressive deterioration in their trade. One such importer wrote to his Dutch supplier in 1742: 'We are pretty much out of Business and entirely discouraged out of the Paper Trade, which is brought here to a very low Ebb, and will decrease more and more, by reason of the great Quantitys made in England, which manufactory encreases every day.'

The Derwent Valley shared in this increase. Paper mills were listed in 1700 at Duffield, Darley Abbey and Masson, and others were known to exist at Little Eaton and Alport. Two of these areas were to see, in future years, more extensive development. Between 1768 and 1772 Robert Shore of Snitterton, the fifth Duke of Devonshire's mining agent at Ecton, went into partnership with George White of Winster, the owner of the Lumb lead-smelting mills at Matlock, to erect a paper mill and waterwheels below Masson Hill. Subsequently sold to Arkwright, it may well, later on, have been worked under lease, for in Pigot's *Commercial Directory* for 1835 John Skidmore at Matlock Bath was listed among the 'paper makers', and some years later William Adam noted that close by Masson Mill 'and on the same side, is an extensive paper mill belonging to Mr. Simons, who carries on a considerable trade in that important article—paper of almost every quality being produced in the mill.'

Whatever its precise location, Shore and White's factory has now disappeared, probably beneath the later Masson Mill extensions; but the largest of the Derwent paper mills survives at Little Eaton, below Duffield Bridge. Peckwash Mill, now disused and part-ruined, was built by Thomas Tempest in 1805, and manufactured paper throughout the nineteenth century till it finally closed in 1906. Tempest secured the renewal of water rights that had first been granted in 1425, and then had them extended, granting him the right, if he so desired, to extract up to 800 horsepower from the river. In 1821 he installed in the mill a new continuous paper-making machine, and periodic expansion in the years that followed turned the plant, by mid-century, into one of the largest paper-producing mills in the country, with five great waterwheels, the marks of which can be traced, even today, on the walls of the wheel pits.

Unfortunately the company, in 1894, was persuaded to forsake the river, and introduced steam turbines as the source of power. A tall chimney, still standing some distance from the mill, was then constructed to carry off the smoke, but the prevailing wind, blowing from the west, carried it instead towards Blue Mountain Cottages on top of the rising ground to the east. The residents complained, and in 1905 one of them secured a legal injunction to restrain the Tempest firm from emitting smoke. The following year the mill closed, though the Brook Mill, a mile downstream, originally also a Tempest concern, still manufactures paper.

Another growing requirement was for narrow fabrics: tapes to tie bundles

Peckwash weir and paper mill, Little Eaton.

of documents together; bindings and braids for the trimming of textiles. The weaving of these small wares, introduced into Derby at the beginning of the nineteenth century, spread from there to Wirksworth, which, by 1880, boasted five separate tape mills and had become the established source of 'red tape' for Government departments. According to Glover's *Peak Guide*, it was the firm of Madeley, Hackett and Riley who commenced weaving tape in 1806 at their Haarlem Works in Derby. They later took over Arkwright's mill at Wirksworth, naming it after their Derby factory, but in 1879 Haarlem at Wirksworth passed into the hands of the Wheatcroft family, who were already producing tape at the Speedwell Mill, close by on the Ecclesbourne. Wheatcrofts rapidly became the main Wirksworth manufacturers of narrow fabrics, the *High Peak News* confiding to its readers on 4 January 1896 'that three tons of tape are turned out every week in the year, and that 108 yards weigh approximately half-a-pound so that the mileage each week must be stupendous, and it is more than possible for the Haarlem and Speedwell tape in one week to cover the circumference of the earth.' Wheatcrofts still produce tape at the Haarlem Mill, though Speedwell has been yielded up to an insulation firm.

Speedwell Mill, Wirksworth.

Diversification, on a minor scale, was also making itself apparent in the valley. New industries were developing, which bore little relation to past activities. At Hathersage, Dale Mill, once one of the many wire works, was re-equipped to manufacture pearl buttons; Stoney Middleton turned to the production of besoms, brooms made of twigs; and Bradwell became the centre of a new domestic industry based on optical glass, turning out spectacles, opera glasses and telescopes. Indeed, this small village on the edge of Hope Valley became the very epitome of diversification, providing a home for lead-smelters, tanneries, cotton and silk weaving establishments, hat factories and sawmills.

But expansion not only created new industries. It gave many old ones a new lease of life, and rooted them in places with which, up to that time, they had had but scant connection. In Belper the small community of frame-work knitters had always had to take second place to the nailers, but with the growth of the Strutts' spinning mills there and at Milford, the town rapidly became a developing centre for master hosiers and their outworkers—

Brettle's Hosiery Works, Belper.

families who hired stocking-frames and used them in their homes. It was in 1802 that William and John Ward made their appearance in what had once been a nailers' stronghold, to be followed a year later by George Brettle. The three men combined their resources to found the hosiery firm of Ward, Brettle and Ward, with a large collecting warehouse in Chapel Street and a network of domestic knitters living anything up to ten miles distant from the town. Glover reported that, as early as 1829, the company, which still flourishes in Belper today, had 400 frames for making silk hose and gloves, and a further 2,500 devoted to cotton hose. At that time they were said to be producing 100,000 dozen pairs of stockings every year.

Yet perhaps the most remarkable of all transformations was that wrought by the steam engine on the mining of lead, the valley's oldest industry. There was little need to look far afield for the evidence. It was apparent in the expanding production at Eyam and Stoney Middleton, Winster and Monyash, of heavy boots and candles; in the shaping at Bradwell of basin-shaped hats made of thick protective felt, known as 'Bradder beavers'; and, close to the river and on the high moors, in the solid, stone-built engine houses raised above the deepening shafts of the lead mines, where New-comen engines, 'accompanied', in the words of Samuel Smiles, 'by an extraordinary amount of wheezing, sighing, creaking and bumping', strove to lift the water that, in the end, drowned the richest workings in Britain.

7   The Balanced Beam

Press'd by the ponderous air the Piston falls
Resistless, sliding through its iron walls;
Quick moves the balanced beam, of giant birth,
Wields his large limbs, and nodding shakes the earth.

Erasmus Darwin: *The Botanic Garden (1789–1791).*

I sell here what all the world desires, power.

Matthew Boulton to James Boswell, during the latter's visit to Soho (1776).

Sixty years before Arkwright took his first determined steps from Preston to Nottingham, and at much the same time as Abraham Darby, in the gorge of the Severn at Coalbrookdale, was experimenting with a series of coke-fired furnaces, an obscure blacksmith–ironmonger from Dartmouth in Devon was grappling with a problem which was threatening the existence of the Cornish mines.

Tin had been mined in Cornwall since ancient times, and vast resources of copper lay hidden below the surface ready to meet the growing demand for brass, but the county's unique geographical setting militated against the deep mining involved. A narrow strip of land, at its broadest point between Bude and Saltash only thirty miles across, it was washed on three separate sides by the sea. There were few places in the county which lay more than fifteen miles from the coast, and from the crest of Brown Willy on Bodmin Moor it was possible, on a clear day, to see the waters of both the Atlantic and the Channel. Mine shafts and workings so close to the sea were inevitably subject to the danger of flooding, especially those in the rich mineral spur of the Land's End Peninsula, north and south of St Just, where the mine buildings clustered close to the cliffs, and where, in some cases, the levels ran for hundreds of yards beneath the sea. It was said, indeed, that men hacking at the rock in Botallack Mine, a mile and a half from St Just, could hear, on stormy days, the beat of the sea above them as they worked, 'the break, flux, ebb and reflex of every wave'; and Wilkie Collins, the novelist, visiting the mine in 1850, reported that, even when the sea was calm, they could feel on their ears 'a long, low mysterious moaning' that never changed.

Because of the uncontrollable encroachment of water, many Cornish mines, at the end of the seventeenth century, were facing the threat of closure, while rich veins of tin and richer veins of copper lay as yet untapped beneath their progressively drowning corridors. Methods of unwatering the workings were primitive. Crude mechanisms operated by hand or by foot; horse-gins for raising and lowering buckets; rag-and-chain pumps; and the long, sloping soughs or drainage tunnels, known in Cornwall as adits, were all ineffective to hold back the rising tide below ground. Neither men nor horses could lift the water faster than it flowed into the mine, and the adits, invaluable in earlier years when ore extraction was confined to shallow workings, proved impracticable once the shafts plunged beneath the level of adjacent rivers or, ultimately, the sea.

If the richest of the Cornish mines were even to survive, let alone look forward to a prosperous future, some method of power pumping, independent of man or animal, and swifter than either, had to be discovered; and this was the task that Thomas Newcomen, in his workshop at Dartmouth, had pledged himself to fulfil.

He was not the first to apply his energies to the problem. Some ten years before, in 1698, 'Captain' Thomas Savery, another Devonshire inventor, had taken out a patent for a pumping device worked by the power of steam.

Comparatively few facts have been unearthed about Savery. Even the title of 'Captain', by which he was known, continues to pose its own problems of origin, suggesting a varied array of possibilities: that he may have been a ship's master, a military engineer or, perhaps more likely, a supervisor in the Cornish mines. He certainly seems to have been well acquainted with the problems of deep mining. He described his device as 'The Miner's Friend', specified it to be a 'new Invention for Raiseing of Water . . . by the Impellent Force of Fire, which will be of great use and Advantage for Drayning Mines', and appended to his patent application an address to 'The Gentlemen Adventurers in the Mines of England'. 'For the draining of mines and coal pits,' he wrote, 'the use of the engine will sufficiently recommend itself in raising water so easie and cheap, and I do not doubt that in a few years it will be a means of making our mining trade, which is no small part of the wealth of this kingdome, double if not treble to what it now is.'

In this conclusion he was far from correct. His pump, though it lifted quantities of water, had fatal limitations inherent in its very method of operation. Steam from a boiler was admitted through a valve into a closed tank. Cold water was then sprayed on the outside of the tank, and the steam inside condensed, producing a vacuum. The vacuum drew water up a suction pipe and through a non-return valve in the bottom of the tank; and, once steam was again admitted, the pressure drove the water out of the tank through another non-return valve and up a delivery pipe. It was a simple and indeed ingenious operation, but since the suction process depended on atmospheric pressure to achieve the initial lift, that lift was limited to thirty-two feet: the maximum height to which a column of water could be raised by the weight of the atmosphere at sea-level; and, even allowing for the combined effect of suction and pressure, it was virtually impossible for the pump to raise water more than fifty feet. Such a modest capability proved of little use in conquering the problems posed by deep mines, and though it was theoretically possible to install a whole series of Savery pumps at fifty-foot intervals down a deep shaft, no record exists to indicate that this was ever attempted.

The Miner's Friend brought no relief to the hard-pressed owners of the Cornish metal mines. Its application was restricted to lifting water in large private houses, and returning it to the headrace of a handful of waterwheels. According to Abraham Rees in his *Cyclopaedia*, an improved version was in use in 1819 to assist the drive of an 18-foot wheel at a London axle-tree factory, but an earlier model installed near the Strand to supply the neighbourhood with water from the Thames was eventually discarded because of its repeated failure, and it was left to Thomas Newcomen to provide the first power pumping mechanism that could be relied upon to operate with any efficiency.

Intensive research into the origins and life of this obscure Devonshire iron-worker has yielded only the barest of details, and he remains, for the genius he undoubtedly was, a shadowy figure. Christened in Dartmouth, thirty miles from the Cornish border, on 24 February 1663, he may well have served some kind of apprenticeship in the town of Exeter before returning to Dartmouth and establishing himself as an ironmonger and smith. It seems that he was a Baptist and a local preacher; that he married late in life at the age of forty-two; that he had a partner, John Calley or Cawley, who was plumber, glazier and tinsmith combined; and that he probably visited the Cornish mines in the course of his business; but practically nothing is known of his experiments with steam until the engine he invented had achieved a sufficiently reliable form to be erected at the head of a mine to pump water.

This, strangely enough, was not in Cornwall but at a colliery in Staffordshire, close to Dudley Castle, in 1712. It could be that Newcomen had already failed with an attempt nearer home. There is certainly some evidence, if it is little more than rumour, that one of his engines was assembled at the head of a tin mine near Breage. Perhaps, there, it proved less than successful, and news of its faults was noised around the county; but this is mere speculation. What we do know for certain is that Newcomen engines consumed inordinate quantities of.coal, and the provision of such fuel in an area lacking coal mines was not an expense to be lightly assumed. A flooded colliery, on the other hand, was an ideal testing ground for such a coal-hungry engine, and it is possible that Newcomen had Baptist friends in the Midlands where Nonconformity was strong.

The actual location of the engine has been much debated, but an engraving by Thomas Barney, made in 1719, suggests it may have stood on the Tipton side of Dudley, and shows its mode of operation in considerable detail. It was a very different piece of mechanism from the Miner's Friend, and bore a greater resemblance, since it was a piston or reciprocating engine, to the model constructed some twenty years before by Denis Papin, a French scientist and assistant to Christiaan Huygens, the Dutch astronomer and natural philosopher. Steam from a boiler was passed into an open-topped cylinder containing a piston, which was packed with leather and sealed by a layer of water on top. The piston was suspended by a chain from one end of a rocking beam, while from the other end the pump rods were similarly suspended. When steam entered the cylinder at slightly more than the pressure of the atmosphere, the weight of the pump rods drew up the piston. The steam valve was then closed, a jet of cold water was injected into the cylinder and the steam condensed, creating a partial vacuum; whereupon atmospheric pressure drove the piston down, thus lifting the rods. This was the working stroke, and the cycle was then repeated. According to Barney's drawing, the size of the engine could hardly be described as its least impressive feature. Accommodated in a house some thirty feet high, it had a cylinder 19 inches in diameter, and the rocking motion of the great oak beam, 25 feet long, raised ten gallons of water 153 feet at each stroke, or, at twelve strokes a minute, 7,200 gallons every hour.

Unfortunately for Newcomen, at the time of its erection Savery was still alive, and his master patent, which covered all devices for raising water by fire, had been extended by Parliament to 1733. In order, therefore, to exploit his invention, Newcomen had to enter into a form of partnership with a man whose own device had proved of little practical value; and there seems to be no doubt that the arrangement assured Captain Savery of the lion's share of the spoils. The fact that these hardly constituted a fortune up to the time of Savery's death in 1715 proved, to Newcomen, little consolation, for the patent was then secured by a syndicate of London speculators, who devised a method of enriching themselves and keeping the inventor well in the background, charging at the same time royalty payments which, in those days, could well have been described as extortionate. In 1725 an engine was erected at the Edmonstone Colliery, Midlothian, in Scotland under licence 'granted by the Committee in London, appointed and authorized by the Proprietors of the Invention for raising Water by Fire'. The costs of engine and erection were over £1,000, and in addition the royalty payable to the syndicate was set at £80 a year for an eight-year period. Such charges very naturally restricted the number of engines built under licence, and Newcomen died in 1729, like William Lee of Calverton, the inventor of the stocking frame, almost unknown and in humbler circumstances than should have been his due.

The fact that, in spite of high costs—and these included a heavy consumption of coal—his engines were at work, some years before his death, in eight separate counties, proves not only that mine owners were fighting a desperate battle against water, but that many of them considered the engine, expensive and voracious of fuel as it was, to be their only reliable means of salvation. The need for it became apparent once the patent expired.

By 1769, according to one estimate, 98 had been erected in Scotland and the north of England; and in 1775 there were reckoned to be something like a hundred at work around the River Tyne, and 60 had, by that time, been installed at the heads of the Cornish mines.

Even so, for the mining magnates of Cornwall, Newcomen's engine proved to be only a partial solution. As the tin and copper shafts were bored ever deeper, it failed to pump dry the lower working levels, and since the cylinder was cooled at every single stroke by cold-water injection, it burnt coal at a truly alarming speed in a county where the cost of such imported fuel was disproportionately high. Robust as it was, simple enough to be constructed by a blacksmith turned millwright, and sufficiently reliable to require little maintenance, it yet failed to provide a satisfactory answer to Cornish problems. These had to be suffered and barely controlled till James Watt, Trevithick and the great engine-builders such as Harveys of Hayle furnished the solution.

It was Watt who achieved the breakthrough by inventing and patenting the separate condenser, perhaps the most vital of all improvements made to the steam engine.

Born at Greenock, on the banks of the Clyde downstream from Glasgow, he trained as a metal craftsman in London before returning to Scotland as instrument maker to Glasgow University. Towards the end of 1763, while working in this capacity, he was asked to repair a small scale model of a Newcomen engine, which was used at the university for demonstration purposes. He restored it to working order, and then set himself the task of reducing its fuel consumption. He realized that the engine was wasting steam, and that this was due to the cooling of the cylinder at each successive stroke; but the upward movement of the pump rods depended on the piston being depressed by the atmosphere, and this, in its turn, depended on a vacuum in the cylinder, which could only be created by an injection of water which had a cooling effect. The solution to the problem consequently lay in devising some new method of creating a vacuum, which would, at the same time, keep the cylinder hot. As he wrote in later years: 'I perceived that, in order to make the best use of steam, it was necessary ... that the cylinder should be maintained always as hot as the steam which entered it.' Because this condition was never fulfilled in the Newcomen engine, steam had to be used to re-heat the cylinder and this accounted for the heavy fuel consumption, since the engine was using, at every stroke, several times as much steam as was required to fill the cylinder.

It was a problem that took him eighteen months to solve, and not until the May of 1765 did the answer present itself. He was, as he said, taking a walk on Glasgow Green on a Sabbath afternoon, 'when the idea came into my mind, that as steam was an elastic body it would rush into a vacuum, and if a communication was made between cylinder and an exhausted vessel, it would rush into it, and might there be condensed without cooling the cylinder.' So was born, at a stroke of genius, the separate condenser: a separate vessel connected to the cylinder, in which the steam was condensed by water injection and the vacuum created, leaving the steam in the cylinder and the vacuum in the condenser to change positions once the valve on the connecting pipe between them was opened. Thus atmospheric pressure could work on the piston, and, once it was depressed, the cylinder was still hot for the re-admission of steam.

But a brilliant idea and its practical application may be many moons apart. Eleven years were to pass before the first effective Watt engine with its separate condenser was erected, by a strange coincidence, at Tipton: eleven years of struggle and near-heartbreak for Watt; eleven years, in the course of which the engine repeatedly failed at its trials, and, to add to his ever increasing despair, his wife, Margaret, died.

His early experiments in Glasgow were financed by a friend at the university, Dr Joseph Black, the Professor of Chemistry, and it was Black who introduced him to Dr John Roebuck, a fellow chemist and master of the new Carron Ironworks, who had taken lease of the Duke of Hamilton's coal mines at Bo'ness, near Falkirk, on the Firth of Forth. The mines were flooded, Newcomen engines ineffective, and, in the hope that Watt's invention might eventually clear the water, Roebuck paid his debt to Black, helped him to take out a patent in 1769 for 'A New Method of Lessening the Consumption of Steam and Fuel in Fire Engines', and assumed, in return, a two-thirds share in the separate condenser.

Watt then moved into Roebuck's mansion, Kinneil House near Bo'ness, where, according to Samuel Smiles, 'he at length fixed upon an outhouse . . . close behind the mansion, by the burnside in the glen, where there was abundance of water and secure privacy'. Here he made detailed drawings of the metal parts required from Roebuck's craftsmen, and here, in course of time, the engine was assembled; but the doctor's workmen at Carron apparently proved incapable of the precision required; vital components, one after another, broke under stress, and by 1773 Roebuck was bankrupt. 'I have met with many disappointments,' Watt was reported as saying, 'and I must have sunk under the burthen of them if I had not been supported by the friendship of Dr Roebuck . . . He has been a most sincere and generous friend, and is a truly worthy man . . . My heart bleeds for him, but I can do nothing to help him: I have stuck by him till I have much hurt myself; I can do so no longer.'

Salvation was provided by Matthew Boulton, to whom Roebuck owed a considerable sum of money. Impressed by what he knew of Watt's invention, Boulton invited him to bring his engine to Birmingham, and, in spite of the fact that most of the doctor's creditors considered it to be worthless, accepted Roebuck's interest in the patent as settlement of his debt.

Had Watt been able to make his own choice of a partner, he could hardly have chosen better. Boulton possessed not only a shrewd head for business, but a buoyant courage and down-to-earth common sense that made him the ideal counterpart to the man Smiles described as 'timid, desponding, painfully anxious, and easily cast down by failure'. He employed, moreover, at his Soho works in Handsworth, six hundred of the finest metal craftsmen in Europe, trained in all the skills that Watt required to translate his still-experimental engine into a valid commercial asset. It was Boulton who urged him to apply to Parliament for an extension of his patent, which had then only eight years still to run; and once that extension had been granted for a further twenty-five years, it was he who took the bold decision to put the engine on the market while Watt was still engaged in perfectionist experiments.

In 1776 three engines were erected: the first at Bloomfield Colliery, near Tipton; another for a distillery at Stratford-le-Bow in London; and a third to increase the blast at John Wilkinson's furnaces at Broseley in Shropshire. This last was a shrewd stroke of business achieved by Boulton. Wilkinson had invented a new type of engine for boring cannon barrels: a device that, adapted to work on a different principle—that of the boring bar—could bore steam-engine cylinders to a greater degree of precision than any other boring machine then in use. Wilkinson bored his own cylinder, and there-after, for almost twenty years, he supplied cast-iron cylinders for Boulton and Watt, dispatching them direct to the places where they were due to be installed. The Birmingham partners, for their part, insisted that their customers ordered from him; and for both the contracting parties it was a profitable arrangement. Wilkinson sold the cylinders, but there can also be little doubt that he made Watt's engine a practical proposition.

Even in 1776 success was apparent. The new engines not only pumped faster than the old, but consumed less than a third of the fuel; and though Newcomen engines survived for many years in colliery districts such as Northumberland where fuel costs were a comparatively unimportant factor, elsewhere they were rapidly superseded. In Cornwall, as early as 1770, over half of the Newcomen engines had been forced into idleness by the mounting cost of the coal they consumed. By the end of the century they had virtually disappeared from the face of the county, and, in their stead, more than fifty Watt engines presided over mines like Great Wheal Busy on the Truro—Redruth road, where the first was erected in 1777.

From Kit Hill in the east to Cape Cornwall in the west Boulton and Watt took control, but theirs was a less than easy occupation. Though, by 1782, Watt had dispensed with atmospheric working and, by closing the top of the cylinder, had produced a pure steam engine which used the steam in a double-acting capacity, to both power the upward movement of the piston and depress it; and though he had, in addition, invented his sun-and-planet device, so that his engines turned wheels and could wind as well as pump, yet the Cornish mine-owners resented their bondage to these 'foreigners' from Birmingham.

The improved engines were certainly far more efficient in terms of water raised as compared with coal consumed, but the costs of engine and installation were still as heavy as before, and the royalties demanded by the Midlands partners, one-third the value of the saving in coal, were regarded by many Cornish owners as penal. Their resentment, nurtured for a quarter of a century, crystallized into a solid determination to free themselves from these extortionate payments as soon as such freedom became a practical possibility; and they were fortunate to possess, among their native engineers, a man whose genius in the field of steam was perhaps the equal of Watt's.

Richard Trevithick was born at Illogan, near Redruth, six years before the first Boulton and Watt engine was installed in the county. As a young man he worked as a mining engineer in the town of Penzance, but when he applied to join the Birmingham firm, his application was rejected, some say on the advice of William Murdock, who was Boulton's principal engine erector in Cornwall. Trevithick then attached himself to Edward Bull, another Cornish engineer, and began to experiment with a new type of engine worked by high-pressure steam.

Bull devised a steam pumping engine which dispensed with the rocking beam, since its cylinder was inverted over the mine shaft, but Boulton and Watt brought a test case against him to protect their monopoly under the patent. They won the legal battle that ensued, and, as Watt had included expansive working in one of his later patents, it was clear that any development in high-pressure steam that Trevithick and his fellow engineers might achieve would be similarly blocked, since high-pressure engines of the type they were investigating used steam expansion through part of the stroke. There was therefore nothing for them to do but work on and wait, with such patience as they could muster, till the patents expired in 1800.

Watt had always worked on pressures below ten pounds per square inch, since the wagon type of boiler used on his engines was incapable of withstanding higher pressures. Trevithick proposed to use steam at nearly three times that pressure, and for this he invented a new kind of boiler, cylindrical in shape with a single internal fire tube extending from end to end. This, the 'Cornish' boiler, was destined to prove the pattern for all high-pressure steam engines till the 'Lancashire' boiler, with a double tube for alternate firing, was patented by William Fairbairn and John Hetherington of Manchester in 1844.

At the turn of the century, when the patents exploited for twenty-five years by Boulton and Watt eventually expired, the way was clear for Trevithick to patent his own high-pressure engine; but the first was not erected at the head of a mine until 1812, when a small version, working at a pressure of 40 pounds per square inch, was installed at the Wheal Prosper mine at Gwithian, between Hayle and Camborne. The engine was designed to economize on fuel by cutting off the steam at one-ninth of the stroke, and the remaining movement of the piston was to be powered by expansion of the steam already in the cylinder. This was the first of a long generation of 'Cornish' engines, slow and ponderous in operation, but ideal for the Cornish mines, since they pumped immense quantities of water at a very much lower consumption of coal.

In 1816 Trevithick left Cornwall to work among the silver mines of Costa Rica and Peru, and, because he remained abroad until 1827, the development of the Cornish engine was left to other engineers, among them Samuel Grose and William West, and to the great engine-building foundries such as Harveys at Hayle.

It was in 1779 that John Harvey, a Cornish blacksmith who owned a forge at Carnhell Green three miles from the town, constructed a small ironworks between the Hayle and Penpol rivers. The foundry prospered and expanded; Jane, his daughter, married Richard Trevithick; and Harveys became the most celebrated engine-builders in Cornwall, their most remarkable construction being the Cruquius engine of 1849, built for the Dutch government to drain Haarlem Meer, which had a cylinder 144 inches in diameter.

Cornish engines with 80-inch cylinders became commonplace, their massive dimensions made necessary because of the expansive working on which they relied. The use of high-pressure steam created problems of power which could only be solved by enlarging the engine. Maximum power could only be achieved by non-expansive working: by admitting steam to the cylinder throughout the whole of the piston stroke; but the Cornish designers had realized that maximum efficiency depended on cutting off the steam when only a fraction of the stroke had been completed, and allowing the expansion of steam trapped in the cylinder and the energy stored in the beam and rods to power the remainder. The trouble was that, in a high-pressure engine, the boiler pressure could not be raised to give increased power; so the only way to strike a balance between power and efficiency, achieving the best of both, was therefore to increase the size of the engine. Cornish engines with cylinders 7 feet in diameter, with a piston-stroke of 12 feet and rocking beams of cast iron weighing thirty tons became an increasingly familiar sight, sweeping the county all but bare of Boulton and Watt engines in much the same way as the Birmingham men, fifty years before, had driven out those of Thomas Newcomen.

The Cornish beam engine was the ultimate in expansive, single-cylinder working. Advance from this was through the great compound and triple-expansion engines, which powered the rope-and-lineshaft drives of the later Lancashire cotton mills; but the engines of Grose and West, Harveys and Holmans, and foundries such as Perran, Charlestown and Copperhouse were exported to France and Spain, Mexico and South America, South Africa and Australia. They acted as standard pumping equipment in the waterworks of Britain for over thirty years; they lifted water in Cornwall for a century and a half, till the last of them, erected at the Greensplat china clay pits, near St Austell, ceased working in 1959; and, like their predecessors, those of Newcomen and Watt, they fought against the rising floods below the Derwent till the water proved too strong and even they could fight no more.

The textile mills in the Derwent Valley, positioned and constructed by rivers and streams to make use of the copious supplies of water, discovered little need for the power of steam, at least until the end of the nineteenth century; and, even at that time, their owners still preferred to install water-turbines rather than bear the cost of purchasing, erecting and fuelling steam engines. Turbines made their appearance at Cressbrook and Darley Abbey in the 1890s, at Arkwright's Masson Mill some thirty years later, and their installation at Bakewell was delayed until as late as 1955, when a gear segment of the older of two waterwheels fractured. At Bamford, though a tandem-compound engine was brought in to drive the spinning and doubling machinery in 1907, turbines were still fitted to provide electricity.

True, a handful of steam engines were installed at mills in the eighteenth century, but mainly to pump the water back from the tail race to a storage pool upstream of the wheel. The one purchased by Arkwright for his Wirksworth Mill was used for this purpose; and, almost without exception, the early factory masters remained wedded to water power till the end of their lives. Masson Mill, built by Arkwright in 1784, took its power from the Derwent; and the following year, far from contemplating steam, he re-organized the water installations at Cromford. Even when, as late as 1837, the young Richard Arkwright lost his battle with the proprietors of the Meerbrook Sough, and so his water supply to the Upper and Lower Mills, he preferred to end production rather than drive his frames by the power of steam. In 1833 a new goit and wheelhouse were constructed at Calver and the weir was enlarged; while at Bakewell the younger of the wheels, still working efficiently when the older one broke, was installed as late as 1852. The one outstanding exception was Belper, where, despite the fact that the Strutts erected a highly expensive but most efficient system of goits, weirs and pools, steam was introduced in the 1850s.

Edward Baines in his *History of the Cotton Manufacture in Great Britain* calculated that in 1833, in the district assigned to Robert J. Saunders, a factory inspector, which comprised Cromford, Belper, Ashbourne and the Derby area, there were twelve textile mills generating, between them, 820 horsepower by water installations and only 48 horsepower by various types of steam engine; while, in the same year, 657 mills in the county of Lancashire were generating by steam over 21,000 horsepower, an average of over 32 horsepower for each.

But if the cotton mill proprietors in the Derwent Valley were reluctant to use the steam engine, the same could not be said of the groups or companies operating lead mines. Water power for pumping was only rarely, for them, a feasible proposition. Lead had to be extracted from the point where it lay. Shafts had to be sunk to tap the veins below ground, and, more often than not, these lay at a considerable distance from the rivers. Waterwheels needed a consistent surface flow, and the mines which had this conveniently available were few and far between. During the eighteenth and nineteenth centuries a number of pumping wheels were certainly erected, among them a mammoth of 52 feet diameter in Lathkill Dale; but there were few enough of them to make them remarkable, and, until the Newcomen engine appeared on the scene, the normal method of drainage was by driving soughs or tunnels from the bank of a river to penetrate the deepest workings of the mine. These soughs inclined downwards from the lowest worked levels at a gradient of perhaps ten feet in every mile, and discharged their water, through arched tails or outfalls, into the Derwent or one of its tributary streams.

The earliest sough to be driven in the valley was probably that commenced about 1629 by the Dutch drainage expert, Sir Cornelius Vermuyden, to unwater the flooded Dove Gang Mine between Cromford and Wirksworth. Vermuyden was first invited to come to England by King James I, about 1621, to stem a breach in the embankment of the Thames near Dagenham; and he continued his work under Charles I, reclaiming land in the Fens and the Isle of Axholme. Reared in a country where drainage was an art and a prime necessity, he was a skilled engineer and a man of enterprise and energy. Precisely how his connection with the Wirksworth mines developed is not very clear, but the sough had been completed as far as the Gang Vein by 1651, and, in recognition of his achievement and in spite of vehement protests from local miners, Vermuyden was granted lead-working rights. He also, according to Samuel Smiles, secured a thirty-year lease of the mine, and, before his death, became the local Barmaster, the chief official of the Barmote Court. His sough lowered the water-table or saturated level, and enabled the mine to be worked for a further twenty years till the search for deeper ores led to the construction of a deeper drainage tunnel, the Cromford Sough, between 1673 and 1682. It was the flow from this sough, together with that provided by Bonsall Brook, that Arkwright employed a century later to power the wheel of his first Cromford mill. Superseded in its turn by the even deeper tunnel called Meerbrook Sough, which debouched into the Derwent at Whatstandwell, its tail can still be seen behind a row of shops above the Market Place at Cromford.

It has been calculated that at least a hundred and fifty soughs were driven through the limestone and shale of the Derbyshire mining areas. Counting their branches, there were possibly, in the end, more than three hundred. Six of them were driven under Wirksworth alone; and the Alport mining field, south of the River Lathkill, was seamed underground by an elaborate network, each branch following the line of a vein, and the majority connecting with Hillcarr Sough, the main drainage level, which discharged into the Derwent at Darley Dale after four and a half subterranean miles.

But, as the ore was worked out and lower veins were explored, the shafts were sunk deeper, and soughs already driven could only be used by hand-pumping water from the new, lower depths to the level of the sough. When this became too difficult, the one remaining solution was to drive another sough, and this could prove a ruinously expensive undertaking. Cromford Sough was estimated to have cost some £30,000; Magpie Sough perhaps £35,000; and Hillcarr, including its extensions and branches, possibly in excess of £50,000. It might take, in addition, between ten and twenty years to complete, by which time the levels had sunk even deeper.

The steam engine, though its fuel costs were likely, in the long run, to entail an even greater expense, was a much more immediately attractive proposition. It could pump water for years before a sough was completed; it could, if the need arose, be moved from shaft to shaft; and, once it became available, those mines which were worked by groups of wealthy share-holders—lead merchants, smelters and landed gentlemen—were not slow to invest in this new prime-mover, which seemed likely, within the foresee-able future, to solve all their most intractable problems of drainage.

The Newcomen engines, commonly known as 'fire-engines' in those early days, invaded the valley. The first made its appearance between 1717 and 1720 at the Yatestoop Mine, near Birchover, where, during the next ten years, two more of a similar type seem to have been erected, since the Reverend James Clegg, a Nonconformist minister, passing by the mine in 1730, re-marked upon '3 curious Engines . . . which by ye force of fire heating water to vapour a prodigious weight of water was raised from a very great depth, and a vast quantity of lead ore laid dry.' He went on to describe their method of working. 'The hott vapour,' he wrote, 'ascends from an iron pan, close covered, through a brass cylinder fixed to the top, and by its expanding force raised one end of the engine, which is brought down again by the sudden introduction of a dash of cold water into ye same cylinder which condenseth the vapour. Thus the hott vapour and cold water act by turns, and give ye clearest demonstration of ye mighty elastic force of air.'

The London Lead Company, a group of enterprising Quakers, was responsible for the introduction of a number of early Newcomen engines. In 1720 the company took the leases of various mines in the Wensley and Winster area, and, almost immediately, opened negotiations with Abraham Darby's foundry at Coalbrookdale, another Quaker concern, to supply engine cylinders made of cast iron, which were cheaper than brass. Four years later, in 1724, a cylinder was cast at Coalbrookdale and transported to Winster; and, since the mines taken over by London Lead were in considerable trouble due to underground water, it seems a reasonable assumption that the cylinder was dispatched on the Company's order. It is certainly on record that the London Lead agent, Anthony Barker, had, by 1733, purchased at least five atmospheric engines, some of them from Coalbrookdale; and in that same year Abraham Darby himself is known to have made a journey into Derbyshire to discuss with a customer the performance of an engine supplied by his foundry. John Farey, writing in 1811, reported that five engines had, at one time or another, been working at Yatestoop, and a further six at mines around Winster.

By 1778 London Lead had ceased its operations in the valley, but not before having purchased from Coalbrookdale another Newcomen engine with a 42-inch cylinder for use at the Old Mill Close Mine at Darley Dale. This engine worked successfully until 1764, when a new sough was driven which cut the Mill Close vein and effectively terminated work at the mine. A minute of a general Court meeting held by the Company records that 'Mill Close Mine, Derbyshire, has . . . been tried under level and there is no prospect of success. Resolved to stop the Fire Engine and sell the coal and store such material as will not spoil.' For four years, in the care of a skeleton staff, the engine remained silent, but in 1768 it was sold to the Gregory Mine partners at Ashover, where it continued to work till the end of the century.

When the London Lead Company pulled out of Derbyshire ten years later, a visitor to the valley could have counted thirteen Newcomen engines, their rocking beams toiling to drag the water from the lead mine shafts. One of these, at the Yatestoop Mine, was, at that time, a recent installation. It had a 70-inch cylinder, exceptionally large for the eighteenth century, and had been built by Francis Thompson, an engineer from Ashover. In his *Treatise on the Steam-Engine*, published in 1827, John Farey listed Thompson as one of the principal makers of atmospheric engines; and his rise to eminence, given his undoubted skill as a mechanical engineer, was inevitable in a county which possessed its own rapidly expanding iron industry, but which, until then, had been forced to incur heavy transport costs by dealing with firms as far distant as the Darbys at Coalbrookdale.

Thompson established a working partnership with Ebenezer Smith, a Sheffield man who, in 1775, had set up an ironworks, the Griffin Foundry, at New Brampton on the western outskirts of Chesterfield. Smith, who was later to expand his business by building a second works, the Adelphi at Duckmanton, contracted to cast and machine the cylinders for Thompson's engines. The 70-inch cylinder for the Yatestoop engine was cast and bored at the Griffin Foundry, as was a slightly smaller one of $64\frac{1}{2}$ inches for a second Thompson engine erected at Yatestoop five years later, in 1782. This was, in its way, an even more remarkable piece of equipment. It had a haystack-type boiler of 20 feet diameter, possibly the largest of its kind ever made, and the whole of the engine was installed underground. An engine house of 1,200 cubic feet, with a 'bob' wall five feet thick on which the rocking bob or beam pivoted, was excavated and lined with gritstone; the materials for its construction and all the engine components being lowered 500 feet down a shaft.

Thompson and Smith continued to work together, as did their sons. Perhaps the last of the Newcomen engines to be erected, for the Magpie Mine at Sheldon in 1825, was built by Joseph Thompson (Francis's son) in conjunction with the Smiths who, among their other achievements, cast wheels and machine parts for the cotton-spinning industry, cannon for the Duke of Wellington's army, and a number, at least, of the cruciform stanchions used by William Strutt in his fire-resistant mills at Belper and Milford.

While Newcomen engines were extensively used on the slopes around the valley, those of Boulton and Watt failed, for a number of reasons, to make the same impact. Birmingham was a considerable distance from the Derwent; Wilkinson's foundries, which bored the Watt cylinders, even further away; and the transport costs involved in moving engine parts, coupled with the heavy royalty demands, were regarded by the Derbyshire lead mine proprietors as uneconomic, especially since, by the time the Watt engine appeared on the market, there were skilled engineers and foundry workers on the fringe of the valley. The Newcomen engines produced so successfully by Thompson and Smith were no longer under patent, and coal was comparatively easy to obtain: Francis Thompson, indeed, built a number of his engines for pumping coal mines, perhaps the most famous being the 57-inch installed at the Oakerthorpe Colliery, close to Alfreton, and now displayed in the Science Museum. The cost of such an engine was infinitely cheaper than one of similar horsepower from Boulton and Watt; added to which, because of heavy demands from other parts of the country, the delivery of the Birmingham engines could be subject to long delays, and a period of two or three years might elapse between the placing of an order and the first effective pumping of water.

The men who held the working leases of the lead mines clung, therefore, to their Newcomen engines; and those erected under licence from Boulton and Watt were mainly confined to a handful of cotton mills or to the richer mines, such as the Gregory at Ashover, operated by wealthy groups of merchants and smelters. Even at Ashover the cost of building and operating steam engines proved, in the end, a direct cause of failure. The first to be installed was the Newcomen engine bought from Mill Close which commenced pumping water in 1768. In 1772 the profit from the mine was over £15,000, with an accumulated profit of £40,000 between 1775 and 1778. The following year, however, water began once again to pose a problem and, to clear it from the workings, a 45-inch engine was ordered from Boulton and Watt. It was immediately successful, using no more than 100 tons of coal in its first quarter's pumping, compared with the 350 tons consumed by the voracious Newcomen engine. Nevertheless, by 1789, production had sunk to less than 500 tons of lead ore a year, and the mine was losing an increasing amount of money. The last attempt to make it pay was by the installation, in 1796, of a small Thompson atmospheric engine; but in 1803, after £23,000 had been spent in 13 years, the mine closed down.

The difficulties of installing and operating Boulton and Watt engines are nowhere more evident than at the Gregory Mine. In 1782, the partners, in one quarter, paid the Birmingham firm over £67 in royalties, calculated on the number of strokes of the engine: a total of over £250 a year, excluding the cost of coal. It is doubtful whether any Derbyshire lead mine could, at that time, have borne such a cost, plus the expense of two other pumping engines, one of them the old Newcomen, which itself consumed 26 tons of coal a week.

Installation was also difficult, because of the distances involved and the poor communications between Birmingham and Ashover. Though many of the parts for the Boulton and Watt engine were cast by Smith's Griffin Foundry at Chesterfield, the piston rod had to travel all the way from the Soho Works. It was dispatched in the July of 1779, by way of Liverpool and the Trent and Mersey Canal, to Shardlow. From there it was to be delivered, presumably by road, though possibly along the Trent and then the Chester-field Canal, to the Angel Inn at Chesterfield. It had still not arrived by the middle of October.

Faced by such delays and the costs of operation, there is little wonder that the lessees of lead mines fought shy of dealing with the Birmingham partners, and that the true successors to the Newcomen engines on the lead fields around the Derwent Valley proved to be the slower, but more economical, expansion engines pioneered in Cornwall.

At much the same time as these Cornish engines began to make their appear-ance, the railway commenced its penetration northwards from Derby along the banks of the river; and the swift, direct links thus established with engineer-ing works at Sheffield and Barnsley, Burton-on-Trent and Bradford assisted their proliferation through the lead mining fields. Apart from odd exceptions like 'Jumbo', the 80-inch monster built by Harveys of Hayle which pumped at the Warren Carr Shaft at Mill Close, these engines were supplied from sources very much closer to the valley, and their components distributed along the new rail network to the nearest stations. The railway made it possible for firms like Grahams of Elsecar, Davy Brothers of Sheffield, Thornewill and Warham of Burton-on-Trent and the Bowling Ironworks at Bradford to disseminate their steam engines, piece by piece, with even greater ease than Thompson and Smith had achieved from nearby Chester-field.

The result was a frenzy of renewed activity in old mining areas where persistent flooding had slowed ore extraction, or where the workings, already at the water-table, had long been abandoned. Pumping engines were im-ported, existing shafts deepened and new soughs driven, mainly by means of capital investment from large mining companies like Alport, Mandale, High Rake and Magpie. Mining fields such as Sheldon, Crich and Calver, Eyam, Alport and Lathkill Dale witnessed a fresh, if short-lived, prosperity.

Shafts were sunk to unprecedented depths, and even workings abandoned eighty years before by the London Lead Company were re-opened in the middle of the nineteenth century, and became for a time the most profitable in Britain. Mill Close miners, by the 1930s, were working a thousand feet below the Derwent, and even as early as 1860 the New Engine Shaft at Eyam had reached a depth of nearly eleven hundred feet.

John Byng, traversing the face of the valley in 1790, had reported that 'all the country is scoop'd by lead mines'. Now the shafts were scooped even deeper, and the windswept heights encircling the Derwent found themselves dotted with tall, rectangular engine houses, built of limestone and gritstone blocks, their massive bob walls, stained with oil and grease, supporting the heavy cast-iron beams which rocked to drag the water from astonishing depths. The result of all this intensive burrowing and building, coupled with frequent injections of capital from the new mining companies, was that the valley produced, between 1845 and 1881, some quarter of a million tons of ore; and small farmer-miner communities like Sheldon, exposed at heights of a thousand feet on the limestone uplands, not only survived their endemic lack of water, but actually grew in size in the intervening years. Sheldon itself, in the 1850s, increased its population by twenty-five per cent; and by 1872, when the Magpie Mine was the third greatest lead producer in Derbyshire, water, to aid the survival of the village, was being pumped, by the grace of lead mining profits, five hundred feet up the side of the hill from the River Wye at Ashford, a mile away.

In general, however, by 1860, production began to fall as lead prices declined. In the next ten years, the majority of mines were one by one abandoned to the wind and the water, and the final disaster came in 1885 when the rich lead-zinc ores of Broken Hill in Australia flooded the world market. From then on, production around the Derwent was largely confined to the Mill Close Mine, and it was almost entirely due to the half-million tons blasted out of this mine between 1861 and 1939 that, even as late as the 1930s, the valley was still producing ninety per cent of all the lead ore extracted in Britain. The rest of the mines by that time were derelict and decaying, a fate that Mill Close itself was at last to suffer in 1940, when the efforts of the powerful Cornish engines, supplemented as they were by an electric pump and two stand-by diesels, failed to stem the water, which was then flowing into the deepest levels at a rate of 5,500 gallons every minute.

To wander today among the surface remains of these derelict mines is to feel, perhaps more than anywhere else in the whole of the valley, that the ghosts of the past are still moving with purpose among the tumbled blocks of stone and across the ravaged ground: not merely the ghosts of the miners themselves, but of those huge Cornish engines which fought, for a century, their losing battle against the powerful subterranean floods. To stand amid the ruins of the engine houses, Magpie and Mill Close, Mandale, Wakebridge and Old End at Crich, is to hear once again the shovelling of coal, the hiss of steam, the clank of the rocking bob, and the gush of water lifted from the shaft; while the miners in flat caps and 'Bradder beavers' plod across the thin, stony soil of the workings like dark, bent figures across the stony streets of a Lowry canvas.

Of all the mining fields, none is more evocative than Lathkill Dale of the desperate struggle against underground water. In this beautiful wooded gorge of the Lathkill, below Over Haddon, there are, within a distance of less than a mile, the remains of sough tails and aqueducts, wheel-pits and engine houses, all testifying mutely to the constant yet unavailing efforts to clear the flooded levels and extract the rich deposits of ore from the Lathkill Dale and the Mandale mines.

There is evidence that lead was mined in this area as early as the end of the thirteenth century, and that working continued intermittently until 1761, when the London Lead Company first acquired the title to Smallpenny Vein, which lay towards the western end of the gorge. A sough, the Lathkill Dale Sough, had already been driven under the bed of the river some seventeen years before, and, probably with the help of waterwheels pumping from an even greater depth, the Company mined the lead from a number of veins for another dozen years; but, in spite of its efforts, the yield of ore diminished after 1773, and in the late midsummer of 1776 the Company decided to sell the whole of the Lathkill Dale mines.

There seems to have been little further activity till 1825 when John Alsop of Lea, a well-known lead smelter, and his friend, Thomas Bateman of Middleton-by-Wirksworth, paid £25 for the Lathkill Dale Vein, and mined it extensively till 1842. They secured a lease from Lord Melbourne to take water from the river to operate a wheel, and in 1836 a colossal wheel of 52 feet diameter and 9 feet across the breast was sunk in a pit some three-quarters of a mile upstream from Lathkill Lodge. Described by Bagshaw in his *History, Gazeteer and Directory of Derbyshire* as the largest wheel 'except one in the Kingdom', it worked six sets of pumps and was said to have been capable of raising 4,000 gallons of water a minute from a depth of a hundred and twenty feet below the river. Constructed at Smith's Adelphi Foundry at Duckmanton, it was reported to have cost over £500 and continued to work till the mine closed down in 1842. Offered for sale in 1849, it had certainly been removed by 1861, for William Adam, in his *Pleasant Walks in Derbyshire*, wrote of the 'leviathan wheel' already dismantled, 'the miners' coes thrown down, and the Agent's cottage, once a picture of life and beauty, its once beautiful garden plot covered with rank weeds.'

It was underneath this cottage, known as Bateman's House after James Bateman, the mining company's agent from 1836 until 1842, that another attempt may well have been made to rid the workings of water. Some six years before Bateman occupied the cottage, an unusually wide shaft was excavated immediately underneath the building. This was probably to house,

Mandale Sough tail, Lathkill Dale.

Aqueduct pillars, Lathkill Dale.

in some degree of secrecy, a new variation on an old type of pump: the hydraulic pump designed by Edward and James Dakeyne, the flax-spinning brothers of Darley Dale. Cast at the Adelphi Foundry in 1831 and worked by a descending column of water tilting a disc or annular ring, it was said to have generated 130 horsepower and was, according to the *Mechanics' Magazine*, 'actually at work' by the January of 1833.

In 1839 John Alsop was appointed agent to the Mandale Mining Company, and the Lathkill Dale and Mandale Mines were, thereupon, amalgamated. The Mandale Vein, a quarter of a mile to the north and running down to the gorge half a mile from Lathkill Lodge, had already been drained by the Mandale Sough, driven over a period of twenty years between 1797 and 1820. As a result of this, the mining company had made two rich strikes of ore in the following three years and, convinced that a profitable body of lead lay untouched below the level of the river, it installed in 1840, on the side of the gorge and above the sough tail, a 35-foot diameter waterwheel. The water to power this wheel was carried from a leat on the other side of the river by means of an aqueduct, composed of wooden troughs supported on the tops of six stone pillars traversing the Lathkill.

The wheel was working by the March of 1841, but, although it pumped from a depth of some ninety feet below the sough, it failed to stem the encroaching water, and in 1847 a Cornish engine was ordered from Grahams' Milton Ironworks at Elsecar, near Barnsley. An engine house and boiler house were constructed of limestone quarried from the dale, and the 65-inch engine, generating 150 horsepower, with a planned capacity to pump from a hundred and sixty feet below the river, was installed and working the following year. The effort was expensive and all to no avail. After a further two years' working, the company was forced to close down the mine, recording a loss of £36,000, and on 28 January 1852 the engine and boilers were offered for sale. Who eventually purchased them no-one seems to know, but there is a story, passed from lip to lip across the years in Over Haddon, that a team of forty horses had to be harnessed to haul the beam up the hill to the village.

A visitor to the gorge, who drags himself today up that tortuous slope, may well be persuaded of the truth of that tale. Many people still do climb

Mandale engine house, Lathkill Dale.

the steep hill, but a limited number of cars can be parked on the verge of the hairpin bend just above Lathkill Lodge, and a walk through the wooded glory of the dale still reveals the tell-tale signs of those artefacts, abandoned now for more than a century, by means of which the nineteenth-century miners strove to clear the water from their lead-lined levels. Here, by the Lodge, is the long-collapsed tail of the Lathkill Dale Sough, still trickling water; and further to the west, at a point where the wood reaches down to the river, the square-arched outfall, dark and dry, of the Mandale Sough. Above it, on the sloping side of the gorge and half-hidden by trees, stands the massive bob wall of the Cornish engine house, and behind it the hollow that housed the Mandale wheel; while a hundred yards to the west, on the bed of the dale, are the stubs of the aqueducts that carried the water from the southern bank. Still further up the gorge, on the bank of the river, two columns of stone are fenced off by wire. These are all that remain of Bateman's House, wired against entry because of the shaft that may once have held the Dakeyne disc engine; and another three hundred stretching paces bring one to a deep, sometimes water-filled hollow, partly lined with stone: the pit where John Alsop's 'leviathan wheel' revolved for six years in a desperate effort to recoup its cost.

Both mines were abandoned by 1852, apart from intermittent working by small groups of men which continued till as late as 1867; but the story of Lathkill Dale and its struggling miners would not be complete without a mention of its gold rush. In 1854, rumours of a gold strike in one of the disused workings brought a flood of speculators into the gorge. Shares in the Over Haddon Gold and Silver Mine, purchased for £1, rose to thirty times that value, and not surprisingly, since two ounces of pure gold were reputed to lie in every ton of the toadstone; but the gold was the gold of fools—iron pyrites, nothing more; the shares fell to zero, the prospectors departed, and the Lathkill Dale mines were left once again to their leaden ghosts: the men with their picks and shovels, their tallow candles and black blasting gun-powder; the ponderous waterwheels creaking as they turned and turned again within their limestone pits; and the huge metal beam of the Cornish engine rocking on its bob wall, pausing with purpose at the end of its up-stroke for the pump valves to close, and then rocking once more: almost as if, as Wordsworth and Coleridge remarked in conversation, the machine were endowed 'with some faculty of intellect' and performed its rhythmical repetitive action 'like a giant with one idea'.

The mines in Lathkill Dale were, in one sense, fortunate. There was surface water available to drive the massive wheels; though, as the mining companies discovered, the flow was often inadequate, since the Lathkill, in dry seasons, disappeared underground, leaving the bed of the gorge exposed and the pumping wheels powerless.

However, in the Alport field, south of the Lathkill, which was worked with high intensity for a century and a half, the operating company turned the presence of underground water to advantage. The lead levels in this field lay at the deepest point of a saturated basin: a focus for water from the catchment area of the Lathkill and Bradford, which, percolating through the joints and bedding planes of the limestone, produced, in winter and early spring, a seepage of some 6,000 gallons every minute. By 1787 a network of soughs had been driven to clear the workings, most of them connected to Hillcarr Sough, which was the main drainage channel; but heavy deposits of ore still lay below the soughs, and it was impossible to drive the network any deeper and still drain the water into the Derwent. The mining company called for estimates of pumping costs, rejected steam pumping as far too expensive, and turned instead to water-pressure engines. In principle not unlike the Dakeyne disc engine, but worked by a descending column of water pressing on a piston, these weighty machines were sunk deep below the surface and underground water was led to downfall pipes directly above them, the engines pumping into Hillcarr Sough and so into the Derwent. By 1848 there were eight in operation at various shafts of the Alport field, the first of them designed by Richard Trevithick and erected inside the Crash Purse Shaft to the south of Youlgreave. The largest, a 50-inch monster constructed at Butterley, with a 10-foot stroke and a piston rod and plunger-pole weighing between them more than fifty tons, was sunk at the Guy Shaft in 1842. Installed two hundred feet below ground, it was said to have discharged, in the wettest of weather, 5,000 gallons a minute into Hillcarr Sough; but all that now remains for the visitor to see is a rubbish-filled hollow in a copse near a junction of two farming tracks: a lifeless patch of ground, once a scene of desperate mechanical activity, now silent except for the song of birds and the summer breezes gently stirring the leaves.

Sheldon's Magpie Mine presents a different scene. Here, half a mile from the village and five hundred feet above the level of the Wye, the most extensive surface remains of any lead mine in Derbyshire stand, stark and deserted, amid the wind-swept fields. The problem of flooding inside the very heart of this limestone hill was complicated by the lack of surface water and a shaft which, as early as 1845, had already been sunk to more than seven hundred feet. Here, at Magpie, steam appeared to be the only possible answer; and high above the ruins of boiler and winding houses, open shafts, jigs, a smithy and a powder store, the massive grey shell of the Cornish engine house and its attendant round chimney rear into the sky. Even in 1820 the underground water was proving an almost unmanageable problem, and three years later £40 a week was being spent to pay men who were operating hand pumps. By 1825 the position was so desperate that the first of a series of steam pumping engines made its appearance: a 42-inch Newcomen: the last of its kind to be installed at the head of a Derbyshire lead mine. The engine and shaft cost £1,000: an outlay partly repaid by the extraction, within a single twelve-

Engine house, Magpie Mine, Sheldon.

month period, of eight hundred tons of ore; but the water rose again, and by 1835 had forced the closure of the mine.

It was re-opened four years later under the guidance of John Taylor, the well-known mining entrepreneur and engineer, who had already had considerable success with Cornish pumping engines at his Consolidated Copper Mines at Gwennap in Cornwall. Under his direction, and with the assistance of a number of Cornish miners brought to live at Sheldon, the Newcomen pump was replaced by a 40-inch Cornish engine, bought for £500 from the South Wheal Towan Mine near Redruth. This enterprise was rewarded by the sale, in four months, of more than £2,000 worth of ore, though not without disaster, for an overseer was crushed to death between the bobplank and the beam as it rocked in descent, and a second man, only a few months later, fell to his death down the engine shaft.

But, despite all Taylor's efforts, the water remorselessly continued to rise and the mine was once again forced into idleness, this time for close upon twenty years. When working was resumed in 1864 by John Fairburn of Sheffield, his company decided that an engine with greater pumping capacity was needed, and, five years later, a 70-inch Cornish engine was imported from Calver Sough, another of Fairburn's mines in the valley. To shelter this massive piece of machinery, weighing three hundred tons, the great Cornish engine house was constructed, and in the next three years ore to the value of £19,000 was extracted from the mine, making it, at that time, the third largest lead producer in Derbyshire. On the debit side, however, lay the operating costs. The engine consumed some eighty tons of coal in the course of every week, and this had to be purchased from the neighbouring coalfields and then transported by rail to Bakewell and from there by road to Sheldon at an annual expense of nearly £2,000; so, in 1873, with the price of coal rising steeply and that of lead falling, the company decided to attempt a cheaper method of drainage. This was to suspend all mining operations, drive a sough from the Wye which would penetrate the shaft at a depth of nearly six hundred feet, and, instead of lifting the water through seven hundred wearisome feet to the surface, use the engine to raise it a mere two hundred to the level of the sough.

The Magpie Sough, the last to be driven for a Derbyshire lead mine, took eight years to cut and was completed in August 1881, an event duly celebrated by a dinner for the workmen. The cost had been planned at £8,000, but the ultimate expenditure may have been in the region of £35,000, and the venture, bold and difficult, proved to be fruitless. In 1883 the price of lead plummeted to less than £15 for every ton, and, unable to sustain the financial burden, the company was forced into liquidation, Fairburn confessing that he had lost 'every shilling' of £10,000 invested in the mine.

Within the last ninety years, numerous attempts have been made to clear the water and re-work the mine, but all have proved to be uneconomic. The final effort was made in 1951 by Waihi Investments and Developments of London. Using electric pumps, they drained off the water to a depth in excess of six hundred feet, but the levels were deep in mud, water still dripped from every crack in the limestone, and in 1958 the company pulled out.

The mine is now the Field Centre of the Peak District Mines Historical Society. The gaunt wreckage of its centuries of surface construction still dominates the skyline above the village of Sheldon, and the tail of the sough, recently restored after a water explosion in 1966, which blew a thirty-foot crater in the steep hillside, still pours some ten million gallons a day into the River Wye half a mile above Ashford.

But by far the greatest triumph and most glorious failure of the massive Cornish engines was at Mill Close Mine, above Darley Bridge, and virtually on the very bank of the Derwent. Abandoned by the London Lead Company in 1764 and its Newcomen engine sold to the Gregory partners at Ashover, it was re-opened by Edward Wass in 1859. A new engine house was constructed above Watts Shaft on the edge of Clough Wood Valley, and within it was installed a 50-inch Cornish engine, later nicknamed 'Baby' and built by Thornewill and Warham of Burton-on-Trent. Fifteen years later, a second such engine, the largest ever erected in the valley, began to pump at the Warren Carr Shaft, half a mile nearer the bank of the river. Made by Harveys of Hayle, this 80-inch giant, immediately christened 'Jumbo', was joined in 1889 by yet a third, known as 'Alice', a 60-inch engine bought

now restored Magpie Sough tail, Ashford-in-the-Water. Site of a water explosion in 1966.

from Wakebridge Mine at Crich, and originally, like 'Baby', built at Burton-on-Trent. In 1896 these three vast Cornish engines were gathered together at the Warren Carr Shaft, from which they pumped water into the old Yatestoop Sough and thence into the Derwent.

Their combined effect was to make Mill Close the richest lead mine in the country, and one of the richest, perhaps, in the whole of the world. Between 1861 and 1939 it produced nearly half a million tons of ore, containing an average of over eighty per cent lead, treasure which today would be worth some £25 million; and in 1931, of the 29,000 tons raised in Britain,

26,000 came from this mine. In 1887 the engines were pumping 1,000 gallons of water a minute; by 1929 2,000 gallons; by 1937 well over 4,000; and in 1938, by which time the workings had sunk to a level of a thousand and twenty feet, the amount had reached more than 5,500, or thirty thousand tons of water a day.

'Jumbo' was scrapped in 1933, but 'Baby' and 'Alice' continued to work, with the help of diesel and electric pumps, until 1938, when, two miles from the shaft and nearly nine hundred feet below the level of the Derwent, shot-firing breached the wall of an underground lake. An immense volume of water poured into the workings, drowning the levels and cutting off access to the main vein of ore.

Mill Close was abandoned the following year; the engines were sold for scrap; and all that now remain to mark the site of this once magnificent mine are the heaps of spoil on the verge of the later Enthoven smelter, the gritstone chimney above Lees Shaft, and the majestic ruin of Watts Engine House standing high above the wild and deep-ravaged hollow of Clough Wood Valley. Like some fallen temple, built to the glory of the old gods of steam, Watts still endures: the one surviving monument to the great rocking beams of 'Jumbo', 'Alice' and 'Baby', toiling tirelessly, defiantly, for long years triumphantly, yet in the end in vain, to hold back the floods that sealed the fate of the mine.

Watts Shaft engine house, Mill Close Mine, Darley Dale.

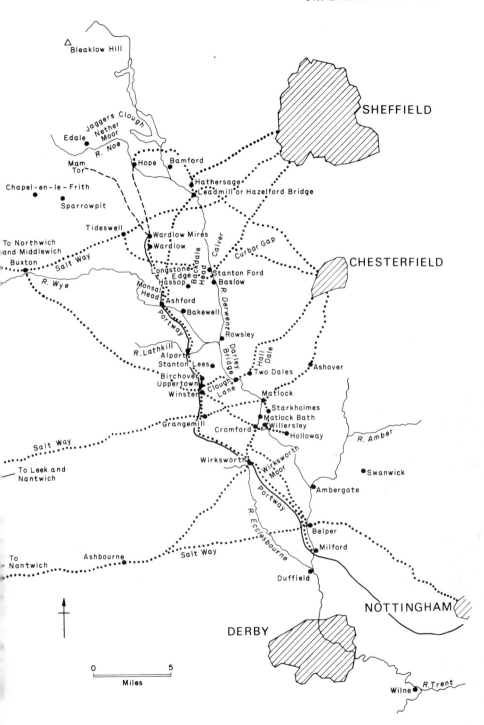

Packhorse Routes.

8   Passable Ways

I purpose to send your wife a chimney back as soon as our Derbyshire ways are passable.

Letter from George Sitwell of Renishaw (1664).

England has more roads and canals than all the rest of Europe put together—and more civilization . . . this is an unfailing effect of an infallible cause. From the want of easy communication, men remain disjoined and isolated; their minds grow cold, their spirit slumbers, they feel no emulation, they experience not the spur of the necessity for satisfying new desires, have little moral development, energy or activity.

Count Giuseppe Pecchio: *Italian Exile* (1833).

A generation before Arkwright built his first mill at Cromford, the roads that traversed the Derwent Valley were little short of deplorable. In the middle of the seventeenth century, Edward Browne, long accustomed to the gentler landscape of Norfolk, had written with feeling of 'the craggy ascents, the rocky unevenness of the roads, the high peaks and the almost perpendicular descents' that beset him in the course of a Derbyshire journey; and in 1676, in Charles Cotton's addendum to Walton's *Compleat Angler*, Viator, his imaginary traveller, had described the road between Derby and Ashbourne as nothing more nor less than 'measures of foul way'.

The ways were still foul and almost perpendicular when, in 1697, Celia Fiennes took to her horse and rode through the valley. She complained—though, one feels, with a perverse satisfaction—of the 'steep precipices' and 'quagmires' and the fact that 'one that is a stranger cannot travell without a Guide, and some of them [the guides] are put to a loss sometymes.' There was clearly no improvement twenty years later, for an agent of the London Lead Company, prospecting near Winster, reported that it was only with the greatest difficulty that he and his companions 'got in and out of the county', and this 'by reason of the badness of the roads, even in the dry season'; while Daniel Defoe, at much the same time, castigated the 'base, stony, mountainous road' that led to Matlock Bath. The ways at that period, wrote William Adam, 'were wretched in the extreme. The difficulties of a Derbyshire road became proverbial. In the lower parts of the valleys, in wet weather, the carriages might sink to the axles; and the steep and rugged acclivities over which they were obliged to pass, often presented formidable obstacles to the traveller's progress.' As the century lengthened, there seemed to be only deterioration. In 1758 it was reliably reported that roads around Swanwick, which normally carried coal, were impassable as early as the middle of October; and in the winter of 1763–4, a mere seven years before Arkwright

Bradford Packhorse Bridge.

arrived at Cromford, the road running south-east from Belper to Nottingham was, for almost six months, in a similar condition.

To men such as Arkwright and Jedediah Strutt, struggling to nurture an infant industry on the banks of the river, the lack of reliable communications must have proved a debilitating handicap. Movement through the valley and over the hills of such bulky commodities as bales of raw cotton, gritstone and limestone for building purposes, iron castings for machinery and water installations, and consignments of finished yarn to the customers must have been constantly frustrated by the unreliability of passage along the roads; and as industry multiplied and spread around the Derwent, the time wasted edging waggons up and down steep hills over calamitous surfaces, the inability to guarantee delivery dates, and the necessity to hold large stocks of raw material and fuel in reserve against the incidence of mud, flood, ice and snow posed a very real threat to financial solvency. The transportation of lead and copper to the smelting plants; coal, steam engine components and pumping equipment to the lead mines; iron ore and limestone to the furnaces and foundries; bar iron to the wire works; chert to the potteries; and agricultural lime from the kilns to scattered farms on the slopes of the hills: all suffered from the inevitable Derbyshire disease of rough, rutted roads, deep in mud and water close to the rivers, and twisting up precipitous ice-ridden slopes from the narrow, hump-backed packhorse bridges that were all that sufficed to carry them across the wet-season torrents.

In the mid-eighteenth century, packhorse ways were, indeed, all that existed; and these medieval trade routes, many of them following ancient tracks, ran in general on a west to east axis, clung to the high ground and only descended to the valley bottom to cross the river, whereas industry developed mainly north to south along the banks of the Derwent. Textile centres such as Cromford and Belper had of necessity to rely on the roads, since the Trent, navigable as far as Burton since 1699, and flowing, like the packhorse trains, roughly west to east, served only the southern tip of the region; while improvements to the Derwent, completed twenty years later, permitted passage only as far north as Derby. Access to the centre of the Derwent Valley from Nottingham, Chesterfield and Sheffield in the east could only be achieved by climbing up the long, hard slope of the gritstone, and then falling, with disconcerting steepness, to the river; while exit to the west meant climbing once again up the steep limestone shelf to the high plateau and the moors around the ancient henge of Arbor Low. Riverside roads between Bamford and Derby were, at that time, evident in only short and unconnected stretches; and traffic into and out of Cromford had, in typical fashion, to descend the steep hill from Matlock by way of Starkholmes, cross the bridge at Willersley, and then toil up the rugged slope on the opposite bank making south for Belper by Wirksworth Moor.

Along such tracks as these passed a multitude of packhorses, sometimes fifty or sixty to a train, each horse accountred with a double-crooked saddle from which panniers were suspended, each train guided through darkness or fog by a tinkling bell that was mounted on the leading animal's collar, and the whole winding procession tended by groups of men known as jaggers, who, though long since departed, have left their name imprinted on Derbyshire maps in the form of Jaggers Lanes at Ashover and Hathersage, and Jaggers Clough, clinging to the crest of Nether Moor on the border of Edale.

On the backs of these horses, malt flowed from Nottingham north-west across the valley to the Lancashire hinterland; salt from the 'wiches'— Northwich, Middlewich and Nantwich in Cheshire—eastwards to Nottingham, Chesterfield and Sheffield. Smelted pigs of lead moved south-east to Nottingham, north-east to Bawtry; coal north, south and west from the eastern measures; chert from Bakewell westwards to Wedgwood's potteries; while wool, milk and lime were carried to and from all points of the compass. Constantly seeking the driest ground, descending the valley sides to the fords and bridges that offered the safest crossings of the Derwent, climbing west to the limestone and east to the gritstone, these slow-moving trains with their swinging panniers bore the products of farms and lead mines, salt pans and bellpits, limekilns and quarries back and forth across the valley along an intricate web of tracks, trodden before them by medieval traders,

Cromford Bridge.

Anglo-Saxon settlers, Roman soldiers, or prehistoric nomads driving their animals to find new pastures.

The crossings of the Derwent, whether they were fords or narrow pack-horse bridges, thus became nodal points for the traffic: places where a series of routes converged, and, having crossed the water, diverged once again to their separate destinations. At Leadmill or Hazelford Bridge, near Hathersage, routes from Chesterfield and Sheffield, from Hope and Ashford all intersected to cross the river; at Cromford ways from Winster, Matlock and Holloway, from Ashbourne and Belper met at the bridge below the village at Willersley; while, in addition to the traffic flowing northwards from Cromford and south-west from Chesterfield by Jaggers Lane at Ashover, Matlock Bridge was a crossing point for the packhorse trains that carried malt into Lancashire, and salt from Nantwich by Leek and Grangemill. An eighteenth-century traveller, passing across the bridge on a journey from Buxton, commented on the 'vast number' of packhorses he saw, 'sixty in a drove', laden with wool and malt, winding up the slopes to the 'naked hills and deserted dales' on the way to Manchester.

Visitors to the valley can still tread many of these old packhorse ways. A further route from Chesterfield probably approached the Derwent by another Jaggers Lane, this time in Hall Dale, clipped the edge of the site where Edward and James Dakeyne later built their flax mill, passed through Two Dales or Toadhole, and then crossed the river at Darley Bridge. From there the track turned eastwards toward Stanton Lees, and then forked to the left up Clough Lane to Clough Wood, passing between the Watts and Warren Carr Shafts of the Mill Close Mine, and so, east of Winster, joining the Portway, the prehistoric track that led south to Wirksworth and north to

Alport. A motorist seeking the Watts Engine House must drive up Clough Lane to a point where the road peters out in the wood, and then take a track winding down to the left; but the packhorse way, still paved in part with its gritstone slabs, carries straight on, climbing steeply through the wood to Uppertown, near Birchover. Traffic on this route probably flowed, in the main, from west to east, the pack ponies transporting ore from the mines or smelted pigs of lead, the weight of which, even in Roman times, may well have been determined by the carrying capacity of a single horse.

The Derwent, Defoe's 'fury of a river', was for most of the year too dangerous to be forded except at certain specified points, and bridges existed from early times. Such fords as were in use were ultimately abandoned or replaced by bridges. Leadmill Bridge at Hazelford, half a mile below Hathersage, was, as its place-name suggests, built on the original site of a ford; but,

Packhorse way through Clough Wood, Darley Dale.

Leadmill Bridge, Hathersage.

north of this point, the river drains a wide area of moorland, and the fording place was often impassable. To ensure safe passage for the many packhorse trains that used this traditional crossing of the Derwent, the construction of 'a wooden bridge with two stone piers and stone abutments' was authorized by Quarter Sessions in 1709, but the waters, in sublime disregard of the Sessions, washed it away before it was completed. The present stone bridge with its five (now widened) arches was built to replace it, raising the cost to £166 in contrast to the original estimate of £50.

One ford that was never replaced by a bridge was Stanton Ford between Calver and Baslow, which gave passage to traffic from Chesterfield and Sheffield through Curbar Gap, by Longstone Edge to Tideswell, and so, very possibly, from there to Manchester. Crossing the river at Stanton, the packhorses made their way up the slope through Bramley Farm to Backdale Head crossroads, and then by Deep Rake on to Longstone Moor. A motorist today can follow part of this track by taking the side road that leads to Bubnell, close beyond the fork where the A619 and A623 diverge at Baslow. If he then follows the lane by the side of the river, he will find it swings down through Bramley Dale and up to Bramley Farm. Here, at the farm, there is a sharp horseshoe bend, and this was the point where the track from Stanton Ford joined the lane. Looking up the track as it climbs the hill from the farm, it is easy to imagine the long processions of heavy-laden horses toiling up the narrow way between the trees and emerging eventually, as the motorist will, at Backdale Head on the Hassop to Calver road, where the track cuts straight across, taking the moors to Tideswell.

This route is known to have been used by medieval traders as early as the year 1432, but two fords of even greater antiquity were those on the Portway at Alport and Ashford. The ancient way, running northwards from Nottingham, forded the Lathkill at Alport and then passed west of Bakewell to cross the Wye at Ashford. This was later an important packhorse route for trains loaded with malt from Derby to Manchester, and the crossing at Alport was particularly dangerous. So hazardous was the passage that, in 1718, a complaint was made to the Derbyshire Sessions that 'great gangs of London carriers as well as drifts of malt-horses and other carriers and passengers goe this ancient waye, which lies in a hollow frequently overflowed by the swollen stream. Heavy rains have so scoured out the channel as to render the ford impassable for as long as 8 or 10 days, whilst at all times carriers with loaden horses and passengers cannot pass the saide road without great danger of being cast away.' Sessions decreed that a horse-bridge be

Packhorse way, climbing from Bramley Farm.

built, and this was later replaced by the turnpike bridge which still crosses the Lathkill at Alport Mill.

Three bridges had already been built, by then, at Ashford, including the picturesque Sheepwash Bridge, but even these proved insufficient for the multiplying traffic. Towards the end of the seventeenth century, three hundred packhorses loaded with malt were said to be passing through Ashford every week on their way to Derby, and Dr Thomas Brushfield, a resident of the village, later remarked that he had seen as many as eighteen coaches crossing the river in a single day; while in 1776 it was recorded that 'Ashford Bridge is so extremely narrow that it is dangerous for Carriages to pass over the same, and that the Battlements are very frequently knocked off by Carriages.'

The route from Ashford passed up the hill to Monsal Head—then also known to travellers as Edgestone Head, Headstone Head, or Hernstone Lane End—and followed from there the track of the Portway through the village of Wardlow to Wardlow Mires. This is probably one of the oldest stretches of road in continuous use in Derbyshire. A section of the Portway, it became in due course a packhorse route, and, in 1758, the final four miles of the turnpike road that ran from Wirksworth Moor as far as Wardlow Mires. Today it carries a link road connecting the A6 with the A623 from Baslow through Sparrowpit to Chapel-en-le-Frith. Mesolithic hunters and Iron Age warriors, Roman legionaries and medieval pedlars, strings of packhorses and stage coach teams have all trodden this route. Now cars filled with tourists use it as access to the commanding viewpoint at Monsal Head, interspersed with the clattering limestone lorries that seem to use, frustratingly,

Alport Bridge.

not merely every major road, but every link and side lane that runs through the Peak.

The deplorable state into which the roads had declined by the beginning of the eighteenth century was due, in no small measure, to the ineffectiveness of the provisions for their maintenance. In the Middle Ages, when feudal rights and duties were of paramount importance, it was the responsibility of each and every parish to preserve the means of passage for the king, the king's officers, and all his subjects. This duty, enforced under Common Law, required each parish to elect a way-warden to serve for a year with the right to insist that every able-bodied man, within that period, set aside four days to labour on the roads; and, in 1555, these customary procedures were codified as statute law by an Act of Parliament which made each parish responsible for the maintenance of highways within its own boundaries. Every such parish was to appoint for a year a surveyor of highways, whose unfortunate task it was to insist that 'every person for every plough land in tillage or pasture' and 'every person keeping a draught of horses or plough in the Parish' provide on four specified days in the year, set aside for road repair, 'one wain or cart furnished after the custom of the country, with oxen, horses or other cattle, and all other necessaries meet to carry things convenient for that purpose, and also two able men with the same'; and that 'every other householder, cottager or labourer able to labour' hold himself available on such appointed days to assist with the work.

Despite the fact that, in 1563, the statutory days were increased to six, the system was inefficient as well as unpopular. The labour days set aside were normally in summer, when farmers and landowners were reluctant to spare either horses or carts from their own very necessary agricultural concerns; the work was unpaid, and labourers, forced to yield up their time, resented the sacrifice of six days' wages; added to which, the principles of road construction and even road maintenance, in decline since Roman times, had long been forgotten, and neither surveyors nor labourers possessed any knowledge of, let alone any skill in, the mending of roads. The great majority merely contented themselves with shovelling rubbish into obvious potholes, and then, twelve months later, by which time the holes had re-appeared and deepened, repeating the process.

Road surfaces, in consequence, progressively deteriorated, and it was perhaps in a mood of desperation that Parliament, early in the eighteenth century, authorized the creation of turnpike trusts. The trustees were usually groups of landowners and other prominent local people empowered, under their own particular Act, to erect barriers and tollhouses on certain specified stretches of road; and, by means of these, to levy a tax on travellers which would pay for maintenance and, if sufficient moneys were forthcoming, provide for improvements. In 1663, in an effort to restore the ancient highway from London to York, the Quarter Sessions of Hertford, Cambridge

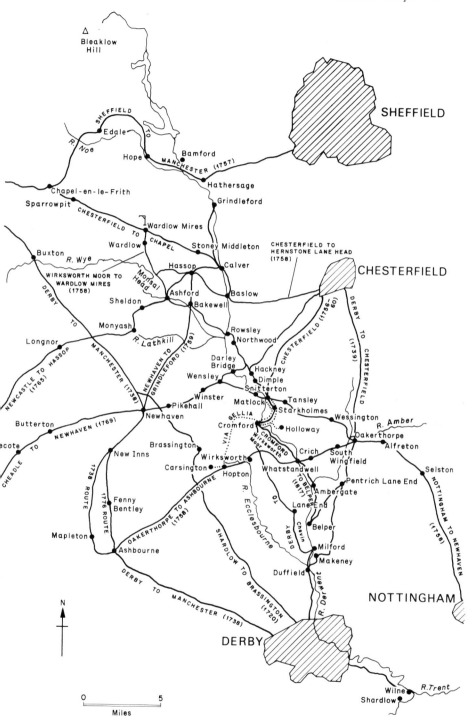

Turnpikes.

and Huntingdon were granted the right to erect their own tollgates at Wadesmill, at Caxton, and also at Stilton; and in 1706 the first turnpike trust was established by Act of Parliament to mend and maintain the road between Fornhill in Bedfordshire and Stony Stratford in Buckinghamshire. By 1838, in England and Wales, there were over a thousand such trusts in existence, maintaining 22,000 miles of road by means of almost 8,000 gates; but even this proliferation of barriers and taxes achieved little more than a marginal improvement till, early in the nineteenth century, a new generation of skilled engineers and road surveyors, led by Telford and Macadam, made their talents available to turnpike trustees; and by that time, ironically, the growing railway network was beginning to make the need for better highways a matter of swiftly diminishing importance.

The first section of road near the Derwent to be turnpiked was a stretch of the London to Manchester highway between the crossing of the Trent at Shardlow and Brassington, west of Cromford. The Act of 1720 which authorized the trust declared its intention 'to amend the dangerous, narrow and at times impassable road' between these two places; and a second such Act in 1738 turnpiked an alternative route to Manchester through Ashbourne and Buxton by way of Newhaven, though the road, for the first five miles north of Ashbourne, ran to the west of its present line, passing through Mapleton and not Fenny Bentley.

The way from Derby to Chesterfield through Wirksworth, Cromford, Starkholmes and Matlock was partially turnpiked in 1756; and that from Sheffield to Manchester by Hathersage, Hope and the Vale of Edale the following year; while 1758 saw the creation of the Nottingham to Newhaven Trust by a comprehensive Act which covered the improvement of seven cross-country roads: Alfreton to Newhaven, Oakerthorpe to Ashbourne, Wirksworth Moor to Wardlow Mires, Chesterfield to Hernstone Lane Head, Bar Brook to Wardlow Mires, Calver Bridge to Baslow Bridge, and Newhaven to Grindleford Bridge.

Most of these routes, turnpiked under the Act of 1758, follow today the lines of minor roads, still marked in places by their milestones, tollhouses and coaching inns. The main Nottingham to Newhaven turnpike, $31\frac{1}{2}$ miles in its total length, was designed to connect Nottingham with the London to Manchester road at Newhaven. Invariably named in the Trust's Minute Books as the Alfreton Turnpike Road, it set out from Nottingham at Hyson Green and proceeded through Selston to the George Hotel at Alfreton, a coaching inn where the horses were changed. From there it continued to Four Lane Ends at Oakerthorpe, took the right-hand turn past the Peacock, another coaching inn on the Belper to Chesterfield turnpike, and then cut off left through Wessington to Matlock. The drop through Tansley to Matlock Bridge was steep, and was matched on the western side of the Derwent by the climb to Snitterton and up the flank of Oaker Hill

Winster West Bank.

to Wensley and Winster, followed by the sharp ascent of Winster West
Bank to the Miners' Standard Inn. The road had, by that time, twisted up
some six hundred feet from the river in less than five miles; but, reaching
the crest of the hill beyond the Standard, it then flattened out to run through
Pikehall to the junction at Newhaven.

Between Alfreton and Newhaven there were three tollhouses and gates: the first at Matlock, the second at Wensley and the third at Pikehall. None of these now survives, but one of the original milestones can still be seen at Snitterton, marking the distance from Nottingham as twenty-six miles; and if little else remains save the line of the road to prove that this, two hundred years ago, was one of the major coaching routes across the valley, yet the hills are still there: hills so steep in parts that the present-day traveller, whether driving in a car or toiling up the inclines step by weary step, can only wonder how horses could ever have dragged a coach, let alone a laden waggon, as far as their crests.

The fact is, of course, that the turnpike trustees recognized the problem and made their own provisions, at an early date, to deal with it in the only way that they possibly could. Meeting together in 1767, they recorded their opinion that the existing regulations were clearly inadequate. 'It is impracticable,' they declared, 'for any Wagon or other 4 wheeled Carriage with the weights allowed by the Act of Parliament without manifest inconvenience and hazard to be drawn up'; and to reduce, if not to eliminate, the dangers, they permitted the hitching of extra horses at the bottom of Oaker Hill and Winster West Bank, instructing their surveyor to mark by some easily visible means the points between which such horses could be used.

Similar concessions must have been made on the turnpike road between Oakerthorpe and Ashbourne, which passed through South Wingfield, Parkhead and Crich, before descending the precipitous side of the valley to Whatstandwell—then known as Hottstandell—Bridge and pressing across the river to climb Longway Bank on to Wirksworth Moor. A visitor taking the branch road to Crich from the eastern end of Whatstandwell Bridge, and scaling the steep ascent with its panoramic view of Francis Hurt's Alderwasley Hall across the valley to the right, can do little but marvel at the endurance of horses and the strong nerves displayed by stage coach passengers in an age when the roads were not yet metalled, when wheels were tyred in iron, and when the only method of braking a vehicle was by the drag shoe or skid, which, on a downward slope, locked the near-hind wheel.

Matlock Bridge, a meeting of the ways for the packhorse trains, continued to hold its place in the turnpike age as a junction of roads and perhaps the most important crossing of the Derwent; and the network of turnpikes converging on the bridge led to the complaint that 'in five directions Toll-bars are placed very near to this Town, one hilly and indifferent Lane only remaining open towards Willersley, by which the Inhabitants can stir abroad without paying Tolls'. Here, at the river, the turnpike road from Nottingham to Newhaven met those climbing steeply up Matlock Bank to Chesterfield and through Dimple and Hackney to Darley Bridge and Rowsley. The road up the Bank to Chesterfield, with its tollhouse at the bottom, still carries the appropriate name of Steep Turnpike; while the bridge itself, *Pontem de Matelock* as it was known in clerk's Latin in the thirteenth century, reveals, even today, on its downstream side, the four pointed arches that probably carried the packhorse trains across the winter surge of the flooded river.

Other old junctions, like Leadmill Bridge at Hathersage, declined in importance with the building of turnpikes; but new ones developed, dominated by their coaching inns, to serve the increasing stage coach traffic that ran between Derby, Nottingham and Manchester. Newhaven, on the road between Ashbourne and Buxton, developed as a busy multiple junction, where turnpikes from Nottingham, Derby and Manchester, Grindleford Bridge and Cheadle in Staffordshire merged from five directions and travellers were accommodated at the Devonshire Arms, 'a large handsome and commodious inn', now the Newhaven Hotel. King George IV, the former Prince Regent, was one who, so the story goes, passed an evening there, perhaps on his way across the border to Scotland in 1822. According to J. B. Firth in his *Highways and Byways in Derbyshire*, he was so regally entertained that he granted the house 'a free and perpetual licence' to serve

Newhaven Hotel.

customers at any hour of the day or the night; though the dispensation was granted to the sixth Duke of Devonshire, who then owned the inn, and it may well have lapsed when, later in the century, the land was transferred to the Rutland estate. The thirsty motorist, passing by at midnight on the road to Buxton, should not therefore expect to find the bar open, even in this allegedly permissive age.

Another stretch of road which became a vital link in the turnpike chain was the ancient way from Ashford by way of Monsal Head to Wardlow and the Mires. This formed the northern end of the tollroad that ran through Matlock and Bakewell from Wirksworth Moor. Joined from the right at Monsal Head by the Chesterfield to Hernstone Lane Head turnpike, which had reached the junction by passing through Baslow, Hassop and Great and Little Longstone, it then continued north to link with the turnpike from Chesterfield to Chapel, now the A623, at Wardlow Mires. Here there was a tollhouse which, in 1815, became a place of notoriety when the gate-keeper, Hannah Oliver, was murdered and robbed of her takings. A young man of twenty-one, Anthony Lingard, was convicted of the crime at Derby Assizes and sentenced to be hanged and then gibbeted by the tollhouse. On

Turnpike junction at Wardlow Mires.

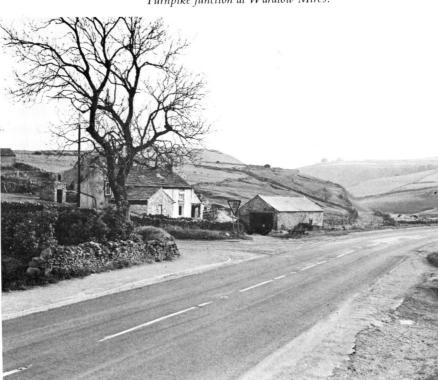

the high ground by the Mires, since known as Gibbet Field, his body was accordingly suspended in chains, and remained there till the flesh had rotted away and the bones began to rattle in the westerly wind that swept across Littonfields from Tideswell. Lingard's father made a pilgrimage alone, in the dead of night, to stand below the gibbet, the last in Derbyshire: a journey that prompted William Newton, the Minstrel of the Peak, who at that time was building Cressbrook Mill, to write his well-meant, if hardly poetic, soliloquy:

> Art thou, my Son, suspended here on high,—
> Ah! What a sight to meet a Father's eye!
> To see what most I prized, what most I loved,
> What most I cherished,—and once approved,
> Hung in mid air to feed the nauseous worm,
> And waving horrid in the midnight storm!...
> If crime demand it, let the offender die,
> But let no more the Gibbet brave the sky;
> No more let vengeance on the dead be hurled,
> But hide the victim from a gazing world.

Newton's mill architecture has stood the test of time better than his verses, but they may well have played their part in ensuring that Lingard's body was the last to be subjected to this grisly treatment; though cynics might claim that the cost of the gibbeting, reputed to have been in excess of £100, proved in the end a more potent deterrent to the officers of the law.

By 1771, when Arkwright established his first mill at Cromford, the turnpike trusts already controlled a web of twisting roads across the face of the valley, yet the village remained as deep in isolation as it had been in Defoe's time, fifty years before. Eighteenth-century trusts rarely pioneered new, direct routes. They restricted themselves to improving and maintaining such roads as existed; and since these followed, with little variation, the old packhorse ways, the new turnpikes avoided the valley bottom except at the points where they crossed the Derwent. In consequence, the tracks that ran into and out of Cromford fell, as they had done since medieval times, down semi-perpendicular slopes to the dale and then climbed from the river up hills that were equally difficult to negotiate.

Even as late as 1788 there was no valley road running by the side of the river from Belper. The Derby to Chesterfield turnpike road swung, west of Milford, around the Chevin to Belper Lane End and Wirksworth Moor, approaching the village down the precipitous slope that led from Bolehill. It then crossed the bridge and wound up the eastern side of the dale through Starkholmes to Matlock: a tortuous, 'hilly and indifferent Lane' that was apparently never controlled by the trust, and so never improved. The second, more direct, Derby to Chesterfield turnpike never touched Cromford. It

Cromford Hill.

crossed to the east of the river at Duffield and swung abruptly right by the Holly Bush Inn at Makeney, where the line of the road is still marked by a stone inscribed 'Derby Coach Road 1739'. From there it proceeded by way of Holbrook to Pentrich Lane End and Oakerthorpe, and thence to Chesterfield along the Roman road known as Ryknield Street.

North of the village, as far as Matlock Bath, there did exist a private carriageway constructed as early as 1745 by two Nottingham gentlemen, Mr Smith and Mr Pennel, who, having purchased the lease of the thermal springs for £1,000, improved the old horseway from Cromford Bridge to guarantee some degree of safe passage to visitors taking the waters at their bath-house. This had almost certainly, by 1771, been extended to Matlock,

Turnpike stone, Holly Bush Inn, Makeney.

but it was not until 1817 that the riverside road running southwards to Belper, now the A6, came into existence under an Act of Parliament 'for making and maintaining a Turnpike Road from the Town of Cromford to the Town of Belper'.

Arkwright, in conjunction with Francis Hurt and Jedediah Strutt, had already, by that time, linked the two places by a private road along the bank of the river, which provided a line for the projected turnpike; but, to the end of his life, he must have had to struggle to move building materials, bales of cotton and consignments of finished yarn, especially since the only two other roads of consequence, providing exit from his dale-locked village, were the old packhorse way toiling up through Lea Bridge to Holloway, and the road through the deep, wooded Griffe Grange Valley, commenced in 1791 by Philip Gell of Hopton Hall, driven from his lead mines at Carsington, west of Wirksworth, and named, in grandiloquent fashion, Via Gellia.

In the spring and autumn rains, in the blizzards and snow drifts of a Derbyshire winter, the movement of vital supplies along the roads must have ground to a halt for weeks, if not for months, at a time; and it was almost certainly in an attempt to circumvent this problem that Arkwright himself, at the end of July 1788, attended a meeting convened at Matlock to support 'a Navigation from Derby to Cromford, and up the River Amber'.

The new canals, or navigations as they were known in Parliamentary language, had already, by that time, touched the fringes of the valley. That they had done so and that Britain possessed, by 1788, a rapidly expanding system of artificial waterways was due largely to the genius of a semi-literate Derbyshire millwright, James Brindley, who, in the words of Samuel Smiles, 'was probably one of the most remarkable instances of self-taught genius to be found in the whole range of biography'.

Brindley was born in 1716 on the edge of the cluster of unpretentious cottages which still today forms the village of Tunstead, in a desolate area of dry stone walls above Great Rocks Dale, three miles east of Buxton. His father, an indigent labouring crofter, was apparently more addicted to the baiting of bulls than he was to the profitable working of the croft; and it seems to have been due mainly to his mother's encouragement that, at the age of seventeen, the boy bound himself apprentice to a millwright near Macclesfield. By 1742 he was a master of his trade, with a business at Leek: a business that at first was chiefly confined to erecting waterwheels and machinery for the silk mills of Macclesfield and the flint-grinding mills of the Staffordshire potteries, but one which he extended to embrace surveying, the construction of tunnels and the drainage of mines.

His local reputation as a man of resource and a skilled engineer brought him to the notice of Earl Gower of Trentham, who engaged him to work on a number of projects, one of which was to make a survey of the possible line for a waterway to link the Trent with the Mersey. It was due to this connection that, in 1759, the earl's brother-in-law, the young Francis Egerton, third Duke of Bridgewater, employed him to survey and cut a canal for coal transportation between his Worsley estate and the town of Manchester. The success of this enterprise, the first of its kind in Britain, sparked off a frenzy of canal construction, earned for Brindley a nationwide reputation, and ensured that, for the remaining dozen years of his life, his self-generated expertise was in constant demand for developing a national network of waterways.

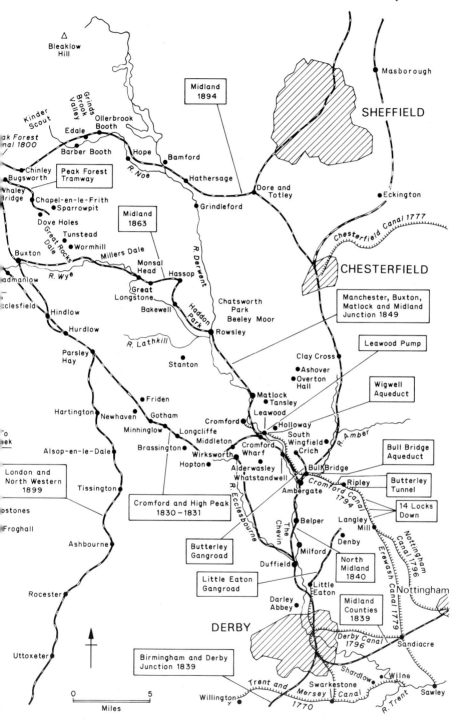

Canals and Railways.

By the time that Smiles published his *Life of James Brindley* in 1862, the family cottage at Tunstead had fallen into ruins. He described its progressive disintegration:

> The walls stood long after the roof had fallen in, and at length the materials were removed to build cowhouses; but in the middle of the ruin there grew up a young ash tree, forcing up one of the flags of the cottage floor. It looked so healthy and thriving a plant, that the labourer employed to remove the stones for the purpose of forming the pathway to the neighbouring farm-house, spared the seedling, and it grew up into the large and flourishing tree, six feet nine inches in girth, standing in the middle of the Croft, and now known as 'Brindley's Tree'. This ash tree is nature's own memorial of the birthplace of the engineer, and it is the only one as yet raised to the genius of Brindley.

Apart from his grave at Turnhurst in Staffordshire, the ash tree remained his only memorial until 1875. Then, at last, a century after his death, the Derbyshire hill folk belatedly recognized that their bare, bleak heights had nurtured a most remarkable man. To commemorate their awakening, they erected over the head of the village well at Wormhill, a mile from his home, a curious structure, triangular in shape and built of stone blocks, with the curt inscription: '1875 In memory of James Brindley, Civil Engineer, Born in this Parish A.D. 1716.'

At Tunstead the old tree alone marked his birthplace, till it fell to a gale sweeping down across the heights from Wormhill Moor. Lacking its gnarled presence, nothing remained to indicate the spot where the cottage had stood but a twist in the lane leading down to the village. It languished unmarked until 1958, when the Local History Section of the Derbyshire Archaeological Society planted a sapling where once the tree had grown, and erected a new memorial: a stone plinth bearing a plaque made of bronze, and the measured and much more impressive dedication:

James Brindley
1716–1772
Millwright and Civil Engineer
Here stood the cottage in which James Brindley
was born. Of humble birth, he became famous as
the pioneer builder of the great canals of
England.

It is difficult today, standing by that twist in the Tunstead lane, to believe that this bleak, inhospitable moor above the valley of the Wye—little changed from the time, according to legend, when Brindley, as a boy whittled pieces of wood into waterwheels of his own contrivance—could possibly have yielded a great engineer to a waiting world. On this wind-swept height, bare of all save its dry stone walls, the words of the naturalist W. H. Hudson, written sixty years ago, seem closer to credibility. The people of the Peak, he took care to explain, lived in isolation from the rest of mankind. They were, he said, 'like the inhabitants of a lonely island'.

Here at Tunstead, itself a lonely island, only the plinth, a dot in the wilderness, bears witness to the fact that from this plot of ground rose an unlettered giant, who towered above the rutted tracks trodden by less imaginative men as the ash tree once towered above the mud-spattered lane by his father's croft.

Brindley Memorial, Tunstead.

It was in the midsummer of 1759 that Brindley commenced his initial survey on behalf of the Duke of Bridgewater. Two years later, almost to the day, the canal was completed; and included in the $10\frac{1}{4}$ miles of its length was the Barton Aqueduct, which carried it at a height of forty feet above the River Irwell and which was justly regarded, in that pioneer age of waterway engineering, as an achievement compounded of imagination, daring, and a high degree of technical skill. The first boat-load of coals crossed the aqueduct to Manchester on 17 July 1761, and Brindley then proceeded to extend the canal westward a further 28 miles to join the Mersey at a point on the natural tideway above the port of Liverpool. This new channel was cut as far as Runcorn by 1767, but, long before its opening, Brindley was engaged in a greater enterprise which was to take his system of continuous waterways to the very edge of the Derwent Valley.

In 1765, largely on the initiative of Josiah Wedgwood, the scheme for linking the Trent and the Mersey, originally conceived by Brindley's old employer, Earl Gower of Trentham, was revived with the support of the Staffordshire potters. The raw materials required by the Potteries—special clays from Devon and Cornwall; flints from the south-east coast and East Anglia—had to travel long distances by tortuous routes, and were subject, at times, to unconscionable delays. The clays were normally shipped to Liverpool and then up the Mersey and its tributary, the Weaver, to Winsford in Cheshire, whence they were transported the rest of the way by packhorse train or rumbling stage-waggon; this was because the more direct route through the port of Bristol involved a journey up the Severn to Bridgnorth or Bewdley, and then an even longer martyrdom on the roads as far as north Staffordshire. The flint-stones, likewise, were carried by sea to Hull, from there along the Trent in barges to Willington, east of Burton, and then again by road; while the earthenware and china subsequently produced made the same expensive and dangerous journeys, this time in reverse. Samuel Smiles wrote:

> Large crates of pot-ware were slung across horses' backs, and thus conveyed to their respective ports, not only at great risk of breakage and pilferage, but also at a heavy cost. The expense of carriage was not less than a shilling a ton per mile, and the lowest charge was eight shillings the ton for ten miles. Besides, the navigation of the rivers above mentioned was most uncertain, arising from floods in winter and droughts in summer. The effect was, to prevent the expansion of the earthenware manufacture, and very greatly to restrict the distribution of the lower-priced articles in common use.

It was therefore natural that Wedgwood and his fellow potters should look with favour on any design to connect the Potteries with the two main rivers of transportation, the Trent and the Mersey, with the option of eventually extending such a waterway to link with the Severn and perhaps with the Thames. This was what Brindley purposed to do, and, once appointed engineer to the project, he let it be known that he preferred to think of the work, not as the Trent and Mersey, but the Grand Trunk Canal: the trunk, as he said, of a great tree that would throw out its branches to east and west: the primary stage of a Grand Cross of waterways to connect the four major rivers of England.

Parliamentary sanction was secured for the canal, after a tedious struggle against vested interests, on 14 May 1766; and two months later Wedgwood himself turned the first sod of earth, Brindley wheeled it away in a barrow, a sheep was roasted whole in the market-place at Burslem, and the Potteries rejoiced. The first faint line of the silver cross of water had been cut between the deep-rutted Staffordshire lanes.

The Grand Trunk, according to Brindley's plan, was to run from Preston Brook, near Runcorn, on the Bridgewater Canal, through the great salt-producing districts of Cheshire, climbing by a series of thirty-five locks to a summit point at Harecastle on the Staffordshire border. Here a tunnel, almost three thousand yards in length, would be cut through the hill, and the canal would then descend by forty further locks, passing Burslem and Stoke, Rugeley and Burton, to join the Trent at Wilden Ferry by the Cavendish Bridge and the mouth of the Derwent.

A resident of Burslem, writing to a friend in 1767, declared that 'the great Mr. Brindley' was 'as plain a looking man as one of the boors of the Peak, or as one of his own carters'; but, 'when he speaks, all ears listen, and every mind is filled with wonder at the things he pronounces to be practicable'. It was eminently practicable, Brindley maintained, to cut a canal tunnel through Harecastle Hill: a belief he always clung to, despite mounting ridicule and allusions to his project as 'a sad misfortune', a 'chimerical idea' and, more wittily perhaps, 'a castle in the air'. He proved in the end that his faith was justified, but the tunnel required eleven years to complete, and though the canal was opened in June 1770 from Wilden Ferry northwards to the neighbourhood of Stafford, it was not until the May of 1777, five years after his death, that boats could navigate the whole of the distance from the Mersey to the Trent. Nonetheless, the final triumph was his, for the opening of the Oxford Canal in 1790 completed the Grand Cross that had been his dream a quarter of a century before.

His waterway, in the words of John Wesley, transformed the Potteries from a 'wilderness' into a 'fruitful field'; it linked Wedgwood's Etruria with the east and west coasts; and to a small cluster of cottages near the mouth of the Derwent, the village of Shardlow, it brought a prosperity that few, except Brindley, could possibly have foreseen.

When the London to Manchester road was turnpiked northwards from the Trent in 1720, the river was crossed by a rope-hauled flat boat at a place then known as Wilden Ferry; but, in 1758, to speed the passage of traffic, an Act of Parliament was obtained for the construction of a bridge. Opened

three years later as the Cavendish Bridge, it gave its name to the settlement
that grew at the crossing. Tolls were collected on the Derbyshire side, and
these, the same as those charged for the ferry, were recorded on a handsome
slate tablet which can still be seen, beside the A6, at the Derby end of the
modern bridge. The charges were heavy: two shillings and sixpence for a
four-wheeled coach, and one and six for a four-wheeled waggon. Even
pedestrians had to pay a penny, though soldiers, 'favour'd' as the scale plainly
stated, were allowed to pass for half that amount; while the charge of a
penny, modest by comparison, for a 'horse (not drawing)' was clearly
considered exorbitant by at least one traveller, for in 1705 Joseph Taylor,
to avoid the ferry toll, rode his horse through the river from bank to bank,
though, as he said, perhaps with typical British understatement, ''twas a
little difficult'.

A few hundred yards in the direction of Derby, along the turnpike road
and beside the river, lay the village of Shardlow: a small, unremarkable
farming community, clustered round its hall, built eighty years before by
Leonard Fosbrooke, a wealthy river carrier and one-time owner of the

Tollboard at Cavendish Bridge, Shardlow.

Wilden Ferry. This quiet village, because of its position on the new navigation, was to be swiftly transformed. A mile from the southern end of the canal and its junction with both the Derwent and the Trent, Shardlow was chosen as the transhipment point where goods were interchanged between the broad river barges and the narrow boats required to negotiate the locks on Brindley's waterway; and since such transhipment was rarely immediate, direct from boat to boat, the village rapidly developed into an inland port of considerable significance, with storage and distribution facilities and a whole range of ancillary crafts such as smithying, rope-making and boat and crane building.

Broughton House and the Navigation Inn, Shardlow.

In 1766, when Brindley had completed what he described as his 'ochilor servey or a ricconitoring', his 'navvies', the inland navigators, arrived at Derwent Mouth to cut the canal; and Shardlow immediately became the place of bustling business activity it was to remain for more than a hundred years. Once the southern half of the canal was opened, warehouses were constructed between the narrow stretch of water and the turnpike road to Derby, basins and inlets were excavated to give access to them, wharves built to accommodate the hundreds of boats, and cranes and hoists to transfer their cargoes: cargoes which ranged from iron, lead and coal through limestone and gypsum, flint and chert, deal and pottery, to ale, cheese and barley, malt and salt.

The Lady in Grey, Shardlow.

Out of the heart of this 'Little Liverpool' two families emerged, the Soresbys and the Suttons, to dominate the carrying trade from the port. The Soresbys ran a fleet of fly-boats on the Trent: express barges drawn by relays of horses; while the Suttons transported goods by river and canal as far as Liverpool, Hull, Birmingham and the Potteries. Both families prospered. The Soresbys built a tasteful, tree-sheltered house called The Lady in Grey; the Suttons another, Broughton House, close by; though James Sutton, the head of the firm, never lived there, preferring the seclusion of Fosbrooke's old hall further to the west.

By the time that John Byng, in the course of his travels, visited the port in 1789, he was suitably impressed. 'Around the navigation of the Trent to the Mersey, at Shardlow,' he wrote, 'are built so many merchants' houses, wharfs etc., sprinkled with gardens looking upon the Trent and to Castle Dunnington Hill as to form as happy a scenery of business and pleasures as can be surveyed.' The population of the village was then about three hundred. It more than quadrupled by 1841, but by that time the railways were penetrating the area, bringing a progressive decline in trade. The warehouses were closed or diverted to corn-milling, the basins infilled, the cranes removed, and the host of inns and taverns—by 1799 there were nine within half a mile of the canal—dwindled as, one by one, they were converted into dwellings; though the Navigation Inn, a riverside tavern before Brindley

Clock Warehouse, Shardlow.

came to Shardlow, survived the contraction and still survives today, despite the ill-usage it once must have suffered at the hands of the boatmen, whom Pastor Moritz, a visitor in 1782, described as being 'wilder' and 'coarser' men than any he had ever met before in his life.

The port of Shardlow is now the Shardlow Wharf Conservation Area; many of the buildings that served the canal are 'listed' as important, preserved for architectural or historical reasons; and, despite the closeness of the busy A6 road, to walk the towpath beside the Grand Trunk today is to feel, as one feels by the Derwent at Darley Abbey, that the years have rolled back to the eighteenth century.

Here is the old Clock Warehouse, built of brick and tile in 1780, with its graceful arch beneath which the boats glided for unloading, and, in its pediment, the vacant circle that once housed the clock. Here are the inns: the Canal Tavern, the Ship, the Malt Shovel, the Navigation. Here is Broughton House, with its Doric columns and network balcony, and The Lady in Grey, still sheltered by trees and now delicate in white. Here are the long parallel hedges of the ropewalk, where the boatmen exchanged their short canal ropes for the longer ones needed for towing on the Trent; and here, on the towpath, a stone's throw from the vast container lorries that throng the A6, the first of many iron mileposts, cast by the Staffordshire firm of Rangeley and Dixon and set mile by mile along the canal. 'Shardlow', it reads on one side; and on the other, 'Preston Brook'—a name unknown to lorry drivers—'92 miles'.

Ninety-two miles of smooth, level water: once the silver shaft of Brindley's Grand Cross.

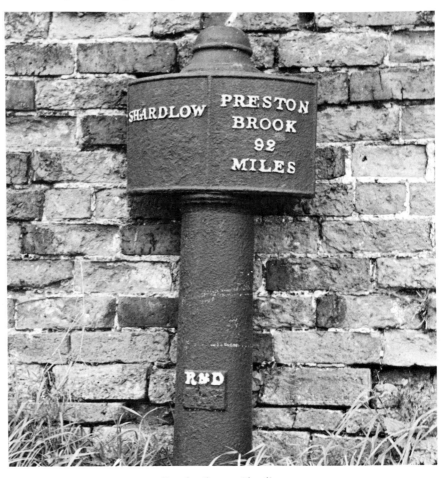

Canal milepost, Shardlow.

The Trent and Mersey Canal made contact with the Derwent at its junction with the Trent, but, while work was in progress in and around Shardlow, Brindley was engaged on yet another waterway, nine miles from the Derwent and further to the north. This, the Chesterfield Canal, was driven from the town by way of Worksop and Retford to join the Trent at Stockwith, eight miles east of Bawtry. Construction work commenced in 1771, but the following year Brindley was caught in a storm while surveying a new branch of the Trent and Mersey between Froghall and Leek. He continued to work, ignoring the fact that his clothes were drenched. 'This,' wrote Samuel Smiles, 'he had often before done with impunity, and he might have done so again; but, unfortunately, he was put into a damp bed in the inn at Ipstones, and this proved too much for his constitution, robust though he naturally was. He became seriously ill, and was disabled from all further work'. It was only when Erasmus Darwin, in his medical capacity, was called in to attend him, that the discovery was made that Brindley was diabetic. Despite Darwin's devotion and daily visits from his friend, Josiah Wedgwood, he never recovered and, in the September of 1772, died at his home at Turnhurst, almost within sight of the unfinished workings at Harecastle Tunnel.

John Varley, his Clerk of Works, succeeded him as engineer to the Chesterfield project, and, following its completion in 1777, was appointed to cut the Erewash Canal. This, the third new waterway to touch the edge of the valley, was designed first and foremost for coal transportation. Running from the Trent at Sawley, three miles east of Shardlow, it followed the line of the Erewash River northwards to Langley Mill, where its terminal point was only fourteen miles to the south-east of Cromford. By 1788, when Arkwright attended his meeting at Matlock, it had been in service for almost nine years and was paying a dividend of more than twenty per cent; and it was against this background of profitability that Sir Richard and a number of his business associates decided to pursue the idea of 'a Navigation' to connect the mills at Cromford with the terminal basin of the canal at Langley Mill, and to ask William Jessop to prepare on their behalf an estimate of cost.

Jessop was then, at the age of forty-three, a canal engineer of considerable experience, and was destined, three years later, along with Benjamin Outram and Francis Beresford, to be a founder-partner in the Butterley Company. Outram and Beresford were members of Arkwright's group, as were the Gells of Hopton and the Hodgkinson family of Overton Hall, near Ashover: a combination of interests that represented iron and cotton, coal, lead and limestone. The advantage to such men of a waterway connecting Cromford with the Trent, with the textile districts centred on Nottingham, and with the two major ports of Liverpool and Hull, was sufficiently plain to render finance a purely academic problem. When, in the December of 1788, a further meeting was held at Alfreton and Jessop submitted his plans for the canal with an estimate of £42,000, half of the money was raised immediately and the remainder inside a couple of weeks.

The Cromford Canal was authorized by Parliament the following year, despite opposition from Jedediah Strutt and Thomas Evans, who feared a distortion of water supplies to their mills at Belper, at Milford and Darley Abbey, lower down the Derwent. Opened in August 1794 at an eventual cost of nearly twice Jessop's estimate, it ran from Cromford Wharf on the site of Arkwright's mills, clinging to the Derwent for a mile and a quarter as far as Leawood, where it swung to the east to cross the river by the Wigwell Aqueduct. At Ambergate it turned still further to the east, crossed the Amber valley by a second aqueduct, this time at Bull Bridge, penetrated directly beneath the Butterley Ironworks by means of a tunnel three thousand yards in length, and then descended by a series of fourteen locks to meet the Erewash Canal at Langley Mill.

Jessop's construction work was not without its problems. Early in 1792 the Bull Bridge Aqueduct, fifty feet high and two hundred yards long, began to crack apart and had to be repaired; while, later the same year, cracks also appeared in the Wigwell Aqueduct, spanning the Derwent. In both cases Jessop accepted the blame and paid the cost of restoration. 'Painful as it is to me to lose the good opinion of my Friends,' he said, 'I would rather receive their censure for the faults of my head than of my heart.' The fault at Wigwell, he declared, was a lack of 'sufficient strength in the front walls': a fault magnified to the point of failure by his use of Crich lime in the building mortar. The lime from Crich, as he discovered too late, was exceptionally pure and contained insufficient clay-like matter to bind the masonry blocks together.

But, in spite of these setbacks which delayed its completion and increased its cost, the Cromford Canal proved a profitable venture. Apart from coal and coke, which consistently provided three-quarters of its trade, it carried gritstone, iron ore and lead. Its boats bore chert from Bakewell bound for the Potteries; limestone from Crich to serve as a flux in the Butterley furnaces; and the multiple products of the furnaces themselves, distributed from Ripley to places as far apart as London Docks, the Gloucester and Cheltenham Railway, Newbottle Colliery in County Durham and the Caledonian Canal through the Great Glen in Scotland.

Wigwell Aqueduct, Cromford Canal.

The completion of the Nottingham and Derby Canals in 1796 by Jessop and Outram provided Cromford with direct water links to the two major textile centres of the Midlands, and increased the already heavy traffic to Langley Mill. Between 1802 and 1803 the waterway carried 155,000 tons of goods, and this amount had doubled by 1842. Then, seven years later, the decline commenced. By 1849 the Manchester, Buxton, Matlock and Midland Junction Railway had extended its lines alongside the western stretch of the canal, and trade sunk progressively: 284,000 tons in 1850; 145,000 in 1870, declining to a mere 45,000 tons by 1888.

The canal was sold to the railway company in 1852, and the sale provoked an increasing disuse. In 1889, by which time the traffic was little more than local, a subsidence closed the Butterley Tunnel for four years and, though it was repaired, colliery shafts running beneath it caused a further collapse in 1903. By that time the cost of possible restoration was uneconomic, and the canal remained split into two separate sections, which for some years operated independently of one another, though most of the section between Butterley and Langley Mill degenerated into a waterless bed, and the upper part to Cromford was eventually closed in 1944 by the L.M.S. Railway. Taken over by the British Waterways Board, its ownership was transferred to the Derbyshire County Council in 1974 and, largely owing to the efforts of the Cromford Canal Society, volunteer work has restored the canal between Cromford and the Wigwell Aqueduct as an amenity waterway, and the Society hopes to reconstitute the towpath as far as Bull Bridge to form a waterside walk and nature reserve.

The Bull Bridge Aqueduct was demolished in 1968 to permit the widening of the road down the Amber Valley, but the Wigwell Aqueduct, with its 80-foot span arching across the Derwent, still stands as sound, to all appearances, as when Jessop rebuilt it. At its northern end is the engine house of the Leawood Pump, its tall gritstone chimney surmounted by a wide cast-iron parapet towering above both aqueduct and canal. The canal company came into existence with the right to take water either from the weir above Arkwright's Masson Mill or from his earlier Cromford Mills. The latter course was adopted, the water being taken by means of pipes which were later replaced by an underground culvert; and for almost fifty years this source, plus a feeder reservoir at Butterley, supplied the canal with water. However, the driving of the new Meerbrook Sough, which by 1846 was tapping most of the lead mine levels under Wirksworth, robbed the Arkwrights of the water supply to their Upper and Lower Mills and reduced to a trickle the feeder supplies to the northern end of Jessop's canal. Because of this the Leawood Pump house was built to raise water from the Derwent, and though, for some time, the canal company hired a pumping engine, they eventually ordered a Watt-type beam engine from Grahams of Elsecar, who, two years before, had supplied the Cornish engine for the Mandale Mine. The engine went to work in 1849, and pumped for ninety-

Leawood pump, Cromford Canal.

nine years whenever there was a surplus of water in the Derwent, raising 31 tons a minute to be poured into the canal. Now restored by willing helpers from the Cromford Canal Society, the boilers are fired on certain days in the year and the massive beam rocks once again under steam.

To follow the line of the canal from the old wharves and warehouses by the church at Cromford down to the second wharf where the Cromford and

Wharf and warehouse, Cromford Canal.

High Peak Railway commenced its spectacular climb to Parsley Hay; then past the Leawood Pump, across the Wigwell Aqueduct, and so, by Whatstandwell, to Bull Bridge, is to walk through one of the most beautiful stretches of the Derwent Valley. But there is more to observe than beauty. Here, juxtaposed, are centuries of progress;·for here, in the narrow valley, the arteries of communication almost touch one another. Enclosed by the slopes that rise to Holloway and Crich, to Alderwasley and Wirksworth, river and road, railway and canal run for some four miles side by side; and though it is only for the briefest of moments, as below Wigwell Aqueduct, that the Derwent, trapped between its woods, seems intent on re-asserting its old isolation, yet to walk the canal towpath is to be constantly aware, not so much of the river, but of the railway track, now singularly peaceful, save when nine times a day the local train from Cromford clanks down to Ambergate. By this quiet, now barely-used stretch of water, the railway seems more immediate than the river, seems to hold more meaning even than the road, for it was these metal lines, stretching away into the distance in the sun, that killed the canal.

Here, displayed within the sweep of a man's gaze, lies all the inevitability of change. First there was only the river, dragging at the piers of its packhorse bridges. Then the canal was cut, smooth and straight, as Brindley might have said, between its strong banks: the first direct link through the floor of the valley with the growing urban centres and their markets to the south. Between those banks, till the railway track was laid, flowed the traffic of the valley. Now the coal and the coke, the limestone and gritstone that once filled the boats trickle from clattering lorries to fall on the tarmac of the A6 road; for the road has, just as surely, drained the life of the railway, as the railway once drained the life of the canal. Only Defoe's ever-furious Derwent, held now in tenuous control by its weirs, still remains as it was: tumbling across the same rough, stony bed, dragging at the piers of the same packhorse bridges as it did in his day, two hundred and fifty years back in the past.

With the construction of Jessop's canal, the only one of the new navigations to penetrate into the heart of the valley, Cromford was connected by water to the four major ports of Brindley's Grand Cross: to Liverpool by the Trent and Mersey Canal; to Hull by means of the Trent Navigation; and to London and Bristol down the Coventry and Birmingham and Fazeley Canals. Yet, ten years later, a discerning traveller, perhaps all the way from Harvey's foundry at Hayle and so with some knowledge of the experimental work of Richard Trevithick, could have forecast, as he floated slowly down the fifteen miles from Cromford to Langley Mill, that the prosperous life of this stretch of water would inevitably be short: little more perhaps than a span of fifty years. This he might have deduced from noting, as he passed, the numerous waggonways already constructed to bring coal and limestone down to the loading wharves from pits and quarries; among them the Butterley Company's Gangroad, clinging to the slope between Hilts Quarry at Crich and the wharf at Bull Bridge. Down this mile-long track, horses could be seen drawing waggons full of limestone, wheels locked against the incline, to be tipped into boats at the side of the canal; and the traveller intent on prophecy might have nodded his head, for these horse-drawn waggon-ways, once the expiration of James Watt's patent enabled Trevithick to produce the locomotive, were to become the steam railways that swiftly drove the canals out of business.

Waggonways, tramroads or gangroads, as they were variously named, had been used in Germany for underground transport in the coal and metal mines as early as the middle of the fifteenth century; but in England their appearance was delayed for a further hundred and fifty years. Then, about the year 1604, Huntington Beaumont, one of the first men to develop exten-sive coalmining interests, laid a wooden track from his coal pits at Strelley, eight miles from the Derwent, to a road distribution point near Wollaton Hall on the western side of Nottingham; but it was in the colliery areas of the north-east of England, where Beaumont also had considerable holdings, that the waggonways became an essential form of transport. In 1676 Roger North, an eminent barrister, saw them in use in the Newcastle area. 'The manner of the carriage,' he wrote, 'is by laying rails of timber from the colliery down to the river, exactly straight and parallel, and bulky carts are made with four rowlets fitting these rails, whereby the carriage is so easy that one horse will draw down four or five chaldrons of coals, and is an immense benefit to coal merchants.'

Both rails and waggon wheels were, at that time, constructed of wood, and though iron wheels began to be used on waggons during the second quarter of the eighteenth century, yet Arthur Young, writing of the Newcastle coalfield some fifty years later, could still describe the tracks as 'pieces of wood let into the road for the wheels of the waggons to run on.' The first recorded use of rails made of iron was in 1767 when, at Coalbrookdale, to quote Samuel Smiles, 'five or six tons of rails were cast, as an experiment, on the suggestion of Mr. Reynolds, one of the partners; and they were shortly after laid down to form a road.' Richard Reynolds, son-in-law of the second Abraham Darby, had been appointed manager of the ironworks four years before, and his granddaughter, speaking many years later, made very clear that the suggestion did, indeed, emanate from him:

> For the conveyance of coal and iron to different parts of the works, and to the river Severn, wooden rails had been in use, which from the great weights carried upon them, were not only soon worn out, but were liable to give way and break occasioning loss of time and interruption to business, and great expense in repairing them. It occurred to him that the inconveniences would be obviated by the use of cast iron. He tried it at first with great caution, but found it to answer so well, that very soon all their railways were made with iron. He did not attempt to secure by patent the advantage of this invention, and the use of cast iron in the construction of railways was afterwards generally adopted.

Brindley had, by that time, cut his first canal; and, as the network was extended, branching east and west to produce his Grand Cross, canal proprietors realised that here, in the horse-drawn waggonways, there already existed a cheap, efficient means of increasing their scope. Tracks were laid down as spurs and as feeders to the wharves, and while some were built at the proprietors' expense under the terms of the original Acts of Parliament, others were financed by the owners of mills and mines, quarries and ironworks to link their establishments to the nearest canal. In Derbyshire alone at least fifty such lines are known to have been constructed, all but five connecting with canals and measuring, between them, a total distance of 77 miles. One of these was the Butterley Gangroad, built and financed by the Butterley Company, connecting Crich with the Cromford Canal, and almost certainly the work of Benjamin Outram.

As partners in the newly-formed Butterley Company, Jessop and Outram proved invaluable to one another and so to their firm. If Jessop was the civil engineer, the expert on canals, Outram was the mechanical engineer, and though he too cut canals, he was the expert on waggonways. The two men worked in harness, and naturally, for supplies, they turned to the ironworks in which they had an interest. Butterley, as a result, not only built up an enviable reputation for producing cast-iron rails, they also turned out waggons, lock gates and mechanisms, winding machinery and stationary steam engines.

The often-repeated rumour that Outram gave his name to the tramroads he constructed has probably little foundation in fact; the term derives, more likely, from the old German word for a beam of wood, a *traam*; but he was, without doubt, their most capable publicist and specialist engineer. He was also a perfectionist, preferring, if possible, to supervise personally the laying of tracks for which Butterley supplied the rails. 'In works of considerable extent,' he wrote, 'it is most agreeable to me to undertake the whole road to make by Contract or to have the management of the Construction as much depends on the manner in which the work is executed.' Among the waggon-ways he laid down in Derbyshire were the Ticknall Tramway, a spur to the Ashby-de-la-Zouch Canal; the Peak Forest Tramway, an extension of his own Peak Forest Canal; and the Little Eaton Gangroad, branching north from a terminal basin of the Derby Canal, which was worked on a system of what would now be described as container traffic.

The Derby Canal, surveyed and built by Outram and opened completely in 1796, connected Derby with the Trent and Mersey Canal at Swarkestone to the south, and with the Erewash Canal at Sandiacre to the east. The Phoenix Cut and Lock in the centre of the town by-passed the weirs and gave traffic on the canal access to the Derwent and so north to Darley Abbey; but the weir providing power for Evans' Boar's Head Mill prevented any further passage upstream, so a branch of the canal was extended to Little Eaton, two miles north of the mill, whence a waggonway, the Gangroad, continued a further four miles to Smithy Houses at Denby. The original plan had been to cut the canal all the way through to the collieries at Denby, and the Gang-road appears to have been Jessop's suggestion. On 3 November 1792, in a paper addressed to the Committee of Subscribers to the Derby Canal, he wrote:

> I am clearly of opinion that the most eligible scheme will be that of a canal from Derby to Little Eaton; and from thence Railways to the Collieries:—If these Railways, which should be of cast iron, are substantially laid upon stone founda-tions, and ascend on a regular Acclivity from Eaton to the Collieries, one horse will easily draw down two wagons with two tons each; and empty they will as easily be drawn up again.

No doubt it was an idea that Benjamin Outram adopted with enthusiasm, for the Derby Canal Act of 1793 contained provisions not only 'for making and maintaining a navigable canal', but also 'to make and maintain a Rail or Wagon Way or Stone Road for the conveyance of Coal, Iron, Ironstone, Lead Ore, Limestone and other articles in carriages or vehicles to be properly constructed for that purpose.'

These vehicles were made up of two components: the tram or bogie, and the box or container. To avoid trans-shipping goods at the wharf at Little Eaton, the coal mine and quarry owners tipped their coal and stone into boxes containing slightly less than two tons. These were then lifted by cranes on to bogies, and teams of four horses drew them in trains of ten to the Little Eaton wharf, where the boxes were once again lifted free by crane and loaded into boats.

The coal trade from the Denby collieries expanded rapidly. In the twelve months that ended in midsummer 1798, 11,500 tons passed down the Gang-road, and five years later this had increased to nearly 28,000 tons. Then, in 1820, with the closure of Joseph Bourne's Belper pottery and the transference of all production to Denby, a new and more fragile pattern of merchandise began to be carried in ever-greater quantity. New branches to collieries at Kilburn and Salterwood, opened to traffic in 1829, added to the heavy mineral tonnage, but as Derby developed as a railway centre and trade on the canal declined, so it did on the waggonway. In 1855, when the Midland Railway opened its branch line to Ripley, the fate of the Little Eaton Gangroad was sealed, and the last load of coal, four horses hauling four trams and their boxes, passed down the track from Smithy Houses to the wharf at Little Eaton in July 1908.

The canal at Little Eaton has now disappeared, and the wharf is a depot for a firm of road hauliers. Only the original wharf house with its still-ticking clock survives to mark the place where Outram's canal ended and his waggon-way began. Where the boxes of coal were once lifted from the trams and dropped into waiting boats, heavy fourteen-wheeled lorries now wait for the coal, while the container traffic, so effectively pioneered on the old sloping gangroad, thunders at speed down the trio of trunk roads that now embrace the site.

The longest and most spectacular of all the waggonways was the Cromford and High Peak Railway, driven across the central barrier of the Peak by Josias Jessop, and climbing, in the course of its 33 miles, to a height of nearly thirteen hundred feet.

When, in 1800, Benjamin Outram linked the developing towns of Lancashire to the quarries of North Derbyshire by the Peak Forest Canal, with its southern branch basin at Whaley Bridge, imaginative engineers began to consider a further possibility: a trans-Peak waterway to link Whaley Bridge with the Cromford Canal, thus connecting the manufacturing districts of the North-West with those of the Midlands by a more direct line than that already provided by Brindley's Grand Trunk.

Already, by 1810, such a scheme had been suggested, and in subsequent years two separate routes reached an early stage of planning: one by way of Tansley, Matlock and Bakewell, and another by Grindleford, Hope and Edale. For the Edale route a prospectus was issued, estimating the cost at

£500,000, but since the promoters could envisage an annual revenue of no more than £6,000, the plan, from its inception, was fated to fail.

The Bakewell route was also abandoned, and a third, across the top of the limestone moors to the valley of the Goyt, presented the same insuperable obstacles: the expense of building locks to raise the canal a thousand feet above its starting point at Cromford, lowering it from the summit another seven hundred and fifty feet to the wharves at Whaley Bridge, and maintaining on the high, porous limestone plateau sufficient water for the purpose.

It was out of this series of successive frustrations that the Cromford and High Peak Railway was born. The engineer appointed to survey the route for a canal across the moors was Josias Jessop, William Jessop's son; and it was therefore perhaps predictable that, faced with the formidable problems of lockage, he should have turned, as Outram and his father had done at Little Eaton, to the cheaper alternative of constructing a waggonway. Nor was it perhaps altogether unexpected that, once the line was authorized, Butterley should be designated as the main contractors. The company, in fact, supplied for the railway almost everything made of metal: surveying equipment and bridgework, rails and waggons, cast-iron window frames, winding mechanisms and eight stationary steam engines to provide haulage power on the inclined planes: planes which were Jessop's ingenious substitute for the innumerable locks a canal would have required.

On 2 May 1825, the subscribers to the line, who included the sixth Duke of Devonshire, Richard Arkwright junior and a number of Manchester bankers, secured their Act of Parliament 'for making and maintaining a Railway or Tram Road' from Cromford to Whaley Bridge 'for passage of waggons and other carriages, to be propelled thereon by Stationary or Locomotive Steam Engines or other sufficient power'. The possibility that steam locomotives might be used on the line was thus envisaged from the very beginning, and this was remarkable at a time when there was little evidence available concerning their capabilities. George Stephenson's Stockton to Darlington Railway was still, even then, four months from completion, and four years were to pass before the 'Rocket', with its revolutionary design, proved the efficiency of steam locomotives at the Rainhill Trials.

Jessop's railway, or, to describe it more truthfully at this stage, his waggonway, constructed on Stephenson's 4 foot 8½ inch gauge, was opened in two sections: the southern half, from Cromford Wharf to Hurdlow, on 29 May 1830, and the northern, from Hurdlow to Whaley Bridge, on 6 July 1831. From the Cromford Canal, 277 feet above sea level, it climbed a further 987 feet to a summit point at Ladmanlow. There, at a height of 1,264 feet, it commenced its descent, falling 747 feet in eight miles to the wharves of Outram's Peak Forest Canal. This rise and fall was achieved by nine inclines or inclined planes connecting level stretches: steep slopes on which the waggons were controlled by chains attached to steam winding engines. The first four inclines, at Cromford, Sheep Pasture, Middleton and Hopton,

Sheep Pasture Incline, Cromford & High Peak Railway.

lifted the line to eleven hundred feet in the course of five miles at gradients ranging from one in eight to one in fourteen. Once on the high plateau the climb was resumed up Hurdlow Incline, mild by comparison at one in sixteen; but then the line fell sharply to Whaley Bridge through four more inclines, the steepest of which was one in seven.

At the head of each incline, except on the final slope at Whaley Bridge which was worked by a horse-gin and counterbalance, stood a gritstone engine house sheltering the Butterley steam winding engine that dragged the endless chain round immense pulley wheels set horizontally below the bed of the track. Between 1855 and 1857 the chains were replaced by ropes made of hemp, and four years later these were superseded by steel wire cables, to which trains of waggons, to a maximum weight of 38 tons, were attached by means of tapering chains, plaited round the cable and tightly secured by leather straps and buckles. But not only waggons were wound up and down by this slow and often hazardous process. In 1841 the railway company fulfilled its promise, enshrined in the words of the original Act of Parliament, by introducing its first steam locomotive. This was the 'Peak', built at Newcastle by Robert Stephenson; and though it was another twenty years before horse traction on the line was completely eliminated, the company, by 1860, had seven locomotives, and these too were hauled up and down the steep slopes, anchored by similar means to the cables.

In between the inclines, since this was a contour railway constructed on the principles of a contour canal, were tunnels, deep cuttings, massive embankments, and curves so tight that only four-wheeled waggons grinding and groaning at the slowest pace were permitted to round them. The Cromford and High Peak did, in fact, contain the sharpest curve on the whole of the British railway system, just as it also, for many years, displayed the steepest gradient climbed unassisted by steam locomotives. The curve was at Gotham, some ten miles from Cromford, where the track turned through eighty degrees in a radius of only some fifty-five yards; while the gradient was at Hopton where, after 1877, locomotives pounded up a slope which, at its steepest, was one in fourteen.

Gotham Curve, C. & H. P. R. Turning eighty degrees in a fifty-five yard radius, the sharpest curve ever worked on British Railways.

Jessop had estimated the cost of the line at £155,000, considerably cheaper than the projected canal. The ultimate cost was £180,000, still cheap by comparison, but even so the railway never fulfilled the financial hopes of its optimistic sponsors. Despite the fact that its proximity stimulated the growth of lead mines, brick works and limestone quarries, most of which had their own branch lines and sidings, the company's accounts, even in the years of heaviest traffic, were perpetually in the red. After twelve years of operation the debts and unpaid interest amounted to nearly £47,000, and even as late as 1855 no dividend had been paid, and debts and interest payments were still undischarged.

Up to this time the company had been authorized to carry merely freight, but an Act of Parliament that same year granted it the power to introduce a passenger service on the line. It seems most unlikely that the directors hoped, by this means, to liquidate the debt; but, if any such hope existed, it must have been dashed in the next twelve months, when, out of a total revenue of £4,026, only £90 was realized from passenger fares. In retrospect, such poor returns were hardly surprising, for to travel on the Cromford and High Peak Railway required not merely a sound constitution and the steadiest of nerves, but some tenacity of purpose, inestimable patience and a full day without any prior engagements. One hardy traveller in 1877 boarded the train at the top of Middleton Incline, intending to make a journey to Buxton:

> My fellow travellers were then a young woman and a child, and the vehicle in which we sat was like an old omnibus. The guard stood in the middle and worked the brake through a hole in the floor. A locomotive now drew us three or four miles to the foot of another incline up which we were drawn by a rope. When reaching the summit the guard remarked, 'We may have to wait at the top.' 'How long?' I enquired. 'Oh! it may be five minutes,' he replied, 'or a few hours. It all depends upon when the engine comes to take us on. Yesterday,' he added, 'it did not come at all.' To while away the time I walked along the line, and my fellow-passengers went mushrooming. In about three hours an engine came from Whaley Bridge to fetch us, and after the driver, fireman and guard had refreshed themselves at a little public house not far away ... we started ... We reached Park Gates, about a mile from Buxton, at seven o'clock, after a journey of about twenty miles in six hours.

Later the same year a passenger was killed, and the company promptly discontinued the service.

Considering the savage gradients on which the railway was worked, serious accidents were comparatively few in the hundred and thirty-seven years of its history. In 1857 the Cromford and Sheep Pasture Inclines were combined to make a continuous slope of over thirteen hundred yards, ascending at a gradient of one in nine and, closer to the top, at one in eight. On the first day of March in 1888 a brake van coupled to a waggon full of limestone broke free of the wire rope just below the crest, and careered down the incline at gathering speed. At the bottom a sharp right-hand curve took the line along the bank of the Cromford Canal, but the waggons were then travelling far too fast to negotiate such a bend. They jumped the metals, cleared the canal and the double track of the Midland Railway and came to rest in a field. There were fortunately no casualties; two railway employees riding in the van leaped clear as soon as the waggons broke loose; but the mishap emphasized the dangers inherent in working steep inclines, and, because of this, a sleeper-lined catchpit was constructed close to the bottom of the slope. Into this dead end trucks could be diverted if, in the judgment of the pointsman, they were exceeding the permitted speed of eight miles an hour; and the wrecked waggon which even now lies in the pit bears witness to the fact that there were odd occasions when all other safety devices failed.

Wrecked waggon in catchpit, Sheep Pasture Incline, Cromford & High Peak Railway.

The most serious accident occurred at the bottom of Hopton Incline in 1937. By then, locomotives had worked the slope by adhesion for sixty years without any major incident; but the gradient was steep, starting at one in sixty, rising to one in thirty, then one in twenty, with a final pitch of two hundred yards at one in fourteen. It required all the power of an 0-6-0 tank with five loaded waggons to crawl across the top in slow-pounding exhaustion; and since the approach to the incline was more or less level and swept round a bend of generous radius, it was the custom of some drivers to speed up in preparation for the slope. On 6 October 1937, the driver of an early morning freight train to Parsley Hay built up excessive speed on the approach. The locomotive spread the track and derailed itself, rolling down an embankment on to the Wirksworth to Brassington road and dragging with it four waggons. In this particular case the driver paid with his life, and a speed limit of forty miles an hour was thereafter, in consequence, enforced on the curve.

The Cromford and High Peak was the only railway built in Britain to connect two canals, and its economic viability, at least in the early years, therefore depended on their prosperous life; but, by 1831, when the line was opened, that life was already being threatened. As the Manchester, Buxton, Matlock and Midland Junction Railway drove its tracks to the north beside the Cromford Canal, the waterway decayed and traffic on the Cromford and High Peak declined. Attempts were made to integrate the line into the growing national system by extensions at both ends, to High Peak Junction in the south and Buxton in the north; but, as the Midland Railway and the

...pton Incline, C. & H. P. R. *With a section at 1 in 14, the steepest steam locomotive-worked gradient in Britain.*

London and North-Western pushed their lines ahead to Manchester and more powerful locomotives rendered the rope-wound inclines and horizontal stretches of track superfluous, it became increasingly clear that the only economic future for the Cromford and High Peak depended on increased exploitation of the mineral deposits on either side of the line. Early this century such exploitation, which had long disappointed the railway's sponsors, began at last to show results; but the expansion came too late, for the increased traffic which could well have saved the line was progressively lost to the lorry and the roads. The last day of service was 21 April 1967, and more recently, with the lifting of the track, what was once a railway has now become a leisure footpath, the Derbyshire County Council's High Peak Trail.

Josias Jessop's line was a remarkable feat of railway engineering, but an anachronism even at the time it was constructed. Conceived and planned on the basis of contour canal technology, it commenced its life as a horse-drawn waggonway and became, almost immediately, a locomotive railway. It was therefore a link not merely between two canals, but three separate ages: the canal age of Brindley, the peak of waggonway performance under Outram, and those later years when George and Robert Stephenson pioneered the development of the modern steam railway. Once described as an attempt by a mad Archimedes to square the circle, it nonetheless excited the wonder and admiration of those who travelled on it or merely stood by the metals and watched it at work. 'Who would have thought,' wrote William Adam, 'of a railway over such acclivities and apparently inaccessible tracts?'

Goods wharf and transit shed for the Cromford & High Peak Railway, Cromford Canal, High Peak Junction.

Middleton Top engine house, Cromford & High Peak Railway.

To climb the High Peak Trail as far as Parsley Hay, the trackbed of the southern half of the Cromford and High Peak, is not simply to command wide-ranging views across some of the most glorious countryside in Derbyshire, but to walk with what remains of perhaps the most unusual railway in Britain. Most people prefer to stroll downhill or from one of the numerous picnic areas to another, but there is only one true way to appreciate the magnitude of Jessop's achievement, and that is by starting from Cromford Wharf and climbing upwards. Only by toiling up them on foot can the savagery of the inclines be fully determined.

Here at the High Peak Junction Wharf is the old transit shed and, a hundred yards ahead, at the foot of the long Sheep Pasture Incline, a paraphernalia of engine sheds, workshops and signals, the horizontal pulleys and broken wire cables of the winding mechanism, and, perhaps most significant of all, set side by side, the stone trough used for watering the horses in waggonway days and the cast-iron tank that provided supplies for the steam locomotives. Beyond the road bridge that carries the A6 across the incline, the single remaining runaway waggon tilts at a crazy angle in the cavern of the catchpit, while at the head of the slope stands the Sheep Pasture engine house, empty and deserted, its window gaps looking out across the valley to Arkwright's Cromford and the wooded gorge that encloses Masson Mill. Middleton has a bridge at the bottom of its incline: Rise End Bridge, one of the oldest iron railway bridges in Britain; and Middleton Top its octagonal engine house, sheltering the lone survivor of eight original winding engines, built at Butterley in 1829 and now carefully, lovingly and glowingly restored by members of the Derbyshire Archaeological Society. Hopton has its tunnel, approached at each end through deep limestone cuttings; Hopton Bank its notorious, now silent slope; and, further north still, carrying the track across a wide valley, is Minninglow Embankment, faced with limestone blocks, and once described as a sight never to be forgotten when seen in the light of a setting summer sun. Then comes Gotham Curve, even now, without its check rail and superelevation, a seemingly almost impossible bend; and four miles ahead there is Newhaven Tunnel, bored beneath the Ashbourne to Buxton road, with the two stone medallions above its portals, still showing, clear-cut, the words 'Cromford and High Peak Railway Co. 1825', the four-wheeled waggon that was the company's crest, and, at the northern end, the inscription 'Jos\ Jessop Esqr. Engineer'.

Just short of Parsley Hay the High Peak Trail meets the Peak Park Planning Board's Tissington Trail, which follows the old London and North-Western line from Ashbourne. Here, almost a thousand feet above Cromford, with Arbor Low less than a mile to the east, it seems difficult to believe that a steam locomotive was operating across this high plateau only twelve years after the construction of the 'Rocket'. But much about the Cromford and High Peak defies belief. The mad Archimedes all but squared his circle, and if the clanking of chains and the creaking of cables are sounds of the past, yet the walker plodding up Hopton Incline must surely, in imagination, step to one side at the blast of a whistle as 0-6-0 58850 storms the Bank at speed, exhaust blasts lengthening at each successive beat, while the smoke and sparks streaming from its funnel curl away low across the old lead workings on Carsington Pastures.

Plaque, north portal, Newhaven Tunnel, Cromford & High Peak Railway.

Minninglow Embankment, Cromford & High Peak Railway.

Hopton Tunnel, Cromford & High Peak Railway.

By the time that Jessop's railway received its passengers' charter in 1855, those who wished to see the sights of the valley could travel by train from Derby along the banks of the Derwent as far north as Rowsley, where Sir Joseph Paxton, the architect of the Crystal Palace, had designed a fine terminal station in gritstone with round-arched windows and wide eaves supported on wooden brackets.

The passenger-carrying railways first reached the valley in 1839, when two separate companies, the Midland Counties and the Birmingham and Derby Junction, drove their lines into Derby. The Midland Counties Railway, formed in 1832 to link Leicester with Derby by way of Nottingham, had as its engineer Charles Blacker Vignoles, who lost £80,000 in attempting to

Paxton's station, Rowsley.

cut the Woodhead Tunnel, but later recouped both his fortune and reputation by constructing a road bridge across the Dnieper at Kiev for Tsar Nicholas 1. It was his line that carried the first train into Derby on 30 May 1839, and two months later, on 12 August, Robert Stephenson's Birmingham and Derby Junction Railway disembarked its first trainload of passengers beside the Derwent.

By then, construction was already under way to the north of the town. As early as 1835 a company had been formed, with George Stephenson as engineer, to build a railway line from Derby to Leeds; and later that same year the route was surveyed and estimates of cost prepared by Stephenson and his assistant, Frederick Swanwick. It was largely due to Swanwick's preparatory work, meticulous in detail, that the North Midland Railway received its Act of Parliament in 1836, and the first ground was broken the following February.

As a result of three and a half years of intensive engineering, through night and day, summer and winter—and, much to the disapproval of the people of Belper, on Sundays as well—the line was completed, throughout its 72 miles, by the summer of 1840. It ran northwards from Derby, clinging to the Derwent as far as Ambergate, where it swung north-east up the Amber Valley to Clay Cross and Chesterfield, and thence by Masborough, West of Rotherham, to Leeds. The *Derby Mercury* described it as a 'mighty undertaking', and if George Stephenson had regarded the topography of the Derwent Valley as a stimulating challenge, then he and his navvies, armed only with blasting materials, picks and shovels and wheel-barrows, answered it with considerable technical skill, allied to forty months of sheer physical labour of a kind unknown in this mechanical age. Samuel Smiles compared the completed work with Napoleon's military road across the Simplon, and maintained that it was an even greater achievement, not merely because 'water was the great enemy to be fought against' in tunnels, bridge foundations, cuttings and embankments, but also because 'Napoleon's grand military road was constructed in six years, at the public cost of the two great kingdoms of France and Italy; while Stephenson's railway was formed in about three years, by a company of private merchants and capitalists out of their own funds, and under their own superintendence'. Added to which the Simplon road was only 45 miles in length and cost some three-quarters of a million pounds, whereas the North Midland, half as long again, cost more than three millions.

The construction of the line was not without its problems. At Milford, Stephenson planned to take the easiest route, along the valley bottom to the west of the Derwent; but the Strutts, as millowners, raised the objection that their water supplies might well be interrupted, and the track had, in consequence, to pierce the long ridge of the Chevin Hill, the most southerly of the gritstone outcrops that fringe the valley. To check the line of the tunnel and to mark the positions of the ventilation shafts, a rotating alignment telescope was used; and, to accommodate this, Stephenson built a gritstone sighting tower, nearly fifty feet high, which still stands on the Chevin. The substantial nature of this now-derelict tower, roofless since a fire some forty years ago, has prompted the thought that other motives may well have been involved in its construction: the need, for instance, to keep an army of navvies under constant supervision in a stretch of valley where observation was difficult, or even—and this has also been suggested—to provide them with work at a time when tunnelling retarded progress. Certainly the navvies must have needed surveillance; they numbered in excess of a battalion; for when, on 10 June 1840, their contracts for work on the Derby to Belper section expired, the company provided dinner for more than fifteen hundred in a field near Duffield station, spreading before them a cooked meal delivered by train from Derby.

Belper, too, presented its problems. The track had to be carried through and below the level of the town by means of a mile-long cutting, walled in gritstone and spanned by ten bridges: an engineering accomplishment which, viewed from Jedediah Strutt's Long Row, became one of the more popular sights of the town; while at Ambergate the cutting of the Toadmoor Tunnel, as Samuel Smiles explained, all but brought one of the contractors to ruin:

> As the cutting proceeded, a seam of shale was cut across, lying at an inclination of 6 to 1; and shortly after, the water getting behind . . . the whole mass of earth along the hill above began to move down across the line of excavation. The accident completely upset the estimates of the contractor, who, instead of fifty thousand cubic yards, found that he had about five hundred thousand to remove; the execution of this part of the railway occupying fifteen months instead of two.

Stephenson's cutting, Belper.

The tunnel, more than a hundred yards long, was therefore built with a flatter arch than normal to resist further landslips, and is now braced by steel hoops at its southern end.

But perhaps the most remarkable of all Stephenson's engineering works on the line was the solution he devised to carry the track below the bed of the Cromford Canal at Bull Bridge. Here he tunnelled through the canal embankment, and took suitable precautions to stop the water seeping through the roof. The *Derby Mercury* reported this highly delicate operation on 13 March 1839. 'In consequence of the railway having to be carried under the bed of the canal,' the reporter wrote, 'an iron tank, 150 feet long, 9 feet wide, and 6 feet deep, was made at the Butterley iron works, for the purpose of preventing the water escaping from the canal. The tank, having previously been conveyed in five different parts to the place where it was intended to be fixed, was rivetted together about midnight, and floated to the spot and there sunk and embedded. The whole of the proceedings were finished in 24 hours, without having interrupted the traffic on the canal.' Here too, within a matter of yards, the track passed over a bridge that spanned the River Amber, and, viewing the scene, Samuel Smiles was both predictably and justifiably impressed. 'Water, bridge, railway and canal,' he wrote, 'were thus piled one above the other, four stories high; such another curious complication probably not existing.'

The 'complication', unfortunately, has now disappeared with the widening of the Ambergate to Ripley road; but here, as in other places along the chosen route, the problems, great as they were, were conquered; the railway was built; and by 1840 three independent companies, competing with one another, were running trains into Derby.

This, for the town's administrators, posed its own immediate problems of planning. To avoid the construction of three separate stations, the council suggested that a joint terminus for all three companies should be built on The Holms; and, though this original site was abandoned because of its susceptibility to flooding, the plan was approved by the railway directors and the nearest high ground, in Castle Fields, was earmarked for the purpose. The eventual result was the Midland Station, described by William Adam as 'one of the most complete and magnificent Stations yet erected', which, with its complex of offices, warehouses and locomotive workshops, the Midland Hotel and the vast Carriage and Waggon Works, transformed the town into one of the most important railway centres in the country. The great station, with its frontage of 1,050 feet, was designed by Francis Thompson, the North Midland's architect, who built a series of highly individual stone stations: Italianate at Eckington, Jacobean at Ambergate and a minor gritstone masterpiece, now derelict, at South Wingfield. Though his initial plan for a long single platform to serve all the companies had to be abandoned because of the keen competition between them, he still produced a station which, as Adam said, was, for those days, on a 'stupendous scale'; where there was

Midland Station, Derby.

'every facility for receiving and despatching four large trains at the same moment, without any possible danger of collision or confusion.' Even though the frontage was considerably altered in 1892, Thompson's design can still be discerned; and the immediate area, with its Midland gas lamps and the houses in Railway Terrace constructed specially for engine-drivers, is still redolent of the age when the railway came to Derby.

In October 1835, the *Derby Mercury* prophesied that its arrival would 'make Derby a centre of communication, and must, we imagine, increase the trade and importance of the town'. The newspaper's hopes were more than justified. As A. W. Davison wrote in 1906 in his book on the rise and progress of Derby, prosperity 'became assured: ironworks sprang up to supply the new means of locomotion with forgings and castings; the railway companies, finding coal and iron close at hand, established engineering works ... for constructing their locomotives and rolling stock, and the town began to grow at a rate never before known.' So rapid was its expansion that the original North Midland railway station built 'out in the country' at the top of Siddals Road was, in a few years, on the verge of the town. By 1851, 43 per cent of the adult population had been born outside the county, and, a quarter of a century later, the buildings of the Midland Railway Company covered an area the size of the whole of Derby before Stephenson's arrival in 1835.

With the completion of the North Midland line through the southern half of the valley to Leeds, attention turned to a possible route north-west from Ambergate to Buxton and Manchester: a route pioneered by a small railway company with a highly pretentious name. The Manchester, Buxton, Matlock and Midland Junction Railway had, by 1849, stretched its line northwards from Ambergate to Rowsley, using temporary wooden 'boxes' to serve as halts, and constructing later, with the assistance of Paxton, a number of small but unique station buildings, among them the Rowsley terminus and the halt at Matlock Bath which, appropriately enough for a place that was known as 'The Switzerland of England', was based on the style of a Swiss chalet.

Matlock Bath Station.

Already, by that time, inspired by George Hudson, the linen-draper who became a business tycoon and earned for himself the title of the 'Railway King', the three original companies operating into Derby had amalgamated to form the Midland Railway. Of this combined company Paxton was both a shareholder and a director, and he and his associates were anxious to control the new line to Rowsley, with the ultimate aim of extending it to Manchester before their rivals, the London and North Western could do so. Faced by pressure from two such powerful, competing sources, the Manchester, Buxton, Matlock and Midland Junction had little chance of survival. It leased the line jointly to the two larger companies in 1852, and sold it outright to the Midland Railway nineteen years later.

The Midland, determined to reach Manchester before its competitors, could not afford to wait for complete control. In May 1860 its directors secured an Act of Parliament to extend the track northwards from Rowsley to Buxton, but the route was still in doubt, problems of way-leave were still unsolved, and it was another two years before work could commence. The major obstacle was the attitude, not unnaturally hostile, of the two great local landed proprietors, the Duke of Devonshire and the Duke of Rutland. The obvious route for the line was north-east from Rowsley, following the bank of the Derwent through Chatsworth Park, but the seventh Duke of Devonshire flatly refused to consider the possibility. The alternative was to build north-westwards through the valley of the Wye, but the Duke of Rutland, likewise, objected to the railway passing Haddon Hall. The Midland had to bargain, to haggle, and eventually to compromise. In 1863, after failing to dent the Duke of Devonshire's resolution, the company came to terms with the Duke of Rutland and accepted his stringent and costly conditions: that the line should not be built through the bottom of the valley in front of the Hall; that it should pass, instead, along the hillside at the rear, and be hidden from view by means of a tunnel; that none of the trees in the park was to be felled or even lopped; that his agents and keepers should supervise the work to ensure there was no damage to game reserves; and that the company should build him a station at Bakewell, where the trains could be halted should he ever decide to use them. At this point, predictably, the Duke of Devonshire also demanded his own station. The Midland, no doubt by this time desperate to proceed no matter what the cost, yielded yet again and built him one at Hassop, a mile from Bakewell, to which he could drive from Chatsworth House.

After these protracted negotiations, work on the line commenced, though the ultimate choice of the Wye Valley route not only made it necessary to build a second, more westerly, station at Rowsley, but also, further north, posed problems of a magnitude to test the skill of the company's engineers. Between Monsal Head and Buxton there were sections where the valley narrowed to a gorge, and the only way to accommodate the line was to tunnel through rock; while at Monsal Head itself a spectacular five-arched viaduct, 300 feet long, had to be constructed to carry the track across a bend in the river. Even so, the work was driven forward at speed. On the first day of June 1863 the first Midland passenger train steamed into Buxton, and four years later the Derby to Manchester link was complete.

But not without trouble from groups of nineteenth-century conservationists. The desecration, as they felt, of a succession of Derbyshire's most beautiful dales—Monsal and Cressbrook, Water-cum-Jolly and Litton, Miller's Dale and Chee Dale—brought a storm of protest, led by that indefatigable crusader, John Ruskin. His anger exploded against the commercialism that he believed was responsible. He turned on the Midland Company's directors, and dipped his pen in vitriol. He wrote:

There was a rocky valley, between Buxton and Bakewell, once upon a time, divine as the Vale of Tempe; you might have seen the Gods there morning and evening—Apollo and all the sweet Muses of the light—walking in fair procession on the lawns of it, and to and fro among the pinnacles of its crags. You cared neither for Gods nor grass, but for cash (which you did not know the way to get); you thought you could get it by what *The Times* calls 'Railroad Enterprise'. You Enterprised a Railroad through the valley—you blasted its rocks away, heaped thousands of tons of shale into its lovely stream. The valley is gone and the Gods with it; and now, every fool in Buxton can be at Bakewell in half-an-hour, and every fool in Bakewell at Buxton; which you think a lucrative process of exchange—you Fools Everywhere.

Ruskin believed that the line should never have been built: it was un-necessary and too expensive to be an economic proposition. His words went unheeded; but it is one of the stranger ironies of history around the Derwent that when a hundred years later Richard Beeching decreed, for similar reasons, that the line was to close, twentieth-century conservationists fought tooth and nail for the preservation of Monsal Dale viaduct: the structure which, in particular, had provoked Ruskin's wrath. They at least had their way, but they must have perceived an additional irony in their very success. The urge to make money had driven the Midland Railway to build this bridge below the old turnpike junction; and it was the urge to save money, rather

Monsal Dale Viaduct.

Cromford Station.

than the moral force of their protests, that led to its retention. Though the
track was lifted, the cost of demolishing the massive stone viaduct was
deemed to be prohibitive, and, spared for that reason, it still remains today,
as solid and commanding a piece of the landscape as Ruskin's pinnacles
trodden by the Gods. The old crusader must have shuddered beneath his
tall cross in Coniston churchyard when, a few years ago, it was listed as a
building of historical and architectural importance.

Yet, in attacking the businessmen who dared to drive a railroad through
his beautiful vale, Ruskin closed his eyes to new vistas of beauty: those
opened up to his Bakewell and Buxton fools, who proved themselves not
so foolish after all, and travelled the route simply to gaze through the windows
of their carriages. There were few more breathtaking sights on any railway
in Britain than the moment when the train burst out of Headstone Tunnel
on to the viaduct with all the Wye Valley spread out below.

Nor did he ever appreciate the beauty of Paxton's work. The Crystal
Palace, to him, was nothing more than a magnified conservatory, fourteen
acres of good ground covered with glass; but even he, though he detested
imitation, might have found, looking closer, perhaps a little to praise in the
station that G. H. Stokes, Paxton's son-in-law and assistant architect, designed
for Cromford: a diminutive and yet exquisite building, with a station-
master's villa, in the same French style, set high above it on the side of a hill,
commanding the meadows that sweep down towards the curve of the
Derwent.

Ruskin knew Monsal Dale before there was a railway. He saw the rocks blasted, the heaps of shale accumulate. We never did. We were born too late to be able, as he was, to judge by comparison. We can only judge by what we see and hear. The Crystal Palace has vanished; the viaduct at Monsal Dale is now a dead piece of stone, its track transformed into a grass-grown pathway; but the station at Cromford is still very much a living part of the railway, and there is something strangely satisfying in the ever-present knowledge that this tiny gem of Victorian architecture, backed by its trees, still echoes to the warning hoot of a diesel.

The country trains have gone. The tank engines with their two small, unassuming carriages no longer trail their streamers of smoke through the valley; but Cromford's pinnacle, its towers and its lattice windows still possess the magic to conjure up visions of heavy-breathing, tall-funnelled steam locomotives, even with the tick and throb of a diesel beating against the walls of the tunnel.

The final phase of main line construction came at the end of the century. In 1894 the Midland completed its trans-Pennine link between Sheffield and Manchester by laying a track through Hope Valley and Edale and driving two great tunnels, one at each end: Totley in the east and Cowburn in the west; while, five years later, the London and North Western at last achieved a route through the Peak to Manchester, when it opened its line from Ashbourne to Buxton. Their fates were very different. The Ashbourne to Buxton route was intended to carry an express service from London to Manchester, but its steep gradients and sharp curves restricted the speed of trains, and it swiftly degenerated into little more than a local line between the two towns. Even this, in the end, proved uneconomic; the route was closed to passengers in 1954, the metals were removed, and the gradients up which the expresses once pounded are now trodden, at weekends, by the heavy boots of hikers, for the trackbed is the Peak Park's Tissington Trail; but the Hope Valley route, with the closure of Woodhead Tunnel to passenger traffic, has become the main line across the south of the Pennines, in addition to carrying a diesel railcar service between Edale, Hathersage, Bamford and Sheffield.

The railways opened up the valley as the turnpike roads and the canals had never done. They provided the first south-to-north through-valley routes, following the banks of the Derwent, the Amber and the Wye. They were swift, direct and cheap, and could transport not merely the bulk commodities such as stone, lead and coal, but, with greater ease than the roads or canals, the massive iron castings for engines and equipment which were so vital a feature of industrial expansion. They freed the owners of quarries, mines and foundries, cotton mills and farms from the bondage of the mediaeval packhorse routes and the lock-bound canals; and industrialists, for their part, responded by opening new quarries, re-developing old mines, expanding their factories, and using the railways to full advantage. A visitor to Rowsley in the 1850s, when Paxton's station was the valley's northern terminus, would have found in the cluttered yard evidence of almost every local industry. Quarrying was predominant. Grindstones from Stanton, millstones from Beeley Moor and chert from the Holme Bank Quarry at Bakewell all found their way to Rowsley where, forsaking the road, they were, as William Adam said, 'conveyed down to the railway' and from there despatched 'to all parts of the kingdom'.

But the railways did more than ease the long-standing transportation problems of industry. They opened up the valley to the outside world. The visitor to Rowsley would, at that time, have been one among many—sixty thousand a year, so Adam was told—who arrived at the station by way of Ambergate to be transported from there along the twisting road to Chatsworth by the horse bus that dutifully met every train. Tourists poured in from every point of the compass, discovering the grandeurs of the Matlock gorge and transforming Matlock Bath from a fashionable, class-conscious summer resort into a paradise for trippers, out for the day, who stepped from the train at the Swiss chalet station below the Heights of Abraham, and then climbed to the caverns or wandered beside the Derwent. Later, when the track was extended to Buxton, the glories of the Wye became available to all who paid a third-class fare; while the Hope Valley line gave the people of Edale, up to that time an isolated, close-knit community of struggling farmers, their first sight of excursion trains, packed with passengers from Sheffield and Manchester. Suddenly the tiny village of Edale, barely known beyond its beautiful, secluded valley, found itself invaded by hundreds of summer tourists discovering villages with strange Derbyshire names, like Barber Booth and Ollerbrook Booth; climbing the wooded Grinds Brook valley, now the starting point of the Pennine Way; and aiming, perhaps with more hope than determination, for the plateau of Kinder Scout. The nineteenth century became the first great age of the Derwent Valley guide book, and if visitors found it difficult to pack in their pockets the four volumes of Edward Rhodes' *Peak Scenery or The Derbyshire Tourist* or even Adam's bulky *Gem of the Peak*, they probably concealed somewhere about their persons Murray's *Guide*, the 'Handbook for travellers in Derbyshire', published at a time, in 1874, when the railways had reached a summit of self-confident achievement.

Thirty years later, at the end of the century, there were more than a hundred miles of passenger-carrying railways in and around the valley, and few villages, even the most isolated, lay more than five miles from the nearest station. Now there are little more than fifty miles of track. No line follows the Derwent north of Matlock, and those who wish to travel from Derby to Manchester must either take to their cars or change at Dore and Totley to the Hope Valley line. Paxton's station at Rowsley is the office for a road-

Wingfield Station, South Wingfield.

construction plant firm; the Duke of Devonshire's at Hassop is in the hands of a group of agricultural engineers. Great Longstone station is a private house, part of Grindleford a snack bar, and the Midland at Rowsley a packing-case store; while Thompson's South Wingfield is a prey to vandals, and his Jacobean Ambergate, along with many others, has disappeared completely.

The railways, emasculated, now merely serve, as the canals once did, the fringes of the valley. The metals of the Cromford and High Peak, the Ashbourne to Buxton, and the Wye Valley route have all gone for scrap; yet the first line ever to penetrate the valley remains the hardiest survivor. George Stephenson's North Midland still carries the express inter-city trains between London and Leeds, and its great engineering works—the tunnels, the bridges, the cuttings and embankments: 'vaster,' as Ruskin bitterly admitted, 'than the walls of Babylon'—remain little altered from the time, a hundred and forty years ago, when they were hewn by the navvies from the face of the valley in a flurry of picks and shovels and sweat.

9 The Best and the Worst

[Arkwright] by his conduct appears to be a man of great understanding and to know the way of making his people do their best. He not only distributes pecuniary rewards, but gives distinguishing dresses to the most deserving of both sexes, which excites great emulation. He also gives two Balls at the Greyhound to the workmen and their wives and families with a weeks jubilee at the time of each ball. This makes them industrious and sober all the rest of the year.

The Diary of Sylas Neville (1767–1788).

I have seen the time when two hand-vices of a pound weight each, more or less, have been screwed to my ears, at Lytton mill in Derbyshire. There are scars still remaining behind my ears.

Evidence of Robert Blincoe: *Employment of Children in Manufactories*, 2nd Report of the Central Board (1833).

If a visitor to the valley walks through the yard at the rear of William Newton's Cressbrook Mill, and then along the track by the old mill leat, he will come to the weir and, above it, the pool that was blasted out of the limestone gorge. From there a path follows the northern bank of the Wye through Water-cum-Jolly Dale, where, on 15 July 1841—St Swithin's Day—William Adam was caught in a violent thunderstorm and had to take shelter in a cleft above a projecting ledge of rock 'canopied over by the towering crag'. He was, he said, jotting down a description of the scene in his notebook, when 'a brilliant flash of lightning crossed the pass . . . almost blinding us with its sudden glare, and then broke immediately over head one of the most terrible peals of thunder we ever heard, shaking the solid rocks beneath us, and rolling and crashing from crag to crag.' For more than an hour he was 'quite land and water locked', and had to crouch in the cleft while 'the dancing rain fell in torrents': an experience which convinced him, though not a believer in 'the watery saint', that the weather, for the rest of that summer, was destined to show little in the way of improvement.

Water-cum-Jolly Dale is one of the more beautiful stretches of the Wye, and the path beside the river is nowadays trodden by climbers, fishermen and, ever more frequently, by families strolling on a Sunday afternoon; but in Adam's time, before the Midland Railway penetrated the gorge, its isolation was extreme and it was so little known that 'no one', as he said, 'could give a name to it.' He described it as 'a profound and obscure spot, where few venture, except perhaps the botanist, or bold angler, and that only occasionally'; where 'the Wye pursues its way between solid walls of limestone, lofty, precipitous, and frequently overhanging.' The path, at that time, ran along the opposite bank of the river. Obliterated perhaps, twenty years later, by the driving of the railway, it was, in his words, no more than a 'goat track', so narrow and at one point leading 'over such a fearful precipice, that only one can cross at a time, and then it must be with a clear head and a sure foot, or be toppled into the deep and dark stream far beneath.'

The visitor today, if he keeps to the path, will eventually come, like the botanists and anglers of the early nineteenth century, to Litton Mill, a mile upstream from Cressbrook. Adam could see it from the cleft in which he sheltered, 'partly shaded with trees' at the top of the dale, 'and the torrent of the sparkling Wye rushing over the weir'. The mill still throbs, producing nylon yarn for the hosiery trade, but it is not the mill he saw. That no longer exists. It was burnt to the ground in 1874 and had to be rebuilt, and since then time and weather have ravaged what remained. Now nothing of the original structure can be traced save a dilapidated gas-generating house, the weir and sluice controls, and the gateposts, capped with iron, that gave access first to a path and then to a bridge that crossed the river to the old apprentice house. But here, in this quiet, deep-secluded valley, is where it once stood; and if Adam could, on that St Swithin's day, have seen into the future, he might perhaps have said of the flames that consumed it, as he did of the thunder and lightning of the storm, that they were 'manifestations of the

Litton Mill today.

Divine Power', for Litton Mill, even before he glimpsed it through the dancing rain, had, deservedly or otherwise, acquired a reputation as the most notorious building in the whole of the valley.

Its first proprietors were Ellis Needham and Thomas Frith. Needham was a farmer from Hargatewall, half a mile to the east of Brindley's birthplace at Tunstead. He could possibly have been classed as a minor landowner, for his father had accumulated quite extensive estates around Bakewell, Tideswell, and Chapel-en-le-Frith, though these, on his death, had been divided between the four of his sons. The Jurors' Books for the period from 1784 to 1815 described Ellis Needham as a 'gentleman' and farmer, and he was certainly a prominent member of the Anglican congregation at Tideswell church and a friend of the vicar. Less is known of Thomas Frith, but he may well have fallen into much the same category: a farmer from Tideswell, who was also a small landowner and an Anglican churchman.

It was about 1782 when they went into partnership and built Litton Mill, powering it apparently, not from the Wye, but by means of a stream that tumbled down the steep hillside to the gorge. Two years later they constructed a weir, possibly to harness the waters of the river, though already, by that time, there were signs that the business was financially unstable. Needham had almost certainly overstretched his resources, selling most of his land to raise the money for construction; and the mill, hidden deep in

Iron-capped gateposts to Apprentice House, Litton Mill.

its isolated valley and beset by problems of communication, had, with equal certainty, struggled to make a profit. In 1786 it was advertised for sale, but seemingly no-one was willing to buy, and the struggle continued, further reducing the partners' assets. By 1795 Needham's inheritance had disappeared completely and he was farming on eighteen acres which he rented, while in 1799 Frith pulled out and left him on his own.

Contraction was inevitable. In 1803 the mill was employing a hundred and sixty apprentices. Four years later the number had halved, and Needham was facing problems that continued to multiply. The Midlands textile industry was passing through a period of serious depression; there was a fire at the mill; and in 1811 the waterwheel broke, which meant that, for a month, the machinery was immobilized and production was lost. Another four years and he lapsed into bankruptcy. Given notice to quit, he had to sell the mill, and it was subsequently bought by William Newton's sons who ran it, for a time, in conjunction with Cressbrook.

Needham, from that time onwards, seems to have declined into near-oblivion. In 1828 he was described as a pauper, his sons were said to be 'vagabonds', and his wife was attempting to earn a little money by teaching children their letters in a dame school at Hathersage; though this information, it must be admitted, appeared in *The Lion*, a Radical publication which could only have taken the utmost delight in uncovering his degradation.

Frith, on the other hand, once he had judiciously withdrawn from the partnership, seems to have prospered, at least to a somewhat limited degree. He built a small spinning-mill to the north of Tideswell, presumably where a small stream flowed through his farm; and when he died in 1820, he described himself as a cotton manufacturer, and bequeathed to his descendants not merely a dwelling-house, outbuildings, lands and farming stock, but also a 'factory' with its 'stock in trade, machinery, looms, materials and other effects' appertaining to the business.

By the time that William Adam looked up the dale towards Litton Mill, its worst days were past, though its notoriety was still of comparatively recent growth. The events that earned it so unenviable a reputation were alleged to have taken place between 1803 and 1807, but they were not made public till 1828. In the January of that year they were revealed in *The Lion*, a weekly periodical published by Richard Carlile, then well known as a Radical propagandist for the factory reform movement. The material, which was issued in five weekly episodes, was a long and somewhat tedious article written, in a style which foreshadowed all the worst in Victorian pathos, by John Brown, a hack journalist from Bolton, who had committed suicide three years earlier. In an age of social and industrial agitation its sensational disclosures about life in a factory were political dynamite, and its impact was so considerable that it seems to have been reprinted twice within the course of the next twelve months. It was clearly considered to be a document of importance: so much so that, four years later, John Doherty, the founder of the National Union of Cotton Spinners, republished it from his printing works at Withy Grove in Manchester under a new and distinctly provocative title. It thus became *A Memoir of Robert Blincoe, An Orphan Boy; sent from the workhouse of St. Pancras, London, at seven years of age, to endure the Horrors of a Cotton-Mill, through his infancy and youth, with a minute detail of his sufferings.*

It was Blincoe himself who, in 1822, told his story to Brown. A parish orphan and probably an illegitimate child, he was born about 1792 and accommodated in the old St Pancras workhouse till he reached the age of seven, when, among a group of eighty parish apprentices, he was sent by waggon to Nottingham to work in Lamberts' cotton mill at Lowdham. He remained there for three years till the mill closed down, and it was then 'his evil fortune', in John Brown's words, to be transferred, along with many of his fellow apprentices, to complete his term under Ellis Needham at Litton.

His sufferings, as the title of the pamphlet promised, were minutely, not to say luridly, described. Blincoe indicted Needham on a number of counts: savage corporal punishment meted out to the apprentices; working hours that were excessively long; food that was repulsive both to see and to taste; inadequate facilities for personal cleanliness; poor accommodation; and an almost complete absence of medical attention. According to Brown, the children were treated with 'a brutal severity', and Needham and his son, John, were little short of sadists. The apprentices were subjected to 'stripes, cuffs and kicks', and their bodies were 'literally covered with weals and contusions'. They were forced to eat candles, lick up tobacco spittle, and open their mouths for the overseers to spit into; their teeth were filed as a punishment, rollers were flung at their heads, and their hair was torn out. Blincoe himself was tied to a beam by his wrists and suspended in this way above a spinning frame. 'To avoid the machinery, he had to draw up his legs every time it came out or returned. If he did not lift them up, he was cruelly beaten over the shins, which were bare.' On other occasions, hand-vices, each of a pound in weight, were screwed to his ears and nose; he was forced to work with 'two half hundredweights slung behind him, hanging one at each shoulder'; and another of the overseers' favourite diversions was to make him stand on one foot on top of a can, till the moving frame knocked it from underneath him and he had to 'throw himself flat upon the floor, that the frame might pass over him'. Those apprentices who were suspected of making plans to run away were delivered to the smith, who riveted irons upon them 'much like the irons usually put on felons. Even young women . . . had irons riveted on their ankles, and reaching by long links and rings up to the hips, and in these they were compelled to walk to and from the mill to work and to sleep.' Needham himself, according to Blincoe, equalled 'the very worst of his servants in cruelty of heart. So far from having taken any care to stop their career, he used to animate them by his own example to inflict punishment in any and every way they pleased.' He 'stands accused of having been in the habit of knocking down the apprentices with his clenched fists; kicking them about when down, beating them to excess with sticks, or flogging them with horse-whips—of seizing them by the ears, lifting them from the ground and forcibly dashing them down on the floor, or pinching them till his nails met'; while John Needham, his son, was 'a tyrant and an oppressor', treating the girls, in particular, 'with an indecency as disgusting as his cruelty was terrific'.

The children were set to work at five in the morning, and continued at the frames, with little intermission, until nine, ten, eleven, or even twelve o'clock at night. Such hours, according to Blincoe, were 'of common occurrence', and at week-ends the children 'often continued' working at the frames not merely till midnight, but through to six o'clock on the Sunday morning. The food supplied to the apprentices was water-porridge and oaten cakes, which were frequently mouldy; bacon-broth and unpared turnips; meal-balls made into dough in the shape of dumplings; and rice puddings boiled in bags, 'the rice being very bad and full of large maggots'. They had no knives, forks or spoons, and the food was, in general, of such a wretched quality that 'if Blincoe happened to see any fresh cabbage leaves, potato or turnip parings, thrown out upon the dunghill, he has run down with a can full of sweepings, as an excuse, and as he threw that dirt on the dunghill, he would eagerly pick the other up, and carry it in his shirt, or in his can, into the mill, wipe the dirt off as well as he could, and greedily eat them up.'

Washing was apparently a weekly, rather than a daily, exercise. It was confined to Friday nights, when the eldest girls had, as best they could, to comb and wash the younger apprentices, whose heads were 'lamentably-infested with vermin ... No soap was allowed—a small quantity of meal was given as a substitute; and this, from the effects of keen hunger, was generally eaten'. The children were lodged some fifty to a room, and the dormitories, like the bedding, reeked of oil and filth; while medical attention was confined to the removal of vermin by applying a pitch cap to the head and then tearing off the scalp, or, when 'contagious fevers arose in the mill', burning pitch and tobacco in the lodging-rooms and sprinkling vinegar on the beds.

If Blincoe's story is to be believed in full, it seems purely fortuitous that he managed to survive his years at Litton Mill; but, though small of build, he seems to have been a hardier, more enduring spirit than many of his associates. He completed his apprenticeship, worked at other factories in Lancashire and Cheshire as an adult operative, and then set himself up, first as a cotton-waste dealer, and then as a manufacturer of thread, owning his own machinery and renting a part of Ormrod's mill in Tib Street, Manchester. A fire, almost immediately, destroyed his machinery which was not insured, and he appears to have been confined, for a short time at least, in the prison at Lancaster Castle for debt. He possessed, nonetheless, sufficient resilience to rebuild his fortunes. By 1832, the year when Doherty published the *Memoir*, he was once again dealing in cotton-waste, manufacturing sheet wadding and running a grocer's shop. He became prosperous enough to send all three of his children to school, and one of his sons proceeded, in course of time, to Queens' College, Cambridge, graduated from there and became an Anglican clergyman: the vicar of St Luke's, Old Street, in London. Blincoe himself died at the age of sixty-eight in December 1860 at his daughter's home in Macclesfield. Abel Heywood, twice Lord Mayor of Manchester, remembered him, some thirty years after his death, as 'a little man in height, his legs being very crooked, the result of his early life in a cotton factory': a description which tallies neatly with Brown's own state-ment, made in 1822, that he was 'diminutive as to stature', and that his knees were 'grievously distorted' due to 'hard, unremitting and unprofitable servitude'.

For more than a century historians of deservedly high reputation accepted the authenticity of John Brown's *Memoir*, and it has only been during the last twenty years that a certain amount of corrective analysis has, with justice, been undertaken. It would be patently unfair to Ellis Needham to condemn his management of Litton Mill solely on the evidence of a single apprentice who might perhaps have borne him a grudge: evidence recorded by a journalist of unreliable reputation, who could well have been seeking to create a sensation, and which was published in a journal recognized as being violently partisan in its views.

It must be admitted, at the outset, that the article was frankly an exercise in propaganda: an attempt to prove, once and for all, the wickedness of the factory system and those devoted to it. Brown's first mention of Needham's mill set the tone for the whole of the subsequent account. 'It was,' he wrote, 'in the gloomy month of November, when this removal [from Lowdham] took place. On the evening of the second day's journey, the devoted children reached Litton Mill. Its situation, at the bottom of a sequestered glen, and surrounded by rugged rocks, remote from any human habitation, marked a place fitted for the foul crimes of frequent occurrence which hurried so many of the friendless victims of insatiate avarice, to an untimely grave.' Even allowing for the fact that the beauty of Miller's Dale would hardly be apparent to a waggon-load of frightened children on a dark November evening at the beginning of the nineteenth century, Brown's writing was prejudicial and his words were emotive.

To be fair to him, they may have reflected, quite faithfully, his own reaction to Blincoe's story. If so, any reader could well accept them as an expression of all-too-genuine repulsion, but there must still remain the undeniable suspicion that the strength of his feelings led him first into gullibility and, from there, to exaggeration. At least some of the statements he set down as fact are difficult to support by surviving evidence. When he came to discuss the 'contagious fevers' that arose in the mill, he claimed that the number of deaths among apprentices was 'such as to require frequent supplies of parish children, to fill up the vacancies'. The mortality, he wrote, was so great 'that Mr Needham felt it adviseable to divide the burials, and a part of the dead were buried in Tadington Churchyard, although the burial fees were double the charge of those at Tideswell'; but the Bishop's Transcripts of the Tideswell Parish Registers, recording the mortality among parish apprentices between 1780 and 1810, tell a different tale. According to their figures, only six such apprentices died at Litton Mill in those thirty years; and even if Brown's statement, clearly derived from Blincoe, be accepted as true, and 'a part' of the dead were indeed interred at Taddington, the death-rate, at a time when the mill employed more than a hundred and fifty apprentices, hardly constitutes a basis for his later contention that 'frequent supplies' of children were needed as replacements.

Such a contention, patently contradicted by available figures, casts doubt on the whole validity of the *Memoir*; and certainly John Farey, whom historians have long regarded as a meticulous observer of the Derbyshire scene, gave it no corroboration. Farey published his *View of the Agriculture and Minerals of Derbyshire* in three volumes between 1811 and 1817, but his survey was carried out from 1807 to 1809, immediately after Blincoe moved away from Litton. In the course of it he paid a visit to Needham, and subsequently wrote, in a section dealing with conditions in cotton-mills:

> I am far from intending to insinuate that great care, and even kind attention, is not bestowed on the cotton-mill apprentices in general throughout this county. In several cases I have seen this to be the case, and a rather sedulous inquiry on this head from others has not disclosed even suspicious hints to the contrary in any instance, as far as I can recollect; nor am I disposed to think or represent that any very considerable or remedial degrees of vice or immorality exist in these apprentice-houses or mills, nor that their employ is as unhealthy as some have represented.

Farey was clearly a disbeliever, but there were many in Britain and indeed around Tideswell, who would eagerly have accepted Blincoe's story and given it wide publicity. The farmers and landowners, the old squirearchy, the traditional rulers of England, were jealous of the growing wealth and power of the new manufacturers; resentful of the way in which, by high bidding, they pushed up the price of land and, by dispensing with apprentices at the end of their term, inflated the parish poor rates. The long struggle was just beginning between the agricultural and the manufacturing interests, which was to culminate in the parliamentary battle between Disraeli and Peel over the duties on corn. The squirearchy believed that to remove the import duties would mean, for them, a step towards ruin, since it would leave them unprotected against foreign competition; the factory owners, on the other hand, remained convinced that, by reducing the price of bread, they could spike the guns of those who felt wages were too low; and in consequence, as a part of their campaign, the farmers adopted the wickedness of the factory system almost as an article of political faith, and were willing to accept, without too much investigation, the accounts of factory life, such as Blincoe's, which appeared to support what they wanted to believe. Certainly, at the time when the *Memoir* was published, there would have been few around Tideswell anxious to offer their sympathies to Needham or even question the allegations that Blincoe had made. The farmers in the district had shown their hostility at the time of his bankruptcy: they had complained to Lord Scarsdale that, by turning off apprentices, he was pushing up the poor rate to an unacceptable level; and the rest of the community, mainly hand-loom weavers and framework knitters, dependent on the purely domestic trade, would have welcomed the downfall of anyone owning a water-powered factory.

For such reasons alone it would be unfair to Needham to accept Blincoe's tale without due reservation; but it would be equally unfair to dismiss it as merely a tissue of lies. If there is evidence to refute, at least in some part, what he told to John Brown, there are independent witnesses who seem to support him. In 1807, the year of his departure, one of the county magistrates, Joshua Denman, visited Litton Mill as he was appointed to do under the Health and Morals of Apprentices Act. He reported that there were then some eighty apprentices and that they worked 'successively in the night, though this is expressly prohibited by the Act'. Nor did he approve of the apprentice house. 'The rooms,' he wrote, 'appear crowded', and 'from the dimensions of the building it appears almost impossible to contain so many persons consistently with health and anything approaching to comfort'. Four years later the mill was again inspected, this time by a different magistrate, Mr Middleton. He commented on the hours of work and also the food. The apprentices, he wrote, 'go into the mill about ten minutes before six o'clock in the morning, and stay there till from ten to fifteen minutes after nine in the evening, excepting the time allowed for dinner, which is from half to three-quarters of an hour . . . they have water porridge for breakfast and supper, and generally oatcake and treacle, or oatcake and poor broth for dinner.'

Blincoe himself repeated a number of his allegations in 1833 when he gave evidence before the Central Board during a government inquiry into the Employment of Children in Manufactories. When he was asked about the 'forms of cruelty' practised on children, he spoke of being suspended from a beam above the frame and having two hand-vices screwed to his ears. 'Here are the scars,' he said, 'still remaining behind my ears ... Then we used to stand up, in a skip, without our shirts, and be beat with straps or sticks; the skip was to prevent us from running away . . . Mind, we were apprentices, without father or mother to take care of us; I don't say that they often do that now.'

Three years later, John Fielden, the M.P. for Oldham—'Honest John Fielden' as he was known to his friends—published his book *The Curse of the Factory System*. He could hardly be accused of ignorance on the subject. At the age of ten he had been set to work in his father's mill, and the experience, as he said, was still 'fresh' in his memory. So were his associates. 'Only a few of them', he wrote, 'are now alive; some dying very young, others living to become men and women; but many of those who lived, have died off before they attained the age of fifty years, having the appearance of being much older, a premature appearance of age which I verily believe was caused by the nature of the employment in which they had been brought up.' He added that he had read John Brown's account of the sufferings of Robert Blincoe. 'I wish,' he continued, 'every man and woman in England would see and read this pamphlet; it is published in Manchester, where the crippled subject of the memoir now lives to testify the truth of all that I have said.'

What then is the truth about Blincoe and Litton Mill? Amid all the imponderables, one thing is certain. No such indictment as Blincoe levelled against Ellis Needham was ever made in respect of the three major owners of cotton-spinning mills in the Derwent Valley. Between them, by 1793, the Arkwright, Strutt and Evans families controlled half of the twenty-four mills in operation. They were setting up their own patriarchal factory villages at Cromford, Belper, Milford and Darley Abbey; and those who, then and later, looked on what they created in an age bereft of public services and local government assistance, left behind them accounts that were occasionally lyrical, frequently enthusiastic, and hardly ever less than favourable. These contemporary commentators were, moreover, not merely local reporters despatched to the scene by the *Derby Mercury* or its Manchester counterpart, eccentric medical versifiers like Erasmus Darwin, or desultory travellers such as Byng, William Bray or Sylas Neville; but acute observers like Farey, meticulous in analysis and scrupulous in judgement. Nor were they all, like Edward Baines and Andrew Ure, protagonists of the factory system; among them were Robert Owen, Leon Faucher and Peter Gaskell, who were numbered among its severest critics.

Labour at Needham's mill was based on the system of parish apprenticeship, under which the parish authorities, particularly in the poorer districts of London, shrugged off their moral and financial responsibilities by farming out workhouse children to factory owners hundreds of miles away, on the tacit understanding that they would be accommodated, clothed and fed and put to useful work. The original statutes which provided for such arrangements were the Elizabethan apprenticeship and poor relief laws of the sixteenth century, by means of which, in an age of domestic labour, the children of poor parents were to receive training as farm or household servants, by billeting them compulsorily on the ratepayers of the parish; but, after 1691, an apprentice who had trained in an area for forty days became the responsibility of the parish of his adoption, and since it was a matter of local expediency to keep the poor rates down, the custom grew of binding parish children to masters who lived in a different parish and paying such masters, since they were not obliged under law to accept the children, a small sum of money for assuming the responsibility.

This practice was condemned as early as 1738 in an 'Enquiry into the Causes of the Increase of the Poor'. Its author roundly chastised the many parishes which had come to indulge in such waywardness:

> A most unhappy practice prevails in most places to apprentice poor children, no matter to what master provided he lives out of the parish; if the child serves the first forty days we are rid of him for ever. The master may be a tiger in cruelty; he may beat, abuse, strip naked, starve, or do what he will to the poor innocent lad, few people take much notice, and the officers who put him out the least of any body: For they rest satisfied with the merit of having shifted him off to a neighbouring parish for three or four pounds, and the duty they owe to every poor child in the parish is no further lay'd to heart.

Even under the domestic system, where work was, for the most part, carried on in a cottage, a lean-to building or adjoining shed, the opportunities for ill-treatment that such a system provided were, given a bad master, obvious enough. With the development of the water-powered cotton-spinning mill, the exploitation of child labour on a much more massive scale—the scale alleged by Blincoe in connection with Litton Mill—became, for the first time, a real possibility.

Needham was not the only factory-owner in the valley to base his economy on parish apprentices. They were also employed, though not, it would seem, under conditions that were like to have produced another *Memoir*, by Bossley and Newton in their mills at Cressbrook, by Gardom and Pares at Calver, Nicholas Cresswell and his partners in the wildness of Edale, and Edward and James Dakeyne at their Ladygrove flax-spinning mill in Darley Dale. There is, on the other hand, no evidence that the Arkwrights, the Strutts or the Evanses ever made use of the parish apprentice system, except on those odd occasions when they chose to accept individual apprentices from the parish overseers.

Needham probably had no alternative. Litton was in a sparsely populated area, where a cotton mill was regarded with little short of scorn, and where local labour was therefore virtually impossible to recruit. Arkwright and Strutt were in a happier position. Arkwright at Cromford could recruit the wives and children of the local lead miners, particularly since that old-established industry was suffering something of a decline in the neighbourhood; Strutt had the families of the Belper nailers similarly available; while Evans, though his Boar's Head Mill was situated in a predominantly agricultural area, had the advantage that farm workers' wages were, at that time, palpably lower than those offered in industry, and he was, in addition, sufficiently close to Derby to draw from its comparatively deep pool of labour those who were attracted by the prospect of learning a trade in a new and rapidly expanding industry.

But the labour had to be attracted, and, once on the pay roll, it had to be held. These difficult tasks all three families performed with consummate skill, accumulating their profits, but always accepting that, as heads of communities, they had a responsibility for their workers' well-being; and, as sound businessmen, realizing that it was in their interests to preserve and promote both the health and good-will of those they employed. By the lights of their time, always acknowledging that those lights were distinctly dimmer than today's, they were good employers, and even the harshest critics of the system they operated found much to commend in their conduct of affairs.

Admittedly, by modern standards, the conditions they provided and those they imposed were far from Utopian, yet they still succeeded in expanding their empires and treating their workers as human beings, even if, like their associate, the great Josiah Wedgwood, they felt impelled to point out, from time to time, to less benevolent employers that such workers, 'our humble friends as somebody beautifully calls them, have like passions with ourselves, and are capable of feeling pain or pleasure, nearly in the same manner as their Masters'.

Nearly in the same manner, but not entirely. Men such as Wedgwood, and that means the Arkwrights, the Strutts and the Evanses regarded their workers from a standpoint of always conscious superiority; though, in so doing, they merely reflected the patterns of thought which prevailed in their time. They believed, in common with most of their fellows, that employers had the right, acknowledged by society, to give orders, fix wages and determine both the hours and conditions of work in their factories; while those whom they employed had a paramount duty to obey those orders, work the hours laid down, and accept the conditions and wages provided.

They were autocrats; they held their own established place in the hierarchy, with a right to wield all the powers and privileges accruing to their position. Almost feudal in their approach, believing that the successive strata of society were a matter of divine, rather than human, ordination, they would un-doubtedly have subscribed to the view of Thomas Guest that it was not merely wrong, but blatantly unchristian, to demand higher wages. 'In providing for your own house,' he was at pains to declare, 'you are not to infringe on the providential order of God, by invading the rights of others, by attempting to force upon those whom God has set over you, the adoption of such regulations and the payment of such wages as would be beneficial to yourselves.'

They were tyrants, these early cotton masters, in the sense that, within the walls of their factories, they possessed a power that was all but absolute, unleavened by any form of union activity; and the ultimate differences that existed between them depended on the way in which they exercised that power. If they permitted themselves to be corrupted by it, they could become the Ellis Needhams of John Brown's *Memoir*; if they had the strength of character to resist such corruption, and accepted the fact that the possession of power imposed responsibilities, they became, at best, benevolent tyrants.

It would therefore be completely unrealistic to expect to find in their mills, especially in those owned by a product of Old Dissent such as Jedediah Strutt, hours of work that were anything but long. The fact that Arkwright, Strutt and Evans were widely regarded as benevolent employers meant purely and simply that the day's work they demanded from their hands occupied not the sixteen hours quoted by Blincoe, which might at weekends have extended to twenty-five, or even the fifteen reported by Mr Middleton, but a mere twelve. Jedediah Strutt junior, giving evidence in 1816 before the Select Committee on Children Employed in Manufactories, admitted that the hours of work at Belper and Milford were, at that time, still twelve, 'six before dinner (which is twelve to one), and six after; each of which six includes the time for breakfast and tea'. They were just as long at Cromford, though slightly less, it would appear, at Darley Abbey, and the workers were mainly women and children. In 1816, of Arkwright's labour force, 37 per cent were under eighteen, and of Strutt's even more: 48 per cent. Children were taken at Cromford from the age of seven and upwards, so Jedediah Strutt reported in 1774; while, sixty years later, nine was still the minimum age of admission at Belper; and though the Strutts were then contemplating raising the age to twelve, and reducing the hours to ten per day, they were swift to point out to a Royal Commission that 'the reduction of time from twelve hours to ten, and the consequent reduction of wages, would have a most serious and lamentable effect on the working class, as well as bring a great injury to the master.' Everything should be done, they said, 'to enable the working class to procure sufficient food and clothing, and the comforts of life, and then there is some chance of making some moral improvement, but it is very difficult to instruct and improve the hungry and the naked, and those who are degraded (against their own will too) into pauperism'.

They made no mention of the fact that it might prove equally difficult to instruct the weary, possibly because by that time night work, expressly forbidden at Darley Abbey, was uncommon in the mills at Belper and Milford; but it was prevalent in the early years in many establishments, and Richard Arkwright junior admitted to the Committee of 1816 that his mills at Cromford had, for twenty-two years, employed 164 boys on a night-shift basis. They 'got extravagant wages', he said, 'and were extremely dissipated, and many of them had seldom more than a few hours sleep'. William Bray confirmed this. Passing by the Upper Mill shortly after it was opened, he reported that it employed 'about 200 persons, chiefly children', who worked 'by turns, night and day'; while Archibald Buchanan, who trained at Cromford and later owned a spinning mill at Deanston in Perthshire, confessed that in his time 'the spinning went on at night.'

Benevolence also meant that the Strutts and the Evanses approached problems of discipline with a greater humanity than Needham was alleged to have shown at Litton. Discipline was essential to these early factory masters: inside the mill to ensure efficiency of production, outside to safeguard the firm's good name: and with a young, often irresponsible and sometimes unruly labour force, it could, from time to time, constitute a problem; but it was a problem that Jedediah Strutt and his sons consistently declined to meet by using corporal punishment. Such punishment, on their orders, was strictly forbidden; nor are there any records of its use by Thomas Evans and his sons at Darley Abbey; and though evidence of the methods of discipline at Cromford appears to have perished along with the rest of Arkwright's business documents, there seems no reason to believe that, with Strutt as a partner for the first ten years, the principles of punishment established there would have differed in any material way from those that prevailed in Jedediah's own mills.

He and his sons preferred to punish misconduct by a system of fines, or 'forfeits' as they were commonly known at Belper. This entailed, for certain offences, the forfeiture of part of the Quarterly Gift Money. The Strutts operated a system of three-month contracts, and held back a sixth of the workers' wages. This was paid in cash at the end of each quarter, but the whole of it could be forfeited for leaving without notice before the end of three months, and a proportion of it for proven misconduct. Such misconduct embraced a number of specified offences, such as being absent without leave; stealing, destroying or damaging mill property; failing to do work as required by the overseers; and failing to comply with the discipline of the mill. The list of forfeits for the period 1805 to 1813 details the offences for which fines were inflicted. Absence without leave comprised such misdemeanours as 'Being off drinking', 'Being off at Heage Feast with a pretence of being ill', and 'Going off with some Militia Men'. Cases of theft involved packthread and yarn, candles, nails and pincers; while among the articles destroyed or damaged were a pair of scales, a thermometer, a drawing frame and a gallows iron; but it is the entries under the fourth category, the failure to comply with discipline, that are the most illuminating and, indeed, entertaining. Here occur such offences as 'Frequently looking thro' window', 'Making T Ride's nose bleed on the hanks', 'Terrifying S. Pearson with her ugly face', 'Being saucy with W. Winson', 'Throwing Water on Ann

Gregory very frequently', and even 'For putting Josh Haynes' dog into a bucket of Hot water'; while forfeits were ordered for a number of workers for 'Rubbing their faces with blood and going about the town to frighten people': conduct which, no doubt, was interpreted as bringing the firm into disrepute. It is, however, heartening to read that, although three girls were fined between them twelve shillings and eightpence for 'Dancing in Room', the entire forfeit was remitted 'by order of J. Strutt'; and in general it seems that, while discipline was tight, leniency was often the order of the day. The percentage of total earnings to be forfeited was small. Between January 1801 and September 1804 it was only £70 out of the £9,650 earned by the spinners; and the case of Thomas Bamford, who was fined five shillings and eightpence and ordered to forfeit Gift Money to the sum of thirty-five shillings and sixpence halfpenny for taking two days off to indulge in a bout of drinking, was unusually harsh. The impression must remain that, more likely than not, he was a persistent offender.

In the Evanses' mills at Darley Abbey fines were imposed in a similar way for an almost identical range of offences, though here there was no Gift Money, and the proceeds of the fines, subtracted directly from the workers' wages, were devoted to a fund for free medical service. Darley Abbey, created and moulded by Thomas Evans and his sons, was much more of a closed community, a company village, than Belper and Cromford could ever possibly be with their former populations of nailers and lead miners; added to which, the family owned almost all the land in and around the village, and, within its bounds, not merely the cotton mill, but also mills for paper, corn and red lead, not to mention a brick works. Dependence on the Evanses was therefore virtually absolute, and their control over workers they employed extended much further beyond the factory gates than did Arkwright's at Cromford. The Strutts' control at Belper was strict enough; they had watchmen posted at points throughout the town, whose task, each day, was to note in a special book any cases of objectionable behaviour by workers; but, with their total command over Darley Abbey, the Evanses could exercise an even more comprehensive control. Misbehaviour in the village was just as likely to be punished as misbehaviour in the mill. The absence of a child from Sunday school without good reason could be the subject of a fine; and returning to the village after ten o'clock at night, especially if under the influence of drink, was regarded as a particularly serious offence, calculated to disturb the peace of the community. The lock-up, constructed by order of the Quarter Sessions at the entrance to the village on the Derby road, was put to frequent use, and a watchman was stationed there every night, whose task, more often than not an unenviable one, was to arrest and imprison any boisterous revellers and enter in a book the names of all women returning from Derby later than ten o'clock. According to legend, the girls were more successful at evasion than the men. On seeing the watchman, they pulled their skirts high above their faces and ran for the village. No doubt, on such occasions, the custodian found his work somewhat more congenial, and was paralysed into fascinated inactivity.

The methods used to maintain discipline lay at the discretion of individual masters, but they had at their disposal a form of retribution which now, in a period of union power and industrial tribunals, is, to an employer, only barely available. They could at least dismiss a worker on the grounds of inefficiency or misbehaviour, and many of them, no doubt, did so; this was their prerogative, and such dismissal could take immediate effect. There is a warning still posted on one of the doors of the Darley Abbey mill that anyone found putting mill waste or washings down the communal closet 'will be fined 5/- and will be liable to instant dismissal'.

Benevolence could only be extended so far. It had to yield place to efficiency of production and reasonable profits. These were the factors, above all others, that controlled hours of work and scales of wages. As the Strutts pointed out, any substantial reduction in hours was likely to 'bring a great injury to the master'; and for similar reasons wages had to be kept at an economic level. Individual wage rates are difficult to calculate, since almost all the mill hands were paid on piecework, and only a few of the account books have survived. One of these is the Reelers' Wages Book kept by the Strutts, which shows that, in the years between 1784 and 1787, reelers, for a six-day, seventy-two hour week, were paid between a shilling and five shillings and sixpence, while overseers received between six and ten shillings. Overtime was paid at a rate of a penny an hour for the hands and twopence an hour for overseers, but it is apparent from the accounts that, though two reelers' overseers, John Chappell and Robert Hodgkinson, regularly worked a thirteen-hour day, there were very few such payments to the reelers themselves. Sir Frederick Eden, in his monumental work, *The State of the Poor*, published in 1797, reported that, at Arkwright's Wirksworth mill, children from eight to fourteen years of age earned between one and five shillings a week, women three to five shillings, and overseers twelve shillings. What precisely was the rate of the 'extravagant wages' paid to Arkwright's 164 boys on night-shift at Cromford is impossible to determine, but it seems very doubtful whether any of them exceeded five shillings a week.

Such hours and wages, though marginally better than those in many other factories, were hardly likely to attract workers from Derby and Nottingham to isolated country mills like Cromford, dependent on the water power of the Derwent and its tributary streams. Nor were they, on their own, likely to entice the lead miners and their families who already, by the middle of the eighteenth century, were on average earning more, living rent free or at a nominal charge, producing their own food and grazing their animals by right on the common. Yet labour had to be attracted and it had to be held; and masters like the Evanses, the Strutts and the Arkwrights appear to have solved these problems with considerable success by offering to their employees not merely substantial houses of unusual quality, but also a wide variety of social services. Cash payments represented but a small proportion of the workers' wages: probably at the Strutts' no more than a sixth; the rest was received in the form of housing, food and coal, and a whole range of miscellaneous goods and services supplied by the firm.

Good housing possessed a singularly high priority, and how well these early masters succeeded in the realm of domestic building can be seen today by taking a stroll around Cromford or Belper, Milford or Darley Abbey. John Farey was suitably impressed by their efforts. He wrote in his *General View* of the county:

> The cottagers throughout Derbyshire are much better provided with habitations than they commonly are in the Southern Counties of England, and they generally keep them in neat and in better order . . . The vast numbers of neat and comfortable Cottages which have been erected, by the late Sir Richard and by the present Mr. Richard Arkwright, by Messrs. Strutts, Mr. Samuel Oldknow and numerous others of the Cotton-spinners and Manufacturers, for the accomodation of their multitudes of work-people, must have had a great influence on the general style and condition, now observable in the Cottages.

The cottages, in those days, must certainly have qualified as neat and comfortable. Those in North Street at Cromford, Long Row at Belper, and Brick Row and Lavender Row at Darley Abbey, architect-designed and substantially constructed in brick or gritstone, are, with their recently renovated interiors, still sought after today and fetch considerable prices. In November 1977, No. 11 Lavender Row, on the hill at Darley Abbey, was offered for sale at £12,950, which is more than six times as much as the sum for which the Evanses insured the Boar's Head Mill and the whole of its machinery in 1792.

At Cromford the first houses that Arkwright built may well have been those in Staffordshire Row on the approach to the Via Gellia, but by 1777 he had completed the terraces on both sides of North Street, named, not because of their position for they stand to the east of the Wirksworth hill and south of the village, but in honour of the then Prime Minister, Lord North. The street was wide and each three-storey house, constructed of local gritstone, had a cellar and a living room, a bedroom and a weaving-room in the attic. The window-frames were a combination of cast-iron bars and small leaded lights, and the attics communicated one with another along the length of the rows. None of the original frames now survives, and most of the continuous top-storey windows have been bricked up, but cast-iron frames can still be seen in houses, built sixty years later, in Victoria Terrace on Cromford Hill.

In 1924 the terraces on North Street passed out of the hands of the Arkwright family, and in 1961 they were bought by Matlock Urban District Council with a view to demolition. It is greatly to the credit of Derbyshire County

North Street, Cromford.

Cast-iron window frames, Wirksworth Road, Cromford.

Long Row, Belper.

The Clusters, Belper.

Hopping Hill, Milford.

Council that they refused to sanction the destruction of the houses, and, as a result, Matlock sold six of them to the Ancient Monuments Society, which, in 1974, offered them for sale to The Landmark Trust. The Trust bought them, with three others, and has since restored them, as it has restored Nicholas Cresswell's mill at Edale, re-roofing them, reorganizing the kitchens and washhouses, building in bathrooms and replacing some of the windows of the attic workrooms. Number Ten has been specifically refurbished as a landmark, and is let by the Trust as holiday accommodation.

The houses in North Street had small back gardens and plots of land higher up the hill; and those built by the Strutts at Belper between 1792 and 1795, the North and South Long Rows, were likewise furnished: a small garden at the front and a considerably larger one at the rear. One side of Long Row was built of gritstone, the other side of brick; and the three-storey terraced houses, still occupied today, were, for their time, of very high quality. The average rents in 1829 were between two shillings and two and fivepence halfpenny a week, and the Strutts made continuous provision for their maintenance: the interior walls were regularly whitewashed, and the chimneys swept quarterly at a charge of twopence.

Adjoining Long Row they built the three streets of houses, George, William, and Joseph Streets, named after Jedediah's sons; and among them, The Clusters, five blocks of unusual design and even better quality: four houses in each rectangular block, constructed back-to-back, two facing on to one street and two on to another. These had even larger gardens and were

Brick Row, Darley Abbey.

Lavender Row, Darley Abbey.

designed for occupation by the factory overseers. The rents were consequently higher, ranging from three shillings to three and fivepence halfpenny a week, and a couple were distinctly more expensive, their occupants paying between four shillings and four and eightpence halfpenny.

By 1831, of the fifteen hundred houses in Belper, three hundred were owned by the Strutts; and at Milford, which consisted in 1781 of only eight small cottages, they built, at much the same time as Long Row at Belper, some sixty houses winding and climbing up the side of Hopping Hill, and others in a curved row at Bank Buildings on the other side of the Derwent. All were of the same high-quality Strutt construction, and are still occupied and in considerable demand today.

The Evanses were equally assiduous at Darley Abbey, building their first workers' houses in 1783 in a series of courts close to the river. Here they erected North Row, Flat Square and West Row, later adding the terraces in Brick Row, Lavender Row and Mile Ash Lane. As early as 1795 the village possessed well over sixty houses, and two-thirds of these had been built by the Evanses. They, like the Strutts, made provision for maintenance. They supplied free lime and employed a regular team of painters, who worked from one end of the village to the other. The houses were mainly of brick, and the rents in 1795, between threepence and one and sixpence a week according to size, appear to have been distinctly cheaper than those at Belper. Notwithstanding this, they were, for their time, quality dwellings; and nowadays, neatly painted and with their modernized interiors, they provide extremely attractive period homes for Derby commuters.

The city authorities, in this instance, have a reason for pride. Over many years they have carelessly destroyed much of historical value in pursuit of their civic development plans; they have threatened to remove Andrew Handyside's bridge, and recently proposed, though thwarted by Derby Civic Society, to demolish the railway settlement round the Midland Station; but they have, at least, shown some concern for Darley Abbey, lending their assistance to the work of conservation and renovation. Streets and squares have been landscaped, lawns have been laid, trees and bushes planted; when re-paving has been done, the materials, cobblestones or coloured tarmacadam, have been chosen to merge with and enhance the surroundings; and, as a result, the settlement has become not merely an eighteenth-century enclave, but a living community and, for the city, a wholly unique architectural asset. It is good, for once in Derby, to see the past preserved in the service of the present; and good to know, in addition, that the Evanses' unpretentious dun-coloured bricks, laid nearly two hundred years ago, were laid solidly enough to be useful and decorative even amid the concrete of twentieth-century construction.

Such houses, set in the pleasantly wooded environment of the valley, built when land and labour were relatively cheap, and immensely superior to most of the industrial housing of the nineteenth century, must have proved in themselves a powerful magnet to workers in the towns; but these early Derbyshire factory masters provided other and equally attractive facilities.

Arkwright at Cromford offered loans to those of his employees who wished to buy a cow, and in 1783 the *Derby Mercury* reported that he had 'generously given to 27 of his principal Workmen, Twenty-Seven fine Milch Cows, worth from £8 to £10 each, for the Service of their respective Families'. He also, as Sylas Neville duly noted, gave rewards to good workers both in money and in kind, and held two annual balls at the Greyhound Inn 'with a weeks jubilee at the time of each ball'; and John Byng, when he visited the village in 1790, described how the landlord of the Greyhound 'has under his care a grand assortment of prizes, from Sr R. Arkwright, to be given at the years end to such bakers, butchers &c, as shall have best furnish'd the market ... They consist of beds, presses, clocks, chairs, &c, and bespeak Sr Rd's prudence and cunning; for without ready provisions, his colony cou'd not prosper.'

Corn mill, Bonsall Brook, Cromford.

Arkwright had built the Greyhound in 1778, to provide accommodation for travellers and to act as a point of focus for his growing community. It stands today virtually unchanged, presiding over the market place with its pediment and clock, its white-painted quoins and window lintels. He also built a corn mill on Bonsall Brook, complete with a mill cottage, storage facilities and a corn-drying kiln: a complex which the Arkwright Society is now restoring as a working museum and information centre; sponsored a number of sick-clubs and provident societies, which guaranteed medical attention at nominal rates and offered some kind of payment if the worker was ill; and, every September, organized what he called his 'candlelighting' festival, when the workers processed around the village led by a band, and, back at the mills, were regaled not merely with buns and ale, but also music and dancing in the evening.

Nor, in course of time, did the Arkwrights neglect the mental and spiritual needs of the community. Probably as early as 1782—almost certainly due to the fact that Strutt and Need were his partners, for Arkwright was an Anglican —a chapel to seat three hundred people was constructed at Cromford; and, shortly before his death, Arkwright himself began to build a church on the site of the old lead-smelting works downstream from the mills. It was consecrated in September 1797 and opened to public worship by his son, Arkwright's body being moved from Matlock and re-interred there in a bricked-up vault. Now St Mary's parish church, it was substantially altered and partly Gothicized in 1858, with the addition of a chancel and a western portico. William Adam, describing it somewhat earlier, was impressed by its simple elegance. 'The material of which it is built,' he wrote, 'is strong and durable, being of hewn small-grained red gritstone found in the neighbourhood.'

In addition there were schools. In 1785 a Sunday school was established in the village, an event which prompted the *Manchester Mercury* to purr with approval. 'Pleasing it is to the friends of humanity,' the reporter wrote of Arkwright, 'when power like his is so happily united with the will to do good.' Joseph Farington was equally impressed sixteen years later. Describing how the boys attended one Sunday and the girls the next, both morning and afternoon, he recorded his opinion that 'the whole plan appears to be such as to do Mr Arkwright great credit.' Richard junior, in 1832, added the school which still stands at the end of North Street, with its two adjoining houses, one for the master and the other for the mistress.

The Strutts were even more active. They supplied their workers not merely with houses, but with coal and milk, meat, fruit and vegetables. John Farey described how 'Messrs Strutts of Belper in order to ensure a constant supply of Milk to the Inhabitants and make it the interest of Cow-keepers, to keep up their stock of Milking Cows through the Winter, engage for a sufficiency of Milk, at 1½d., 2d., 2½d. and even 3d. per quart, during different periods of the year according to the expense and difficulties of procuring the article, and a person serves it out to their numerous Work-people in the Cotton Works, and keeps accounts until the end of the week, when they pay for it out of their wages.' The Strutts' Milk Account shows that, in 1813, the roundswoman was paid between four and sixpence and five shillings a week, and that between 1807 and 1830 the company sold 524,000 gallons of milk, making, in the process, a profit of £70. Much of the milk and vegetables were supplied from the Strutts' own farms—Wyver, which was close to Belper Lane End; Black Brook, which lay to the north of the Chevin; and Moscow, constructed in 1812, the year of Napoleon's disastrous retreat, on the eastern fringe of the Milford to Duffield road—while many of their houses had gardens of quite appreciable size, and workers could, if they wished, rent additional land in the form of 'potatoe lots' for a penny a week. According to the Provision Books, which have fortunately survived, the firm sold to its workpeople potatoes, onions and peas; scarlet runner beans, leeks, cabbages and cauli-flowers; Brussels sprouts, cucumbers and radishes; cherries, pears and apples; gooseberries, damascenes and rhubarb; together with dripping, butter, bacon, pork and ewe lamb; and in the Belper and Milford mills, workers who wished to buy a pint of tea or coffee every morning and evening could do so on the payment of a penny a day.

The Strutts also, for a time, provided medical advice for all the women they employed, and by 1832 they were paying £12 a year into a compensation fund: the money to be distributed to those involved in accidents during their work. It was under this scheme that, in 1828, a worker named William Potter received compensation when he 'hurt his Head and Legg with a fall from [the] Third Window in [the] North Mill'.

As Dissenters, they were zealous in providing places of worship. They built Unitarian and Wesleyan chapels at Milford, and a Baptist church; while

Moscow Farm, Milford.

at Belper, in addition to Jedediah's chapel of 1788, they contributed, with more than a little generosity, towards the provision of an Anglican church. The *Derby Mercury*, referring to their schools, purred even more loudly than its Manchester counterpart had about Arkwright's. They established Sunday schools at both Belper and Milford, and in a reference to that at Belper in 1785 the newspaper commented: 'We hear from Belpar that Mr. Strutt has, (with a Liberality which does Honour to the human Heart) entirely at his own Expense, instituted a SUNDAY SCHOOL for the Benefit of ALL the Youth of both Sexes employed in his Cotton Mill at that Town; and provides them with all necessary Books, &c for learning to read and write . . . An Example worthy of Imitation by all whom Providence has blessed with Affluence'. Jedediah's sons, William and Joseph, proceeded even further. They had met Joseph Lancaster, the educational pioneer, during a visit he made to Derby in 1802, and five years later they set up a school in accordance with his principles in the attic of Belper North Mill, adding a second the same year at Milford. These were both later moved into specialized buildings, holding between them nine hundred pupils. Milford School is still in use, and so is the one at Belper, at the bottom of Long Row, though now completely rebuilt and extended.

Nor did the family prove parsimonious when it came to celebrating national events. They organized festivities on the centenary of the 1688 Revolution, the signing of the Peace of Amiens in 1802, the capture of Napoleon in 1814, the coronation of George IV in 1821 and the passing of the Parliamentary Reform Act eleven years later. To celebrate Napoleon's exile to Elba they spent £10,000 in Derby alone, and the *Mercury* was prompt in its appreciation of the parallel rejoicings at Belper:

> Friday se'n-night at 9 o'clock in the forenoon, a discharge of cannon summoned the numerous people employed at Messrs. Strutt's manufactory at Belper to meet at the mills ... (where) after parading the town ... 750 sat down to a plentiful dinner of Roast Beef and Plumb Pudding, and the remainder, amounting at least to 450 more, were abundantly supplied with the same excellent fare, and an ample quantity of ale at their own houses. The dining room was decorated with great taste and elegance. On the one end over the head of the table were G. R. Peace, P.R. in large letters composed of gilt and plain laurel leaves and ribbons; the other end over a long range of barrels of ale, the word 'Plenty' was very appositely placed, and on the end of one wing along which four tables extended, appeared the immortal name of 'Wellington'.

The Strutts were more than satisfied with the results of their efforts. In their evidence, offered in 1815 to the Select Committee on Children employed in Manufactories, they wrote: 'It is well-known in this neighbourhood that before the establishment of these works, the inhabitants were notorious for vice and immorality, and many of the children were maintained by begging; now their industry, decorous behaviour, attendance on public worship, and general good conduct, compared with the neighbouring villages, where no manufactures are established, is very conspicuous.'

The Evanses, likewise, took care to make provision for the welfare of their employees. At Darley Abbey the proceeds of fines were diverted to a special benefits fund, which met the full cost of such medical treatment as the workers might require, and provided, if this were felt to be necessary, a period of convalescence at Llandudno in North Wales. If neither of these methods of treatment were successful, and the patient died, the Evanses arranged that burial should be free and supplied an engraved memorial stone. They also cooked hot dinners for the old and the sick which could be collected, when needed, direct from Darley Hall; they laid out playing fields to the south of the mill on the bank of the river; built in 1819, on rising ground to the north of the village, the beautiful Gothic church of St Matthew; and, seven years later, at the end of Brick Row, contrived a village school of advanced design, with spacious, tall-windowed, high-ceilinged rooms and a pedimented clock which, mechanically sound at the end of a hundred and fifty years, still continues to show the correct time of day to Derby commuters.

This constant provision of houses and churches; chapels and schools; fruit and vegetables; meat, milk and coal; provident societies, sick-clubs and Welsh convalescences seems far removed from the tribulations that Blincoe claimed to have suffered at Litton Mill; but, as Peter Gaskell wrote in 1836, 'it would be ... unjust to take as the sole ground for examination, the establishment of the Messrs. Strutt, in the valley of the Derwent, or any other

Village School, Darley Abbey.

country mill, conducted by men of enlarged benevolence and active philanthropy . . . The instances adduced are rather beautiful examples of what may
be done, than illustrations of what is done.'

Since little evidence, apart from Blincoe's, has survived about Litton; and
since the chances that more will in time become available are, to say the least,
slim; it seems probable that no-one will ever be in a position to establish the
truth. We can only hazard a guess that if conditions at Cromford and Belper,
Milford and Darley Abbey were the best in the valley, those which the
apprentices suffered at Litton were probably the worst. In general, where a
firm's finances were sound, conditions were better; where a master or a
partnership was continually struggling against insolvency, the money was
never available to provide any more than the bleakest necessities. Arkwright,
Strutt and Evans operated from assured positions; they had created their
communities, felt responsible for them and possessed the wealth to invest in
their workers. Ellis Needham, on the other hand, was never in a sufficiently
stable position to sacrifice his profits either by paying his workers or by
reducing their hours, nor had he the resources to indulge in the building of
schools and houses or in schemes of social welfare. He was not in fact rich
enough to own and run a cotton mill, set in a remote and secluded valley, far
from his markets, in a period of depression, except by starving it of capital
investment; using apprentice labour; providing poor food, overcrowded
conditions and the most primitive of facilities; and keeping his children at
work for long hours with the aid of a scourge.

Judged on present-day standards, conditions of work, even in the better mills like Belper and Cromford, were far from ideal. Twelve hours' work a day at the age of seven, or even at nine, would be far beyond the bounds of modern toleration; and, assessed on such standards, conditions at Litton were probably appalling; but, while condemning Ellis Needham, it would perhaps also be prudent to realize that those who, like William Cobbett, railed against the factories and looked back with nostalgia to the Golden Age of domestic industry were, at best, self-deluding and, at worst, hypocritical.

For the generations who toiled in cottage industries the age was far from golden. The nailers' shops of Belper, though often family concerns, were undeniably sweat shops; and Defoe's lead miner, 'lean as a skeleton, pale as a dead corpse', squeezing himself from a 'groove' in the ground and living in a hollow gap in the rock, could hardly be said to have enjoyed a silvery, let alone a golden shade of existence. When Wordsworth wrote of the cotton mills as temples, 'where is offered up to Gain, the master idol of the realm, perpetual sacrifice', he could well have applied the words to a blanket-weaver's shed, a hand-loom weaver's cellar or a breeches-maker's workshop. Arthur Young, reporting on the blanket-weavers of Witney in 1767, noted that their hours were from four in the morning to eight at night, and in winter they worked by candle-light; hand-loom weavers in Lancashire, as late as 1843, were said to be at work 'from 5 in the morning till 12 at night . . . in their cold, dark, damp cellars, without any fire or means of ventilation, and the atmosphere . . . foetid with the breath of the inmates', and others 'in cellars dug out of an undrained swamp; the streets formed by their houses without sewers, and flooded with rain; the water therefore running down the bare walls of the cellars, and rendering them unfit for the abode of dogs or rats'. Francis Place, who, in his early days, was a journeyman breeches-maker, lived, worked and slept, along with his wife, in a single room in London. 'We now,' he wrote, 'worked full 16, and sometimes 18, hours a day, Sundays and all. I never went out of the house for many weeks, and could not find time for a month to shave myself'. He added a revealing comment on the state of mind of the domestic worker. 'I know not how to describe,' he continued, 'the sickening aversion which at times steals over the working-man and utterly disables him, for a longer or shorter period, from following his usual occupation, and compels him to indulge in idleness. I have felt it, resisted it to the utmost of my power, but have been obliged to submit and run away from my work. This is the case with every workman I have ever known.'

And not merely workmen. If the long tradition of domestic toil had sanctified a day that was likely to last for at least twelve hours, it had also sanctified the labour of children as a social ideal. To the more enlightened minds of the seventeenth and eighteenth centuries, child labour, at a very early age, was of great social value. John Locke, the philosopher, recommended in 1697 that all 'children of labouring people', above the age of three, should be taught to earn their living at working schools for spinning and knitting, since 'what they can have at home from their parents is seldom more than bread and water, and that very scantily'. Defoe, on his journey through 'the island of Great Britain', remarked approvingly of the domestic woollen industry in the neighbourhood of Halifax, that there was 'hardly any thing above four years old, but its hands are sufficient to it self'; and an American loyalist, visiting the same place fifty years later, expressed what was still, in 1777, the unquestioned attitude towards child labour. Having watched some children making wire cards for carding the wool, he wrote in his diary, faithfully following Locke and Defoe, that such employment 'not only keeps their little minds from vice but . . . takes a heavy burden from their poor parents'; while Jedediah Strutt junior, as late as 1834, defending the admission of nine-year-old children to work in his mills, pointed out with some justice to the Factory Commissioners that 'many, indeed most of the females, have been previously employed, some even from five years old, at lace running or tambouring', and that, in the course of such work, they had been 'shut up in small ill-ventilated rooms for twelve or thirteen hours a day, or even longer, at an employment more injurious to health, and particularly so to eye-sight, than any employment they would be put to in a well regulated cotton factory.'

It would perhaps be prudent, too, to take note of the fact that punishments for children which we would regard as excessively cruel were, in Needham's time, not merely tolerated, but actively encouraged by those who were deemed to be progressive thinkers. Joseph Lancaster, whose educational theories so impressed the Strutts, was then recommending the use in his schools of a punishment called 'the log'. If a child was caught talking, a piece of wood weighing four to six pounds was to be fixed to its neck in such a way that any movement transformed it into a dead weight. In the face of such evidence and the light of pure logic, Needham could almost be classed as a progressive.

The consciences of even the best of men were not, in those days, ours; and in exercising judgment we should recognize this fact. Theirs was a world in which hardship was the normal pattern of living and physical violence a commonplace, where the treadmill was regarded as an improvement on the pillory, where parents took their children to public executions as a moral entertainment, where the Lingards of the time were gibbeted in chains, and suicides were still buried in the darkness at crossroads with a stake through their hearts.

Perhaps, looking back, we see things in reflex, as if in a mirror, and draw the wrong conclusions. Perhaps the wonder is not that such an age should produce men like Ellis Needham, his sons and his overseers, but rather that it could, from time to time, reveal those of 'enlarged benevolence and active philanthropy', such as Jedediah Strutt and old Thomas Evans.

10   The Bludgeon and the Rod

The jurors of our Lord the King upon their oath present that Thomas Bacon, late of the parish of Pentrich, in the County of Derby, labourer; Jeremiah Brandreth . . . otherwise called the Nottingham Captain . . . William Turner . . . (etc. etc.) . . . together with a great multitude of false traitors . . . to the number of five hundred and more, arrayed and armed in a war-like manner, that is to say with swords, pistols, clubs, bludgeons, and other weapons . . . did then with great force and violence parade and march in a hostile manner in and through divers villages, places and public highways . . . and did then and there maliciously and traitorously attempt and endeavour by force of arms to subvert and destroy the Government and Constitution of this realm as by law established . . .

First Count of the Indictment of Thomas Bacon, Jeremiah Brandreth, and others for High Treason before the King's Justices at Derby (1817).

But yesterday a naked sod
The dandies sneered from Rotten Row
And cantered o'er it to and fro;
And see 'tis done!
As though 'twere by a wizard's rod
A blazing arch of lucid glass
Leaps like a fountain from the grass
To meet the sun!

W. M. Thackeray, on the Crystal Palace (1851).

By the end of the eighteenth century, though the landscape of the valley was in parts undergoing a rapid transformation, the old way of life was, for the majority of its inhabitants, changing only slowly. The beginnings of capital investment in lead mines by the larger mining companies had extended the workings; the cotton mills were rising beside the tumbling streams in the depths of the valley, and ancillary industries were either taking root or expanding their traditionally limited production; but this wealth of development had had little effect on the rural communities in which most of the people had always passed their lives. The roads, apart from the few cross-country routes which had already been improved, were still in a thoroughly deplorable condition; access and exit to and from the valley were operations fraught with considerable difficulty; and the villages remained, in consequence, the homes of closely-knit groups of people, isolated and independent, many of whom were still to live, a hundred years later, 'like the inhabitants of a lonely island'.

The turnpike roads and later the railways were to change this pattern, and change it substantially, passing, as they did, either through or close to most of the villages, yet the connection with the outside world that they achieved was never more than partial. There were communities at a distance from turnpike roads, ignored and by-passed by railway constructors; and until the age of the petrol engine, they still remained on the lip of nowhere, their inhabitants rarely moving far in a lifetime. The contraction of the railway network, of recent years, and the pruning of other forms of public transport have reinforced an isolation which, for many places, was never entirely dispelled; and, even today, villages like Tunstead, half a mile from the thunder of one of the world's largest quarries, and Ible, perched only a quarter of a mile above the busy Via Gellia, can still, despite the motor car, retain a sense of almost medieval isolation.

The building of the turnpikes and the construction of the railways, while they made access easier and brought people in their thousands from Derby and Nottingham, Manchester and Sheffield to the heart of the valley, never wholly eradicated such ingrained insularity, and, in some cases, by the very perversity of progress, served merely to strengthen it. There were village communities, by no means few in their numbers, whose detachment from the mainstream of trade and activity was, quite literally, fortified. These were the villages where, in earlier times, markets had flourished, serving as centres which farmers, driving their reluctant flocks and herds, could reach and return from in the course of a day. At a time when passage could only be accomplished over twisting, climbing, uneven roads, such markets were essential and consequently prosperous, each serving an area which ranged,

Ible village.

at its widest, no more than ten miles from the centre of the village; but swifter transportation by turnpike and railway altered the geographical patterns of trade; markets in such numbers were no longer required and had no hope of survival, especially if the village found itself ignored by the planners of the railway. In such a case the market inevitably died, leaving, as at places like Tideswell and Hartington, Litton and Monyash, that empty space—a green, a square or a broad main street, marked by a cross or an abandoned market hall—which is so characteristic of many village centres in and around the valley.

Two and a half miles from the A6 road, close to Darley Bridge, an old crossing of the Derwent, and in the middle of an area that was richer in lead than any in the valley, lies the small town of Winster. The visitor, climbing steadily from Darley Bridge to the limestone moors, will find it a place of both character and charm, still fossilized in its eighteenth-century prosperity. Winster was once a thriving community of miners, merchants and lead mine proprietors, and boasted a market which Llewellyn Jewitt, the Derby-shire historian who lived at Winster Hall, described, in the words of an old inhabitant, as having 'long rows o' stalls and the people so thick and throng together you could a walk'd a top o' their heads'. The wide main street still retains its grace, mingling, among the plainer cottages of the miners, a number of more elaborate merchant dwellings and a pair of houses which Sir Nikolaus Pevsner recorded as being 'Palladian ... with two Tuscan porches and between them on the ground floor and the upper floor a Venetian window'; but the chief of buildings, which dominates the street, is the now-deserted Market House with its infilled arches, built and extended between the fifteenth

Market House and Main Street, Winster.

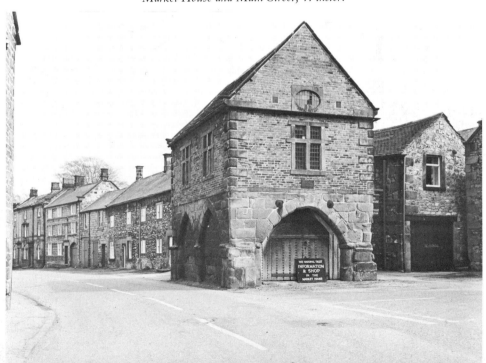

and early eighteenth centuries, and now in the possession of the National Trust. This, once the centre of so much activity, shadows little more today than a couple of fruit and vegetable stalls, for, as Jewitt remarked nearly a century ago, the market has 'for many years fallen into desuetude', and 'the old venerable Market House' is 'but rarely open'd except at the time of the annual wakes'.

Winster's market was only one among many that passed into oblivion. Even the Arkwrights, for all their great wealth and local pre-eminence, could not invest Sir Richard's new market at Cromford with any degree of stability. Its trade, despite and because of the railway, departed, some of it to Bakewell, some to Matlock, and the rest to the old nailers' market at Belper.

Change there was, in abundance; but, by its very nature, such change was at once both progressive and retrogressive. While Belper, under the influence of the Strutts, was expanding from a poor nailers' village into the second largest town in the county; while the railway was bringing renewed wealth to Derby and an increasing flood of tourists to Matlock Bath, other, less fortunate places were declining: some because altered lines of communication were carrying their trade elsewhere, others because their prosperity had depended either on mineral deposits, the extraction of which was growing uneconomic, or on the traditional domestic branches of industry which were failing in the face of competition from the factories. At much the same time as the railway companies were bringing traffic to Rowsley and adding the name of Ambergate to maps of the valley, they were, in conjunction with the water frames, spinning mules and depressed lead prices, stealing away the trade from Tideswell and Winster.

This developing pattern of progression and retrogression affected individuals in much the same way as it did villages and towns. The lead miner who sent his wife and children to work in the mill was merely compensating for a decline in his earning capacity by taking advantage of a newer form of work that was, at that time, enjoying prosperity. A silk manufacturer like Jedediah Strutt, who diverted his resources to the spinning of cotton, was simply acknowledging an economic fact: that the trade in silk, because of its restricted market, was capable of only limited expansion, and that the future lay with the cheaper cotton goods. To some, those cast in the mould of Arkwright and Robert Owen, this age of evolution offered limitless opportunities which, allied to good fortune, energy and talent, could be turned into gold; to others, robbed of their hard-acquired skills by new inventions and powered machinery, it brought little beyond idleness, poverty and despair; and, in the context of the Derwent and its changing valley, it would be difficult to find two better examples of this contrast in fortunes than on the one hand Joseph Paxton, the gardener's boy who became not merely an architect of distinction but also the greatest gardener of his time, and on the other the unemployed stocking-knitter, Jeremiah Brandreth, and the men of Pentrich who followed him to disaster on the Nottingham road.

Joseph Paxton was born at Milton Bryan, a small village in Bedfordshire, in 1803, at a time when the old social order was in flux and the belief was gaining currency that those of even the lowliest birth had the right by self-help—by making the most of their energies and talents, and turning good fortune to their own advantage—to rise in the social scale and make themselves masters in whatever trade or profession they chose to adopt.

His father was a farmer, and he was the seventh son, which perhaps explains why, at the age of fifteen, he was working as a garden boy at Battlesden Park, near Woburn, the country seat of Sir Gregory Page-Turner. It is a measure of the way in which Paxton helped himself that, nearly half a century later, in 1864, Sir Gregory's son employed him as architect-in-charge when Battlesden was rebuilt. The years that lay between were those in which he seized the varied opportunities presented by fortune, and used his energies and talents to equip himself with a wide range of necessary skills.

A number of positions as garden boy followed the one at Battlesden, and then, in 1823, he moved to the gardens of the Horticultural Society at Chiswick. These adjoined Chiswick House, one of the sixth Duke of Devonshire's numerous residences, and the land was leased from him. This was the fortunate combination of circumstances that provided Paxton with his first great opportunity. The Duke was in the habit of strolling through the gardens, and, on more than one occasion, he stopped to have a word with this youthful gardener, who not only showed an interest in the work he was doing, but also displayed an unusual skill. The Duke was impressed, and when, three years later, he found himself in need of a new head gardener at Chatsworth House, he offered the post to Paxton, who consequently, at the age of twenty-three, found himself responsible for one of the finest landscaped gardens in England.

The Duke was not, at that time, at Chatsworth; he was preparing to leave for Russia to attend the coronation of his cousin, the Emperor Nicholas; but Paxton was not disposed to wait for his new employer. Within forty-eight hours he was on the Chesterfield coach, and some years later he described to the Duke his first morning at Chatsworth:

> I left London by the Comet Coach for Chesterfield, and arrived at Chatsworth at half-past four o'clock in the morning of the ninth of May, 1826. As no person was to be seen at that early hour, I got over the greenhouse gate by the old covered way, explored the pleasure grounds and looked round the outside of the house. I then went down to the kitchen gardens, scaled the outside wall and saw the whole of the place, set the men to work there at six o'clock; then returned to Chatsworth and got Thomas Weldon to play me the water works and afterwards went to breakfast with poor dear Mrs Gregory and her niece, the latter fell in love with me and I with her, and thus completed my first morning's work, at Chatsworth, before nine o'clock.

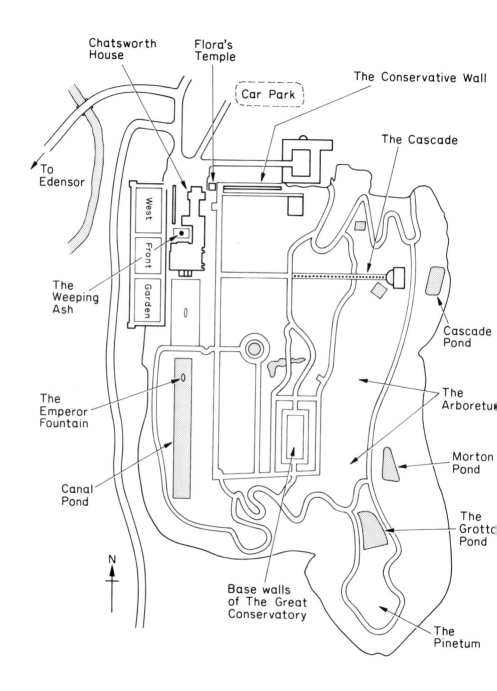

Chatsworth House

Flora's Temple

The Conservative Wall

Car Park

The Cascade

To Edensor

West Front Garden

The Weeping Ash

Cascade Pond

The Arboretum

The Emperor Fountain

Morton Pond

Canal Pond

The Grotto Pond

N

Base walls of The Great Conservatory

The Pinetum

Chatsworth.

It was a profitable morning's work in more senses than one. Mrs Gregory was the housekeeper, and her niece, Sarah Bown, was the daughter of a farmer and mill-owner at Matlock. Paxton married her eight months later on his head gardener's salary of £70 a year, but she brought with her a dowry of £5,000, a capacity for management that relieved him of much of the routine work at Chatsworth, and a dedication to his career which provided him with a lifetime of loyalty and devotion, even when his success swept him away from Derbyshire and left her a lonely, frustrated woman, fortified by repeated cups of strong coffee, toiling late into the night on the Duke's estate papers.

Her concern for these stemmed from the fact that Paxton became much more than gardener to the Duke. The initial respect that each had for the other—the Duke for this industrious, talented young man; Paxton for the solitary, cultured bachelor, whose deafness led him to shun public life—developed into a friendship that lasted till the Duke's death in 1858. Three years after he was appointed head gardener, Paxton assumed the additional duties of head forester at Chatsworth, responsible for all the woodlands on the estate; and gradually, across the years, his sphere of influence widened till he was acting as the Duke's agent, not merely for Chatsworth, but for most of the other Devonshire estates. The bond between the two was particularly close. In a letter to Paxton the Duke once wrote: 'I had rather all the flowers in the garden were dead than you ill'; and when, in 1835, he declined to accept a post in the government, Lady Grenville chided him. 'You and your Paxton,' she wrote, 'sitting under a red rhododendron at Chatsworth . . . and no thought of your country's weal and woe.' Perhaps there was a hint of jealousy in her words, but they pointed to a truth. Even then, after only nine years at Chatsworth, Paxton was, to the Duke, becoming indispensable.

By that time he had redesigned a section of the gardens to accommodate the new north wing of the house, which Jeffry Wyatt, later Sir Jeffry Wyatville, had recently built on behalf of the Duke; planted a pinetum, a collection of conifers that included the Chilean Pine or monkey-puzzle tree and a Douglas fir, which, according to the Duke, 'came down in Mr Paxton's hat' in 1829, and by 1845 was 35 feet high; and was forming the arboretum, a comprehensive collection of all kinds of tree, which still remains a feature of Chatsworth Park. Covering an area of forty acres, it comprised over fifteen hundred different species, some of which were transported considerable distances and then replanted.

Paxton, in the process, developed more than a little skill in moving large trees, and one of those he introduced still stands as a monument to what must have been a mammoth operation. This is the weeping ash planted in the new north forecourt at Chatsworth. An account of its journey was given in the *Derbyshire Courier* in April 1830.

This tree was purchased by His Grace from Messrs Wilson, and was removed from the gardens in the Kedleston Road, Derby (where it had been an ornament upwards of forty years), under the superintendence of the proprietors and of Mr Paxton, upon a machine constructed by Messrs Strutt of Belper. This was a carriage improved from Stewart's principle, and lent for the purpose to His Grace; and though the tree, with earth attached, weighed nearly eight tons, it arrived at its destination in eighteen hours, the distance being twenty-eight miles; and, contrary to expectation, it was able to pass through the different toll-bars, with one exception, without displacing them. The greatest difficulty occurred at the Milford toll-bar; but this, by the skill and exertion of Mr Anthony Strutt, was considerably lessened. The gates and wall at the entrance to Chatsworth Park were, however, obliged to be taken down, and the branches of some trees in the park lopped off. His Grace met the tree at the entrance to the Park, and was much gratified by its safe arrival.

He wrote in his diary, 'Miraculous to have come so far. I was enchanted with it.'

Paxton had also, by 1828, embarked on that work which, a quarter of a century later, was to provide him with his greatest opportunity for fame: his long series of experiments on the construction of glasshouses. When he first arrived at Chatsworth, such glasshouses as there were in the kitchen gardens were few in number and much dilapidated, and there had, up to that time, been little attempt by scientific horticulturists to rationalize any principles of design. The main realization already achieved was that the optimum transmission of sunlight to the plants depended on the slope of the glass, which, in its turn, was dependent on latitude, season and time of day; but such structures as existed were built with heavy frameworks and richly ornamented, which meant that they were both expensive to construct and, obstructing rather than transmitting the light, were unsuitable for plants.

Paxton's aim was to devise something lighter, cheaper and simpler to construct. This he achieved in those early days at Chatsworth, not by using cast iron, then a somewhat novel building material, but by framing his roofs in wood. 'My opinion is,' he said, 'after great experience'—and this was as late as 1852, twelve months after the erection of the Crystal Palace—that:

> Wood will last longer than iron in such a place. Wherever my experience goes, that is the result, and I have tried the roofs in every possible way. If I had tomorrow to put up a roof, and you gave me the money to spend for doing it in metal, I have no doubt I could put it up so much cheaper in wood, that the interest of the money I should have over would put a perpetual roof on for everlasting ... You have only to take care that the water is quickly delivered from it, and to keep it well painted, and there is no end almost to the time that good wood would last.

To drain off the water he devised his famous Paxton gutter, a wooden glazing bar, combining the functions of rafter and gutter in one piece of timber, with an outside channel for rainwater and another inside to catch

Weeping Ash, Chatsworth House.

condensation; while, to ensure the maximum transmission of sunlight and increase its heating effect, he refined and developed the ridge and furrow roof, so that the sheets of glass were, as far as possible, at right angles to the morning and evening rays of the sun. He wrote:

It occurred to us that wooden roofs would admit much more light, if the sashes were fixed in angles. We tried a small range of houses on this principle, with the sash bars fixed lengthways, the usual way, and rafters to bear up the lights. These houses were very light, and the plan appeared to possess several advantages—1st., more morning and evening sun were received, and at an earlier hour than a flat roof house; and 2ndly., the violence of the midday sun was mitigated by the disposition of the angled lights receiving the sun's rays in an oblique direction.

Later, in 1850, encouraged by Robert Chance, the Birmingham glass manufacturer, Paxton protected these ideas by a patent. By then, his system of wood-and-glass roofing had, as a result of numerous experiments, reached a point of development at which it was composed of standardized elements and could therefore be used for much larger buildings.

Most of these experiments were carried out at Chatsworth, producing in their course two remarkable structures: The Great Conservatory or Stove, and the Victoria Regia House.

Between 1828 and 1836 he erected a number of glasshouses in the kitchen gardens. The early ones he built in the normal flat-roofed style, but in 1832 he converted one of the existing houses, by that time more than a century old, to a ridge and furrow roof; and in the next two years, developing the new roofing system as he progressed, he added a small experimental pine-house and an extensive greenhouse, nearly 100 feet in length and 15 feet high.

By 1836 he had almost perfected his new technique, but the next step he took was of formidable proportions: the erection of a Great Conservatory to house exotic trees and plants of the largest size. Dr A. B. Granville, in his book *The Spas of England*, in 1841, described it as a 'truly gigantic' building; and compared with what Paxton, or indeed any previous constructor of glasshouses, had already attempted, the description was accurate. When completed, four and a half years later, it was 277 feet long, 123 feet wide and 67 feet high, set upon a basement gritstone wall composed of arches that held iron valves for ventilation. From the wall, which was two feet six inches in height, sprang the lower side-aisles of curving glass, supported on thirty-six cast-iron pillars; while above these rose the curves of the main glass span, the ribs and framework of which were of wood. The glass itself was a technical achievement. Robert Chance had introduced, some years before, a new method of manufacture, which enabled him to produce sheets of glass three feet in length. Paxton demanded that his panes should be four feet, and Chance, by skilful blowing of the glass, ensured that his order was fulfilled to the inch.

The Conservatory was heated by eight subterranean boilers feeding seven miles of iron piping, and the whole structure cost more than £30,000. It contained a carriageway running from end to end, so that visitors, driving through, could observe the trees and plants, the tropical birds and the gold and silver fish in their specially constructed pools. In 1843, when the Queen drove through in an open carriage, the building was illuminated by twelve thousand lamps fixed along the ribs; and the Duke of Wellington, who accompanied her, is reported to have said that though he had 'witnessed many scenes of surpassing grandeur', he had never in his life seen anything so magnificent.

The Queen and the Duke were only two of the many distinguished guests who came, in the course of the next eighty years, to view this latest of

Chatsworth's wonders, but the First World War, with its shortages both of labour and fuel, doomed it to destruction. Many plants were lost, and shortly after the end of the war it was demolished; though it was, even then, so sound in its construction that five attempts at demolition all ended in failure, and the sixth, by Paxton's grandson, only succeeded with the aid of dynamite.

Six years after the completion of what William Adam called 'this immense mountain of glass', some of the seeds of a giant water-lily, Victoria Regia, which had been discovered on the Amazon in 1836, were sent to Kew Gardens. From these, plants were grown, but they obstinately refused to flower; and so, in the August of 1849, Sir William Hooker, the director of the gardens, gave one to Paxton, who placed it in one of his existing glass-houses and constructed a tank to hold it, reproducing, as far as he possibly could, by heating, lighting and water agitation, the conditions under which it had flourished in South America. By the middle of September the tank had to be enlarged, since the leaves were already three and a half feet in diameter. A month later they measured four and a half feet, and by November the giant lily was in flower, much to the delight of the Duke of Devonshire, who, on hearing the news, travelled post-haste from Ireland.

But still the lily grew, and it soon became obvious that a much larger tank and a new type of building were required to contain it. The result was

Paxton's Great Conservatory, Chatsworth.

the Victoria Regia House, the structure of which, Paxton later acknowledged, was inspired by the structure of the lily itself. The leaves of the plant appeared, at first sight, to be unusually fragile: a flat upper surface supported by webs that touched one another only intermittently and resembled a set of miniature cantilevers; but, as Paxton discovered, their structure concealed a considerable strength, for, when he lifted his seven-year-old daughter on to one of them, it bore her weight with ease. On this principle the ridge and furrow roof of the new lily house was thereupon constructed. Sixty-one feet long and forty-six feet wide, the building incorporated all the features refined by Paxton's many years of glasshouse experiments: the wood-and-glass roof with its angled panes, the ingenious gutters, the supporting cast-iron columns which were hollow to act as rainwater drains, and the slatted wooden floor to increase ventilation and reduce the amount of dust, which could simply be swept through the gaps between the slats.

In its new surroundings Victoria Regia continued to flourish, producing in twelve months 112 flowers and 140 leaves; but, more important still, as Paxton declared two years later at a banquet held in his honour at Derby, the lily—whatever part was played by the crystal caverns of the Ecton Mine—provided the inspiration for the greatest of all his long line of glasshouses. 'I was erecting,' he said, 'a house of peculiar construction, which I had designed for the growth of that most remarkable plant, the Victoria Regia; and it is to this plant and to this circumstance that the Crystal Palace owes its direct origin.'

By the time that the lily house was rising at Chatsworth, plans were already well advanced for a 'Great Exhibition of the Works of Industry of All Nations' to be held in London in 1851. The idea had been conceived at the Royal Society of Arts, under the guidance of its President, Albert, the Prince Consort and Henry Cole, a civil servant who had helped Rowland Hill to launch the penny post. A site had been chosen on the south side of Hyde Park, and in January 1850 a Royal Commission had been appointed to organize the project, with Prince Albert as Chairman and Gladstone, Richard Cobden and the Prime Minister, Lord John Russell, among its members.

That same month the Commission delegated a part of its duties to a Building Committee, which included, among others, Robert Stephenson and Isambard Kingdom Brunel; and on 13 March this committee announced an international competition to design a building to house the exhibition. By the end of April, 245 designs had been received, but though two, both essays in glass and iron—one by Richard Turner, the architect and builder of the Palm House at Kew, and the other by Hector Horeau, the designer of the Paris Halles—were given a 'special mention', all were rejected as either too expensive or impossible to construct within the given time.

The committee members then produced their own design, which could only be described as a hybrid monstrosity, composed, as it was, of fifteen million bricks and surmounted by a dome, two hundred feet in diameter, for which, perhaps sadly, Brunel was responsible. This, as many critics were swift to point out, was not merely ugly, but likely to prove even more expensive, incapable of quick erection and difficult to remove; and since one of the conditions of using the Hyde Park site was that the building should be dismantled immediately the exhibition was over, it appeared to place in jeopardy not only the open beauty of the Park, but the very stipulations the Commission had undertaken to observe.

The Times was in no doubt about the implications of the committee's design. It declared in a leader on 27 June:

> We are not to have a 'booth' nor a mere timber shed, but a solid, substantial edifice of brick, and iron, and stone, calculated to endure the wear and tear of the next 100 years. In fact, a building is about to be erected in Hyde Park to the full as substantial as Buckingham Palace ... not only is a vast pile of masonry to be heaped up in the Park, but one feature of the plan is, that there shall be a dome of 200 feet in diameter—considerably larger than the dome of St Pauls ... By the stroke of a pen our pleasant Park—nearly the only spot where Londoners can get a breath of fresh air—is to be turned into something between Wolverhampton and Greenwich Fair ... Can anyone be weak enough to suppose that a building erected on such a scale will ever be removed? ... The first and main reason therefore, why we protest against the erection of this huge structure on such a site is that it is equivalent to the permanent mutilation of Hyde Park.

The design met with general public derision, and proved a strong weapon in the hands of those protesters, by no means few, who regarded the exhibition as a dangerous waste of money. Among the most vociferous was Colonel Charles Sibthorp, the 67-year-old member for Lincoln, who, within the privileged walls of the Commons, voiced his objections with scant regard either for truth or proportion. He thundered:

> As for the object for which Hyde Park is to be desecrated, it is the greatest trash, the greatest fraud, and the greatest imposition ever attempted to be palmed upon the people of this country. The object of its promoters is to introduce amongst us foreign stuff of every description—live and dead stock—without regard to quantity or quality. It is meant to bring down prices in this Country, and to pave the way for the establishment of the cheap and nasty trash and trumpery system ... All the bad characters at present scattered over the country will be attracted to Hyde Park ... That being the case, I would advise persons residing near the Park to keep a sharp lookout after their silver forks and spoons and servant maids.

His invective was both infectious and popular, and the protests multiplied. Even *The Times*, though couching its criticism in more moderate language, came out in his support. 'The whole of Hyde Park,' it ventured to prophesy, ' ... will be turned into the bivouac of all the vagabonds of London.'

Under fire from all sides—Press, Parliament and public—the Commissioners found themselves holding an untenable position, especially when Colonel Sibthorp, their constant scourge, turned his attention to a clump of elm trees which, to accommodate their building, they proposed to cut down. The attacks rose, at the end of June, to a crescendo, and Prince Albert was close to the edge of despair. 'The whole public,' he wrote, 'led on by *The Times*, has all at once made a set against me and the Exhibition, on the ground of interference with Hyde Park. We are to pack out of London with our nuisance to the Isle of Dogs.'

He had reason to be concerned. The whole scheme of an exhibition seemed to be threatened.

It was at this point that Paxton rescued the Commissioners. On 7 June, in his capacity as a director of the Midland Railway, he visited London to meet the Midland chairman, John Ellis, who was, in addition, a Member of Parliament. The meeting took place in the House of Commons, and, quite by accident, Paxton was present while the acoustics of the newly-built House were being tested. The results were poor, and Paxton remarked that this was by no means an isolated instance of planning mistakes. 'I told Mr Ellis,' he said, that 'I was afraid they would also commit a blunder in the building for the Industrial Exhibition'; that I too 'had a notion in my head, and that I would ascertain whether it was too late to send in a design.' Ellis, well aware of Paxton's talent, urged him to do so, and took him immediately to see Henry Cole at the Board of Trade. The result was that, though specifications for the official design were already being prepared, Cole agreed, on behalf of the Building Committee, to look at the new plans, provided that they could be swiftly produced. Paxton promised to have them ready in nine days' time, and, before he left London, visited Hyde Park to examine the site.

All this happened on a Friday, but it proved quite impossible to commit his plans to paper over the weekend, since he had already promised Robert Stephenson that he would travel to North Wales to see the third tube of the Britannia Railway Bridge raised above the Menai Straits on the Monday. On the Tuesday, however, he was back at Derby to attend another meeting as chairman of the Works and Ways Committee of the Midland Railway. In the course of the meeting, members of the committee noted that their chairman, contrary to normal practice, was making extensive notes on a large sheet of blotting-paper. Since they were merely enquiring into a minor misdemeanour by one of the company's pointsmen, the members thought this curious; but Paxton, while absorbing the details of the case, was working on something that bore little relation to the company's business. At the end of the meeting, he held up the blotting-paper and announced to his fellow members: 'This is a design for the Great Industrial Exhibition to be held in Hyde Park.'

That sheet of paper, now in the Victoria and Albert Museum, contained a cross-section and end elevation of a building to be based on the principles of the Victoria Regia House; and, although the proposed structure was on a very much larger scale, it embraced all the essential features of the Chatsworth lily house: the same roofing system, the same exterior cladding, the same principles of roof drainage by means of hollow columns supporting the structure, and the same slatted floor.

Paxton returned to Chatsworth with his sketch, and in eight days of feverish activity he and his staff prepared a set of plans, which he took to London, by train from Rowsley, on 20 June. Two days later the plans were shown to members of the Royal Commission, and, before another forty-eight hours had elapsed, Paxton was summoned to meet Prince Albert. The Commission then met again, but some members stubbornly refused to be rescued, maintaining that the question of design was settled. At this juncture, Paxton, always impatient, made up his mind to by-pass the Commission and appeal to the public. On 6 July he had his plans published in the *Illustrated London News*, with an accompanying article which ended with the words:

> No single feature, but the structure as a whole, would form a peculiar novelty in mechanical science; and, when we consider the manner of supporting a vast glass roof covering twenty-one acres on the most secure and scientific principles, and filling in a structure of such magnitude wholly with glass, Mr Paxton ventures to think that such a plan would meet with the almost universal approval of the British public, whilst it would be unrivalled in the world.

The public agreed, with considerable enthusiasm; the Commissioners, the majority perhaps with secret relief, yielded to the pressure; and on 15 July Paxton was able to telegraph Chatsworth, telling Sarah that his design had been unanimously approved. Alterations, it is true, were insisted upon, but the only radical variation was the addition of a vaulted semi-circular transept, and this possessed the distinct advantage of roofing in Colonel Sibthorp's elms which, with a little discreet lopping, were permitted, for a time, to grow in the very heart of the Exhibition.

Once the design had been accepted, the great structure rose with remarkable speed, despite predictions of disaster, voiced mainly by those whose schemes had been rejected. In little more than six months, Hyde Park was graced by a light and airy, economical building of massive proportions: 1,848 feet long, 408 feet wide, with a transept 72 feet wide and 108 feet high. It did not collapse beneath its own weight, as the vengeful pessimists had forecast it would; the wind did not level it, nor did rain seep through or hailstones shatter its three hundred thousand panes of glass. Douglas Jerrold, of *Punch*, christened it, in a moment of inspiration, the Crystal Palace; Thackeray described it as 'a blazing arch of lucid glass'; and even *The Times*, so critical of the Building Committee's previous efforts, was moved to rhapsodize:

The vast fabric may be seen, by any one who visits that part of the town, in its full dimensions—an Arabian Night's structure, full of light, and with a certain airy unsubstantial character about it, which belongs more to an enchanted land than to this gross material world of ours. The eye, accustomed to the solid heavy details of stone and lime, or brick-and-mortar architecture, wanders along those extended and transparent aisles, with their terraced outlines, almost distrusting its own conclusions on the reality of what it sees, for the whole looks like a splendid phantasm, which the heat of the noon-day sun would dissolve, or a gust of wind scatter into fragments, or a London fog utterly extinguish . . . Everything is done by the rule, and yet everything is graceful, and it might almost be said grand . . . and it is certainly curious to reflect, now that the work has been accomplished, and the great result stands patent to the world, that, with the facilities we possessed, glass and iron have hitherto been so little employed by our architects.

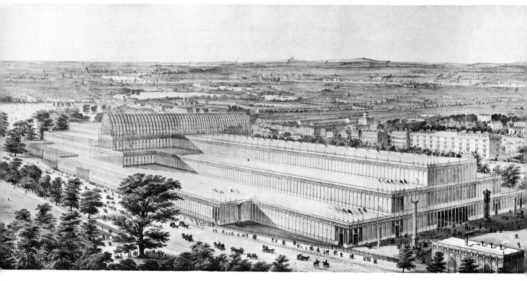

The Crystal Palace, 1851. The so-called 'aeronautic view' from the north-west.

It was a unique building, designed for a purpose which it admirably served, and yet a complete denial of the then-accepted architectural styles. The roof construction, as in the glasshouses at Chatsworth, was mainly of wood, and the whole was composed of mass-produced components, standardized in size, which could be assembled and dismounted with incredible facility. Once inside the Palace, it was difficult to see how its weight was supported; it seemed translucent; its structure cast no internal shadows; the side walls were too far apart to be embraced at a glance, and the ends of the building faded into insubstantiality. James Fergusson, writing in his *History of the Modern Styles of Architecture* a dozen years later, summed up the whole of Paxton's achievement, when he said:

At a time when men were puzzling themselves over domes to rival the Pantheon, or halls to surpass the Baths of Caracalla, it was wonderful that a man could be found to suggest a thing which had no other merit than being the best, and indeed, the only thing then known which could answer the purpose; and a still more remarkable piece of good fortune that the Commissioners had the courage to adopt it.

The success of the Crystal Palace earned Paxton a knighthood and £5,000 from the profits of the Exhibition; while the temporary preservation of Colonel Sibthorp's elms, according to the famous if apocryphal story, provided the Duke of Wellington with the last of his victories. Some of the trees were in due course cut down, but the largest of 'John Bull's Trees of Liberty', as they came to be called at the height of the controversy, attracted the London sparrows. They assembled in their hundreds under the transept roof, fouling the stands and the marvels of art and industry. To shoot them was impossible without breaking half the glass in the building, and all attempts to deter them ended in failure. At last, so the story goes, the Queen sent for Wellington. 'Try sparrow-hawks, Ma'am', the Duke replied gruffly, and the problem was solved.

Three other aspects of Paxton's work at Chatsworth are worthy of mention: the Conservative Wall, the Emperor Fountain and the rebuilding of Edensor.

The village of Edensor, up to 1838, stood where the access drive to the House now joins the carriage road through the park, but the additions and

Edensor village.

alterations made to the House by the sixth Duke brought the village within view of the west-front windows. Because of this, he decided to remove it, with Paxton's help, to a less conspicuous position. A number of the tenants were re-housed at Pilsley, on the Bakewell road, and others at Beeley, on the road to Rowsley; but this was to be merely a temporary move, till a new version of Edensor village was completed. The Duke chose a site comparatively close to the original one, but on the far side of the carriage road, on the edge of the park, and hidden from view by a small ravine; and in this hollow, around the old church, Paxton designed one of the best known of model villages in Britain. He was aided by John Robertson, then employed as his architectural assistant at Chatsworth. Robertson had worked for almost a decade as architectural draughtsman to J. C. Loudon, the foremost gardener-botanist of his day, and had drawn the explanatory diagrams and designs for Loudon's *Encyclopaedia of Cottage, Farm and Villa Architecture.* Paxton, very naturally, had had dealings with Loudon, and this may have been the reason why, in February 1840, Robertson moved to Chatsworth. By that time the village had already been planned and a number of cottages designed, but Robertson, in the course of the next two years, though still a subordinate, made his own contribution, notably by designing the castellated entrance lodge, one of the last of the village buildings to be completed.

The result of their efforts was a loose, informal grouping of cottages and villas stretching from the village green and the church up the twin slopes of Japp Lane and Edensor Lane: the whole a delightful compendium of styles: Norman, Elizabethan and Georgian; Italianate and Swiss; and a number of picturesque but hybrid buildings, which defied any rigid classification save that their designs were, like Edensor itself, a mingling of facets culled from many ages and many widely separated parts of the world.

From the site of old Edensor, the access road runs north of the House, and those who wish to walk through the gardens enter them beside Flora's Temple. This was one of the original features of the classical garden created by the first Duke in the seventeenth century. It was, at that time, a Bowling-Green House and stood to the south-west of the main Chatsworth buildings. The fourth Duke later moved it to the north-east corner and renamed it Flora's Temple. Linking it to the stables, further to the east, and climbing up a slope of one in thirteen, the sixth Duke built a wooden covered walk, and it was this that Paxton transformed into his Conservative Wall. The change was effected over a period of years. First he replaced the walk by a wall, 340 feet long and 18 feet high. This, on its south face, was covered with a wooden trellis on which plants could be trained, and he proceeded to use it for a series of horticultural experiments. To the coping, which projected twelve inches, a curtain rod was fixed, and from this hempen curtains were suspended which protected the plants in inclement weather, but could be drawn aside to display them in summer. The wall remained like this until 1848, when Paxton built, to cover it, a wood-and-glass frame, seven feet wide, stretching almost its entire length and divided into ten separate bays to accommodate the slope. In the centre was a specially ornamented bay, projecting above and beyond the main line of the frame and approached by a flight of seven stone steps; the roof, from end to end, was ridge and furrow; the floor was wooden slats; ventilation was controlled by a system of rods; and the whole structure was broad enough to form a covered walk, inside the glass, more than a hundred yards long. Two years later, in the central bay, he planted two rare camellias which still flourish today, filling the entire thirty-foot-square case and resplendent with flowers throughout March and April.

The Conservative Wall, Chatsworth, 1848.

From this impressive glass-encased wall, those who visit Chatsworth can see, beyond the House, the towering jet of the Emperor Fountain. This, perhaps the most remarkable surviving feature of Paxton's work in the gardens, was completed in 1844: the year when the Emperor Nicholas I of Russia, the sixth Duke's cousin, visited England. Paxton had already started work on the fountain when the visit was announced, and because it was expected that the Emperor would come to Chatsworth, he suggested that the whole endeavour should be completed and that the fountain should play to celebrate the occasion. Since this was to be the highest fountain jet in the world dependent on purely gravitational pressure, the work entailed building a water conduit two and a half miles long from Wadshelf Brook on the

Chesterfield Road; moving by means of shovel and wheelbarrow a hundred thousand cubic yards of soil to make a reservoir lake three hundred and fifty feet above the House; and installing pipes and valves to carry the water safely down to the gardens. All was completed within six months, and though the Emperor never found the time to travel as far as Derbyshire, Paxton named the fountain in his honour. It was indeed, at that time, the highest jet in the world, playing, with a normal supply of water, to 267 feet, and even higher than that when the reservoir was full. It was the most spectacular of all the many water works in Chatsworth Park: a glory unmatched by anything to be seen in the magnificent, formal gardens of the Continent.

From his early years at Chatsworth, the Duke allowed Paxton a certain licence. While still head gardener, he could undertake for other people commissions that had no connection with the Chatsworth estate; and, once he assumed the position of agent, there was an understanding, never contractual but merely implicit, that he could if he wished enlist for such commissions the help of his numerous estate assistants. He took full advantage of these facilities. As the years passed by his private practice, both as an architect and a planner of public gardens, grew to formidable proportions, and his business interests and extraneous duties drew him away from Chatsworth for longer and longer periods. His work on the Crystal Palace and its removal to Sydenham;

Site of the Great Conservatory, Chatsworth.

his construction of the Liverpool and Birkenhead Parks, Kelvingrove Park at Glasgow and the People's Park at Halifax; his extension of the Spa buildings and their grounds at Scarborough; his commissions to build and landscape Mentmore in Buckinghamshire and Ferrières, near Paris, for the Rothschild family; his duties as Member of Parliament for Coventry and as one of the directors of the Midland Railway all conspired to make his absences from Chatsworth more and more frequent. Sarah was left to deal with the routine work of the Devonshire estates, and often, for months, the only communication between them was by means of her letters, complaining that she was lonely, that he was missing the beauty of the rhododendrons and that he ought to pay a visit if only to see the gardens in bloom. 'O Fame,' she wrote once in a mood of despair, 'would that I could break your trumpet.'

That she could never do. When the sixth Duke died at last in 1858, Paxton resigned all his offices at Chatsworth; but, though Sarah, too, laid down her duties, she continued to spend the greater part of the year at Barbrook, their house on the Chatsworth estate, while he remained in London, working on such schemes as the Thames Graving Dock, fulfilling his Parliamentary duties, and entertaining both the rich and the famous.

Eventually the strain of his many activities took its toll of his health. He withdrew from Parliament, and though, in the May of 1865, he attended a flower show at the Crystal Palace, he had to be wheeled through the building in a chair. The following month he died. He was only sixty-one.

He was a man of varied talents, widespread interests and manifold achievements; but amid all the tributes paid, as was only natural, to the designer of the great glass palace in Hyde Park, *The Times*, generously and with discernment, pointed out that perhaps future generations would choose to see him in a different light than framed by his 'blazing arch of lucid glass'. 'His real title,' it said, 'to the regrets of his contemporaries and the regard of those who come after, is the work which he did as a gardener and garden architect, the impulse which he has given to the love of the beautiful in nature, especially among our great town populations; above all, the English breadth and genuineness of his character, which made him the object of affectionate regard to so many friends.'

Certainly, though the Crystal Palace has vanished, consumed by fire more than forty years ago, Paxton's spirit still pervades the glorious gardens at Chatsworth. Those who stroll through them can still admire the delicate vertical lines of the Conservative Wall; wonder at the soaring waters of the fountain; and imagine, looking down on the arched gritstone base of the Great Conservatory, the massive curvilinear structure of glass that it once supported, and the lamps flaring beneath its ridge and furrow roof as the Queen, in her carriage procession, drove through the gates. They can marvel at the spreading beauty of his camellias, the giant green saucers of his Victoria Regia still flourishing in the new, almost space-age, greenhouse; and then, making their way to Edensor, they can climb the slope behind the church to the sixth Duke's grave. Looking back down the hill from this simple, low stone, a much more imposing, rectangular tomb seems to dominate the churchyard. Beneath it lies the man who, in the words of *The Times*, 'rose from the ranks to be the greatest gardener of his time', and beside him, his wife, the Lady Sarah Paxton, who served him as faithfully across many years as he served his own friend and employer, the Duke.

Paxton's grave at Edensor.

Paxton was a man endowed with many talents and blessed by good fortune, who seized the right opportunities when they were presented. Brandreth and his fellow conspirators from Pentrich possessed none but common skills, were dogged by misfortune and snatched at the wrong opportunity when it came.

The village of Pentrich lies three miles to the east of the Derwent, above the Amber Valley and a mile from the Butterley Ironworks at Ripley. John Neal, who, some eighty years ago, wrote a history of its tragic and pitiful revolution, described the village, as he knew it then, in words which could well apply to the present. It was, he said, a 'quiet little hamlet', and anyone who happened to visit the place 'could not fail to be favourably impressed with the tranquillity and picturesqueness of the scene. No one would dream that such a peaceful, and to all appearance so innocent a locality, had ever been the scene of a revolution. The beauty of the surroundings seems so much out of character with anything pertaining to strife, that it is almost impossible to believe it had ever been thrown into a state of rebellion.'

He did, however, make the point that, in 1817, it was 'a much larger village'; in those days of more importance than Ripley. He wrote:

> The inhabitants of Ripley used to go to Pentrich Church, and nearly all marriage ceremonies in the district had to be celebrated there. The village was quite busy on Saturday evenings, and all kinds of sport was freely indulged in. Gambling of every description took place, quite openly, in the public thoroughfares. During the feast week, people from the surrounding villages would make their way to Pentrich to join in the festivities, knowing full well that plenty of life and animation was to be found there.

But there was more afoot in Pentrich in that early summer of 1817 than gambling and merrymaking. This was a time, two years after Wellington's victory at Waterloo, when the long-awaited peace had brought with it not

Pentrich village. The church stands to the left, and beyond it on the right was the White Horse Inn, in the tiny parlour of which the Pentrich Revolution was planned.

plenty, but increasing distress. For more than half a century the progressive mechanization of industry, coupled with a population explosion, had been creating a situation where more men were constantly seeking fewer jobs; and, with the end of the war, a number of new economic factors combined not merely to make regular employment hazardous, but also to depress the wages of those who had work, and to inflate in particular the price of bread. The end of government contracts for war materials and a sudden influx of foreign grain depressed home demand and produced a partial collapse of both industry and agriculture; nor did the export market revive with the lifting of Napoleon's Continental System, since European industries began to expand, and British firms, already hit by a slump, found competition difficult. Action by the government only made matters worse. The quarter of a million men immediately disbanded from the army and navy did nothing but swell the numbers of unemployed; the repeal of the income tax in 1816 threw the burden of war debts on to indirect taxation and drove prices still higher; while the Corn Law, designed to assist the farmers, produced in twelve months a 40 per cent rise in the cost of a quartern loaf. The weather, too, conspired against recovery. Sir Henry Fitzherbert described 1816 as 'the worst year, which was ever recollected' in Derbyshire. 'The Spring,' he wrote, 'was most severely cold, the snow falling as late as the 7th June. The autumn was unusually wet, so that the Harvest throughout England was very bad, and in the higher parts of Derbyshire, the oats were not cut till October, and in many places they were never housed.'

The men of Pentrich were bound to suffer from this savage depression. Apart from some desultory mining and quarrying, the major sources of employment in the village were industries under considerable pressure: farming, hosiery and iron manufacture. The biggest single employer was the Butterley Ironworks, and the majority of those who were not working there were framework knitters, using in their cottages stocking-frames rented by master hosiers. The ironworks, a prosperous wartime arsenal, had suffered a setback with the coming of peace; iron prices had fallen, and the tonnage of coal shipped down to the Trent by the Erewash Valley Coal-masters' Association, of which Butterley was a member, had fallen from a peak of 321,000 tons in 1809 to 242,000 by 1817. In addition, the hosiery trade was stagnant. Wages on the Derbyshire-Nottinghamshire border had been steadily declining since 1790 and prices had been rising throughout the same period, while, to complicate the problem, the Derby Rib machine, on which many of the workers had long and painfully acquired their skills, had ceased to be profitable due to changes in fashion. Nottingham provided the index of hosiery prosperity, and, by the Christmas of 1816, the labouring poor of the city and its surrounding districts were said to be suffering the worst conditions for forty years. Of the twenty-three men convicted for their part in the Pentrich Revolution, no less than eight, by far the largest occupational group, were framework knitters.

The Pentrich area had already seen outbreaks of Luddite violence. In two separate riots during the winter months of 1811–12, twenty-five frames had been smashed in the village, and others close by at South Wingfield and Swanwick. Such disturbances were part of an epidemic of machine-breaking that spread from Nottinghamshire into Derbyshire and Leicestershire: action directed against the master hosiers who, the stockingers believed, were by-passing their skills by using unapprenticed workers to produce cheap 'cut ups': types of stocking that were cut and sewn not from fashioned shapes, but from straight and therefore unfashioned widths. These sporadic outbreaks had continued to the end of 1816, spawning associated violence as far afield as the West Riding of Yorkshire where shearing-frames and gig-mills were attacked and destroyed, and Lancashire and Cheshire where the workers' violence was turned against factories that housed the new steam-looms.

But the Luddite attacks were merely local symptoms of a general malaise that was affecting the nation. Falling wages and rising prices had led to serious food riots in the spring of 1812 in the cotton towns of Lancashire and north-east Cheshire; and these were repeated on a much wider scale in the twelve months that followed the end of the war, when places as far apart as Newcastle and Bideford, Bury and Ely, London and Nottingham, Glasgow and Merthyr Tydfil suffered from increasingly violent disturbances. At Littleport in the Isle of Ely the town was sacked by the fenmen in a desperate search for food, and, once they had left, it looked for all the world, said one observer, as if an invading army had passed through the place. As a result of this episode alone, five men were hanged and a number of others transported.

Behind the economic lay a much more sinister political discontent. In the later years of the previous century a variety of men for a variety of reasons had suggested reforms to the political system: notably the extension of voting rights, the end of the 'rotten boroughs' through which a handful of wealthy landowners controlled elections to the House of Commons, and the enfranchisement of the new industrial towns, many of which, like Manchester and Birmingham, growing fast, had still no Members of Parliament to represent them. This campaign for Parliamentary reform had, in the 1780s, attracted to itself powerful and, indeed, official support, in particular from the Prime Minister, the young William Pitt who, in 1785, had proposed reforms of the type suggested. Then came the French Revolution, the Reign of Terror and the protracted war against the militant Jacobins and finally Napoleon. Reform became synonymous with mob violence and the shadow of the guillotine, and Pitt's Tory government turned to reaction, arresting members of the London reform societies and charging them with treason, pushing measures through Parliament making it possible to speak and to write treason as well as to act it, and banning workers' combinations, the embryonic trade unions, out of fear that they would merely provide a cover for political agitation. Such restrictions remained, in one form or other, till the end of the war, though the voices of reformers were never entirely silenced and small bands of men continued to meet in secret to carry on the fight.

At that time the government undoubtedly had the backing of public opinion. Samuel Taylor Coleridge, himself a reformer, acknowledged as much. 'There was not a city, no, not a town,' he wrote, 'in which a man suspected of holding democratic principles could move abroad without receiving some unpleasant proof of the hatred in which his supposed opinions were held by the great majority of the people'; and Horne Tooke, tried on a charge of treason and acquitted, was told, as late as 1805, that his political principles were as much out of fashion as were his clothes. 'I know it,' he replied, 'but the fashion must one day return or the nation be undone.'

That fashion returned with the coming of peace; and when another Tory government, led by Lord Liverpool, answered the revived demands of the reformers with a strict conservatism and equally harsh measures of repression, there were those who despaired of ever achieving peaceful constitutional reform and turned their thoughts to violent revolution. For them the hosiery areas of the Midlands, racked with unemployment and rising prices, provided fertile ground.

Twelve years were still to pass before the first police force—the Metropolitan—was established in London. Lacking the help of such an organization, Lord Sidmouth, the Home Secretary, relied for information on the detective work of magistrates and paid informers, and in the spring of 1817 reports began to reach him of a rising in the Midlands planned to start on the night of 9 June. In the Home Office files these reports began to multiply. A parcel of daggers was said to have arrived at a public house at Hinckley; five thousand pikes, so it was rumoured, had been smuggled into Leicester; and orders for handles for another three thousand delivered to a village carpenter near Stamford. Since officials at the Home Office had already composed a list of places 'where Riots have actually occurred, or where from the Appearance of the Lower Orders of the People, Disturbances may be expected', and this included towns in twenty-two counties of England and Wales, the scraps of information that came filtering through from the Midlands area merely served to confirm what the government had long suspected, especially since it was aware of the existence of secret committees in the Midland towns, designed to co-ordinate revolutionary activities.

There was, in Nottingham, a secret committee. Its chairman was a needlemaker, William Stevens, described by one of the government informers as 'a great talker'; and its delegate from the Pentrich and South Wingfield district, a dozen miles away, was a framework knitter named Thomas Bacon. Bacon was sixty-four years old, silver-haired, of medium height, and with a pock-marked face. He was a man who had been set in his republican beliefs for thirty years, and was described in the prosecution brief at his trial as a person of 'rude and uncultivated' appearance, yet possessing 'a degree of knowledge far beyond the attainment of men of his condition of life and a most artful and insidious manner'. His name was already in the Home Office files, as a suspect in connection with Luddite activities.

It was he who organized a series of meetings in the May and early June of 1817 at a barn half-way between Pentrich village and the Butterley iron-works, telling those who attended that widespread preparations were being made for a revolution, that there was a need to use force, and that plans for the rising were so far advanced that, when the tide began to flow, the government would be helpless.

At much the same time he began questioning men employed at the iron-works, enquiring about the methods of manufacturing pikes and cannon, and the materials that might be used for making 'crow's feet', which were spiked obstructions for throwing in the path of charging cavalry. He also asked about a cannon that was standing outside the works, wondering aloud how it might perhaps be moved to Nottingham and how long such a journey was likely to take.

It was on 5 June that he attended a meeting of the Nottingham committee, and returned in the company of Jeremiah Brandreth, the deputy appointed by Stevens and his fellows to command the men of Pentrich and lead them through the night to Nottingham Forest, an open space on the edge of the town, where, according to plan, they would be met by contingents from widely scattered parts of the Midlands and the North.

Brandreth, later to be known as the Nottingham Captain, was an unemployed Derby Rib stockinger from Sutton-in-Ashfield, seven miles north-east of Pentrich. Thirty-one years old, he was living with his wife and two children in Nottingham. When he appeared for the first time that evening at the barn, there were those among the Pentrich men who had their doubts about his capacity as a leader. John Cope, a cleaner at the Butterley iron-works, was depressed by what he called Brandreth's 'mean appearance', and Ormond Booth, a fellow framework knitter, described him as wearing 'a brown top coat, a shabby green undercoat and light-coloured trousers.' He seemed, he said, to be 'rather ill-looking, a person having a large nose with a thin face and yellowish complexion.' John Neal, however, wrote of his 'commanding appearance, his depth of character, wonderful powers of will and thorough determination' which, he said, had 'the means of establishing in the minds of many, that confidence which creates a deep feeling of resentment against whomsoever and whatsoever he thought fit to denounce.' These gifts, he continued, were later to produce a 'process closely resembling that of deification, in the eyes of his most ardent supporters.' Subsequently, in jail, he cultivated a profuse black beard, and Thomas Denman, the lawyer who defended him and who was, in course of time, to assume the office of Lord Chief Justice, spoke of him as 'active, decisive and commanding', quoting from Byron's poem, 'The Corsair':

> Sun-burnt his cheek, his forehead high and pale
> The sable curls in wild profusion veil;
> There breathe but few whose aspect might defy
> The full encounter of his searching eye;
> There was a laughing devil in his sneer,
> That raised emotions both of rage and fear;
> And where his frown of hatred darkly fell,
> Hope withering fled—and mercy sighed farewell.

The Noble Poet, he said, must have taken for his model someone who possessed a striking resemblance to the Nottingham Captain. 'There was,' he declared, 'a wild daring in his look, a desperate decision in his manner, and a furious energy in his conduct which bespoke the man capable of a commanding influence upon common minds.'

That evening, in the barn, Brandreth promised his men that, once they arrived in Nottingham, each would be provided with bread, beef and ale and a hundred guineas. There were, he told them, sixteen thousand men there, ready to rise at midnight. Between them they would seize the barracks in the town, and, once Nottingham was taken, they would proceed in boats down the Trent to mount an attack on Newark. The statement he made was unequivocal and stirring, and he ended the meeting by calling on them to attend a further one next morning at the White Horse tavern.

The White Horse, demolished in the middle of the nineteenth century, was a small stone-built inn at the northern end of Pentrich village, roughly opposite the churchyard; and, since its keeper was Thomas Bacon's sister, a widow called Nanny Weightman, it was an ideal haven. Mrs Weightman, later described as 'a Bitch of a mother who deserves hanging worse than those condemned', was an almost fanatical supporter of the cause, and was said to have taken a poker to one of her sons to make sure he joined the rising. All four of them took part: one of them, William, was sent to jail, and another, George, a Pentrich sawyer, was transported for life.

It was here, in the tiny parlour of the inn, that England's last revolution was planned. On the morning of Sunday 8 June, Brandreth presided at a final meeting. He traced the projected route on a map, and distributed some verses, which were later to be used against him with telling effect by the Solicitor-General, as proving intent to commit high treason:

> Every man his skill must try,
> He must turn out and not deny;
> No bloody soldier must he dread,
> He must turn out and fight for bread.
> The time is come, you plainly see,
> The Government opposed must be.

Among those who heard him read out the verses were William Turner and Isaac Ludlam, later to be charged with him as ringleaders of the rebellion.

Turner had served in the army in Egypt, fighting against Napoleon, and, following his trade as a stonemason, had built a house in South Wingfield where he lived with his parents. It was he who proposed to murder Colonel Wingfield Halton, the local squire and magistrate, by setting fire to some straw in front of his house and then shooting him when he stepped outside to investigate. Ludlam was a farmer who, reduced to bankruptcy by the agricultural depression, had taken to quarrying. He owned the small Colburn Quarry by the side of a lane connecting South Wingfield with Pentrich Lane End, and there, hidden behind trees and the slope of the hill, he had stowed away a modest armoury of pikes to be handed out to the men on the march.

Brandreth, that Sunday morning, repeated his pledge of bread, beef and ale, and though he reduced his promise of cash to a hundred pounds a man, he added a pint of spirits as compensation. They were, he told them, to assemble at ten o'clock the following Monday night at Hunt's Barn to the west of South Wingfield. From there they would march in the direction of Pentrich, knocking on the doors of intervening houses and demanding from each a man and a gun. Those inhabitants who refused to comply with this

William Turner's house, South Wingfield.

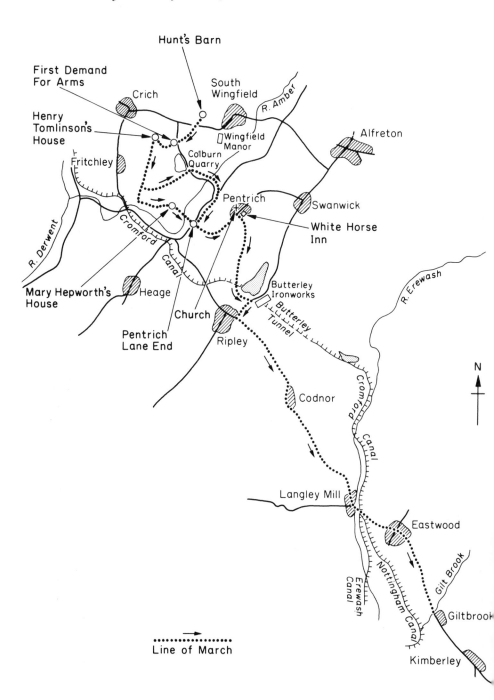

The Pentrich Revolution.

request would be instantly shot. The march would then proceed by Colburn Quarry and Pentrich Lane End to the village of Pentrich, and down the hill towards the Butterley ironworks, which one of the men described as 'a rare place to make arms at'. From there the route would lead through Ripley, Codnor, Langley Mill and Eastwood to the Forest at Nottingham, and thence to Newark. By that time, he implied, their company would be swollen by a multitude of men from Nottinghamshire and Leicestershire, Lancashire, Yorkshire, Staffordshire and Northamptonshire, and together they would all go forward to establish a new 'provision' government in London, which would provide work for those who were unemployed and food for those who were unable to afford it.

They would arm themselves with guns collected on the march, and with Ludlam's pikes. A number of bullets had already been cast, and they were to steal more lead from the roofs of churches; two barrels of gunpowder were stored for their use in a grocer's warehouse, close by, at Heage; and, as Brandreth hinted, there was always Butterley. There the Chesterfield men were due to meet them, and he expected that 'something of importance would occur. When asked what this 'something of importance' might be, Brandreth replied that they would kill the three senior officials: young William Jessop, who was managing partner and brother of Josias, the engineer of the Cromford and High Peak Railway; George Goodwin, the agent; and Samuel Wragg, the works manager. After that they would take possession of the ironworks, and pillage it for weapons and ammunition. 'Vermin' who opposed them would have to be eradicated; England, Scotland and Ireland would rise in rebellion on the stroke of ten o'clock, and all who refused to take up arms would be shot. The wave of revolution would sweep them in triumph along the road to London.

Whether Brandreth's multitudes of men throughout the Midlands were even aware of the projected revolution seems, in retrospect, unlikely; but Sidmouth at the Home Office certainly was. The day before the march— the Sunday of the final White Horse meeting—Henry Enfield, the town clerk of Nottingham, wrote to London saying, 'We have Scouts out—My confidential clerk is on the lookout near Pentridge watching the result of Old Bacon's threatened movements'; and, three days after the whole affair was over, the Lord Lieutenant of Nottinghamshire, the Duke of Newcastle, informed Lord Sidmouth that 'As Your Lordship is aware the plot had been hatching for some time, which we knew, and were prepared accordingly. We thought it much more desirable to let the matter come to a Crisis, than to endeavour to crush it before the Designs were openly disclosed.' This calculated inaction was successful in netting most of the conspirators, and the action the authorities eventually took, though belated, was sufficient. The London Radicals never intended to support such an ill-conceived rising; the immense forces ready to march from the north and various parts of the

Midlands never materialized; the only other disturbance on the night of 9 June was the shooting of a yeomanry horse at Huddersfield; and the Pentrich men were left to act out their tragic farce unsupported, and to suffer the rigours of a penal code the laws of which, as Sir Samuel Romilly said, were 'written in blood', that others, in years to come, might be abundantly discouraged from following in their footsteps.

But if Sidmouth's agents kept him well informed, the suspicion must remain that one of them, William Oliver—'Oliver the Spy' as he came to be known—interpreted his brief very loosely indeed. If it still remains to be proved that he was acting on instructions as an *agent provocateur*, he certainly encouraged Brandreth and his fellow marchers in their folly, and led them to expect the widespread support that they never received, including, as he told a meeting at Wakefield to which Thomas Bacon was one of the delegates, seventy thousand men who were waiting in London to rise 'in three or four Hours notice'. Earl Fitzwilliam, the Lord Lieutenant of the West Riding, later informed Sidmouth that opinion in the country was that recent events were largely due to 'the presence and active agitation of Mr Oliver'; William Turner's last words, spoken on the scaffold, were 'This is the work of the Government and Oliver'; and even Lord Liverpool, speaking in a Lords' debate a week after the rising, at least half admitted his agent's responsibility. 'Spies and informers,' he said, 'have at all times been employed by all governments and ever must be. And this being granted it would and must sometimes happen that such persons from zeal in their business would sometimes go further than they ought.' Fourteen years later, Lord Melbourne, who was at that time the Whig Home Secretary, declared his belief in less cautious terms. Referring in a letter to 'the transactions of the year 1817', he wrote that 'there is too much reason to suspect that the rising in Derbyshire, which cost the lives of three men upon the scaffold and the transportation of many more, was stimulated, if not produced, by the artifices of Oliver, a spy employed by the Government of that day.'

But of this the men of Pentrich were sublimely ignorant when, at ten o'clock on the night of 9 June, they began to assemble, as Brandreth had ordered, at Hunt's Barn, close to South Wingfield village. At that time they numbered in the region of fifty, and Brandreth, armed with a pistol and a shotgun, immediately made his presence felt by threatening that any man who refused to join the march would have his brains blown out. He then ordered them off in the direction of Wingfield Park, subsequently splitting them into two separate groups to recruit as many men and seize as many guns as they possibly could.

They proceeded, for four hours, to terrify the neighbourhood, rousing men and women roughly from their beds, forcing fathers and sons at pistol point to follow them, and demanding the use of any guns they possessed.

Henry Tomlinson, a South Wingfield farmer, showed more courage than many. Warned of their approach, he locked up his house and awaited them outside. Confronted by Brandreth and a gang of men waving guns and pikes, he coolly demanded to know their business, and, when told that they wanted both him and his gun, he replied that, as far as he was concerned, they would have neither. Even when Brandreth levelled his gun and threatened to blow his head off, Tomlinson refused. His gun, he said, had gone to be repaired. Wisely perhaps, in view of what happened further down the road into Wingfield Park, he at length agreed, though with obvious reluctance, to join the march. He was given a pike to carry, but, a quarter of a mile further on, George Weightman, Nanny's son, nudged him in the darkness and told him to go back home to his wife. It was, almost certainly, Tomlinson's evidence that saved Weightman, four months later, from the gallows.

Brandreth's group then approached a small farmhouse in Wingfield Park, where a widow, Mary Hepworth, lived with her two sons. They pounded on the door, but Mrs Hepworth refused to open it, whereupon Brandreth made his way round to the back. Some of his men broke the kitchen window and forced in the shutters, while Brandreth himself fired a shot into the house, killing a servant, Robert Walters, as he bent to lace his boots. To their credit, a number of the Pentrich men demurred at this wanton act of murder, but Brandreth's reply was typical of his belligerent attitude that night. It was, he said, his duty to shoot the man, and, if they displayed a whit more insolence, he would shoot them as well.

The two groups reassembled at Pentrich Lane End, where Brandreth and William Turner formed the men into ranks: those with guns at the front, and the motley collection of swords, pikes, crowbars, scythes and other weapons bringing up the rear. Brandreth then commanded them to march and they made their way up the narrow, winding lane to Pentrich village, rousing from their sleep more frightened householders, before turning down the hill in a drizzle of rain towards Butterley ironworks. There, by the small hexagonal office, they were confronted by George Goodwin, backed by a handful of special constables armed with pikes. When they hammered on the locked gates of the foundry yard, Goodwin appeared from inside the lighted office and asked them what they wanted. 'We want your men,' Brandreth replied. Goodwin was determined to protect the works and, if necessary, to fight. 'You shall not have them,' he said. 'You are too many already except your purpose was better. Disperse. The law will be too strong for you. You are going with halters about your necks, and you will all be hanged.' Brandreth made no answer. He seemed, indeed, to be taken aback by Goodwin's determination; and the agent, recognizing some of the men, seized the initiative. He opened the gates and walked straight to Isaac Ludlam. 'Good God,' he exclaimed, 'what are you doing on such a business as this? You've got a halter about your neck. Go home'; and he took him by the shoulder and

The hexagonal office, Butterley Ironworks.

pushed him towards the office. Ludlam shuddered at the words, yet he wrenched himself free. 'I must go on,' he muttered, 'I cannot go back'; but three of the more reluctant marchers slipped past Goodwin and into the office; and seeing this, Brandreth, perhaps because he feared a sudden mass defection, gave the order to march, and the men fell back in some disarray towards the main road and set off towards Ripley.

There they broke into houses, dragooning men to join them and seizing what they could find in the way of weapons. At Codnor and Langley Mill they roused a number of publicans, demanding and consuming gallons of ale and pounds of bread and cheese; but it was now raining heavily, and Brandreth's indecision at the Butterley gates had awakened a feeling of mis- placed trust among many of his followers, while Goodwin's threatening words about the gallows had demoralized the waverers. Drenched to the skin by the teeming rain, men began to slip away in the darkness and make their ways home. So it was that Brandreth's diminishing army, bedraggled and disheartened, toiled on through Eastwood and stumbled down to the bottom of a valley where the Gilt Brook crossed the Kimberley road. There, by a tanyard, they raised their eyes to the crest of the hill and saw the one thing that they had, at the back of their minds, always dreaded: soldiers on horseback riding down towards them.

There were only twenty: men of the 15th Regiment of Light Dragoons; but they were more than enough. The marchers broke and fled, throwing away their weapons, hiding in ditches, in barns and haylofts, cowering under hedgerows, desperately seeking to conceal themselves from the searching soldiers. They had little success. Some forty were rounded up in the course of the morning, and though Brandreth escaped with Turner and Ludlam, Turner was captured just before mid-day hiding in a ditch between Codnor and Langley Mill, and by the middle of June eighty-five of the marchers were in Nottingham and Derby Gaols. Brandreth, Ludlam and George Weightman took longer to find. It was mid-July before they were taken: Weightman near Sheffield, Brandreth at Bulwell, and Ludlam as far away as Uttoxeter in Staffordshire. The last to be captured was old Thomas Bacon. This veteran agitator, hearing that there was a warrant out for his arrest, had already gone into hiding before the march began. He had played no part in the disastrous events of that rainswept night, and his absence, in the end, probably saved his life; but the authorities were determined to track him down; a reward of a hundred guineas was offered for his capture; and eventually, on 15 August, he was arrested, after a struggle, at St Ives in Huntingdonshire.

So ended the active phase of the rebellion. The men were brought to trial two months later at the County Hall in Derby, charged, among other things, with 'maliciously and traitorously' endeavouring, 'by force of arms, to subvert and destroy the Government and Constitution'. Twenty-three were convicted. Three were sentenced to transportation for fourteen years; a further eleven, including George Weightman and Thomas Bacon, to transportation for life; and, for the crime of high treason, Brandreth, Ludlam and Turner were condemned to death. But for such a crime the penalty exacted by the law of the land was not a simple hanging. The Chief Baron of the Court of Exchequer, Sir Richard Richards, made this very clear:

> Your insurrection, thank God, did not last long, but whilst it continued it was marked with violence and with the murder of an innocent man who did not offer the least provocation. That conduct has shown the ferocity of your hearts. Your object was to wade through the blood of your countrymen, to extinguish the law and constitution of the country, and to substitute for the liberty of your fellow subjects anarchy and the most complete ruin. God be praised, your purpose failed.

Then, wearing the black cap, he passed upon them what he rightly called the awful sentence of the law, which is, that you and each of you be taken hence to the gaol whence you came, from whence you must be drawn on a hurdle to the place of execution, and be there severally hanged by the neck until you are dead; your heads must then be severed from your bodies, which are to be divided into four quarters, and to be at his Majesty's disposal.'

The Prince Regent, on behalf of his father, George III, graciously remitted the customary quartering, but the rest of the savage sentence was carried out on 7 November on Nun's Green in front of Derby Gaol, the executioner holding up the severed heads to the view of the crowd that pressed around the scaffold. Apart from Turner's indictment of William Oliver, the three men had little to say at the end. Perhaps Brandreth had said all he needed to say while he was in gaol. Warned by a magistrate that he was likely to die for the crime he had committed, he had spoken his epitaph. 'I need not care whether I live or die,' he had said, 'for there are no Derbyshire Ribs now.'

A hundred and sixty years after his death, Pentrich is quieter than ever he was to know it. The White Horse has vanished, and so has Mrs Hepworth's farmhouse in Wingfield Park, where Robert Walters bent down to lace his boots and died. Isaac Ludlam's quarry, where the pikes were stored, lies deserted, overgrown; but the narrow, twisting roads that sounded that night to the tramping of feet, the shouts of angry men, the battering of doors and the smashing of windows still wind deep through the fields between Wingfield and Ripley, and, beside the old trunk road from Alfreton to Derby, the sombre hexagonal office still guards the entrance to Butterley ironworks, as it did when George Goodwin stood face to face with Brandreth, and the shadow of the gallows fell for the first time across the men of Pentrich.

11 Sublime Discord

When I consider the striking natural beauties of such a river as that at Matlock, and the effect of the seven-storey buildings that have been raised there, and on other beautiful streams, for cotton manufactories, I am inclined to think that nothing can equal them for the purpose of disbeautifying an enchanting piece of scenery; and that economy had produced, what the greatest ingenuity, if a prize were given for ugliness, could not surpass.

Uvedale Price: *Essays on the Picturesque* (1810).

These cotton mills, seven stories high, and fill'd with inhabitants, remind me of a first rate man of war; and when they are lighted up, on a dark night, look most luminously beautiful.

Hon. John Byng: *The Torrington Diaries* (1790).

The Derwent Valley, through the work of Cotchett, Lombe and Sorocold, and subsequently Arkwright, Strutt and Need, pioneered those developments in factory industry which were later to spread to more distant parts of Britain. Thus it was only fitting that the Crystal Palace, designed to display the triumphs of the factory system, should also have had its genesis on the banks of the river; and it was equally appropriate that the domestic workers, who were, after all, the first unfortunate victims of that system, should have conjured up their last despairing act of defiance in the shadow of those water mills where it all began.

A hundred and thirteen years, but only ten miles, separated the silk mill that Thomas Cotchett raised on the By-Flatt at Derby, from the dark, wet lanes of that violent night around the village of Pentrich; seventy-nine years, and yet merely nine miles, the building of that first, forbidding, fortress-like factory by Arkwright at Cromford and the more delicate structure of Paxton's Victoria Regia House at Chatsworth.

The valley, indeed, for a century and a half, provided within its sixty-mile course a microcosm of the nation's development; but there were those who saw a sombre side to all this activity, and deplored the destruction of natural beauty by the repeated invasions of man and his artefacts. Ruskin was not the only writer to lament the desecration of the Vale of Tempe and its lovely stream. Sir Uvedale Price, the champion of the Picturesque style in painting, spoke of the cotton mills 'disbeautifying an enchanting piece of scenery'; and John Byng, during his visit to Cromford in the June of 1790, remarked on the way in which Arkwright's mills had disfigured the valley:

'Arkwright's Cotton Mills at Cromford by Moonlight', by Joseph Wright, 1783.

I dare not, perhaps I shou'd not, repine at the increase of our trade, and (partial) population; yet speaking as a tourist, these vales have lost all their beauties; the rural cot has given place to the lofty red mill, and the grand houses of overseers; the stream perverted from its course by sluices, and aqueducts, will not longer ripple and cascade.—Every rural sound is sunk in the clamours of cotton works; and the simple peasant (for to be simple we must be sequester'd) is changed into the impudent mechanic:—the woods find their way into the canals; and the rocks are disfigured for lime stone. So that the intention of retirement is much lost here; and the citizen or the tourist, may soon seek in vain for quiet, and wild scenery ... The bold rock opposite this house is now disfigur'd by a row of new houses built under it; and the vales are every way block'd up by mills.

And yet, that same evening, the sight of those mills with their gleaming rows of candle-lit windows reminded him of battleships afloat on the stream. They looked, he said, 'most luminously beautiful', glowing in the immemorial darkness of the valley. It was a new kind of beauty, which others discovered in addition to Byng. Joseph Wright of Derby, born twelve years after Lombe completed his silk mill, was the first of all professional painters to enshrine in his work the spirit of this new industrial revolution. He was fascinated by light, both natural and artificial, and his canvases reflect his repeated experiments to capture in paint the glow of iron furnaces, pottery ovens and factory windows set against streamers of moon-lit cloud or star-bestrewn skies. Arkwright's mills, with the night shift at work, every window blazing with naked candles, and the moon emerging from storm-tossed cloud,

'The Great Day of His Wrath', by John Martin.

provided a subject ideal for his empirical talent. He named his work, with dramatic understatement, 'View of Cromford, near Matlock'.

Wright and the other painters who succeeded him were moving slowly towards the appreciation of an element that Arthur Young, the great traveller and agriculturist, was discovering for himself at much the same time: that of sublime discord: a knowledge that the contrast between the beauty of the landscape and the ugliness of man's industrial work could, and often did, contain an element of sublimity. Making his way through Shropshire in 1776, he came to Coalbrookdale, its roaring furnaces and hammer-ridden forges. The dale, he wrote, 'is a very romantic spot, it is a winding glen between two immense hills which break into various forms, and all thickly covered with wood, forming the most beautiful sheets of hanging wood'; and, he went on, 'that variety of horrors art has spread at the bottom: the noise of the forges, mills, &c. with all their vast machinery, the flames bursting from the furnaces with the burning of the coal and the smoak of the lime kilns, are altogether sublime.'

Edmund Burke, the Irish statesman and philosopher, attempted to define this new sublimity. 'In nature,' he wrote, 'dark, confused, uncertain images have a greater power on the fancy to form the grander passions than those

'Coalbrookdale at Night', by P. J. de Loutherbourg, 1801.

have which are more clear and determinate . . . The passions which belong
to self-preservation turn on pain and danger; they are simply painful when
their causes immediately effect us; they are delightful when we have an idea
of pain and danger, without being actually in such circumstances . . . What
ever excites this delight, I call sublime.'

It was an element that exercised a powerful fascination over the world of
art for three-quarters of a century and achieved its consummation in the
work of John Martin, who painted his storm-racked landscapes of Hell and
enclosed within that Hell the industrial image. His finest work, 'The Great
Day of his Wrath', painted in 1850, was, according to his son, inspired by a
journey deep into the Black Country in the middle of the night. 'The glow
of the furnaces,' he declared, 'the red blaze of light, together with the liquid
fire, seemed to his mind truly sublime and awful. He could not imagine
anything more terrible even in the regions of everlasting punishment. All he
had done or attempted in ideal painting fell far short, very far short, of the
fearful sublimity.'

Coalbrookdale and its immediate vicinity commanded the attention of
innumerable artists, among them Robertson, de Loutherbourg and Turner,
but those who sought for the Sublime, as Burke had defined it, could well
have found much to inspire them by the Derwent. The smoking ovens and
flaming furnaces of Francis Hurt's ironworks at Morley Park, the gigantic
candles of Stephenson's limekilns burning on the floor of the valley at Ambergate, and the blazing shell of Arkwright's mill at Cressbrook, incandescent
in the depths of the River Wye gorge, would all have provided ideal subjects.
So would Efford's 'monstrous cavern' at Ecton, with its haze of sulphur and
its flickering lights; the waters of the Derwent, tossed into storm, sweeping
to destruction the old Calver Bridge; the sombre passage of Arkwright's

'The Limekiln at Coalbrookdale', by J. M. W. Turner.

funeral beneath High Tor; William Adam's forks of lightning breaking through the thunder clouds above Litton Mill; and the desolate figure of Lingard's father raising his eyes to his son's swinging body on the darkness of the gibbet at Wardlow Mires.

The other artistic movement, contemporaneous with that of the Sublime, was the depiction of what was known as the Picturesque. This, according to the artist and traveller, William Gilpin, who, in his essays on landscape painting, attempted to give it systematic expression, was an appreciation of the rough rather than the smooth. 'Make it rough,' he wrote, 'and you make it also picturesque . . . A piece of Palladian architecture may be elegant to the last degree . . . Should we wish to give it a picturesque beauty . . . we must beat down one half of it, deface the other, and throw the mutilated members around in heaps. In short, from a smooth building we must turn it into a rough ruin.' Gilpin rejected the arts of industry as proper subjects for painting, but Sir Uvedale Price, who tried, two years later, to give greater precision to Gilpin's theories, admitted mills and quarries to his list of chosen subjects, provided that time and weather had broken them down or softened their outlines.

Perhaps Edward Rhodes was making the same admission when, in the early 1820s, in his *Peak Scenery or The Derbyshire Tourist*, he commented sadly on the net of dry stone walls that parliamentary enclosure had cast upon the landscape. The moors, south of Brindley's birthplace at Tunstead, were, he said, 'everywhere disfigured with stone wall-fences', which, 'if not absolutely repulsive', were at least 'unlovely'; and, he added, they would remain so, until a lapse of years had 'introduced the softer graces and the richer clothing of cultivation'.

Since the time of Price and Rhodes, the mills and the quarries, the lead mines and ironworks, the canals and the railways have acquired those softer graces. What was the Sublime has become the Picturesque. Time and weather have slowly transformed into a strange kind of harmony the discord that Arthur Young perceived and that Joseph Wright, de Loutherbourg and Turner recorded. The landscape has absorbed the gritstone and limestone, the dun-coloured brick, the iron and steel artefacts of industry and communication, and made them inescapably a part of itself. Nature, run wild, has concealed some in brambles and covered them with twitch-grass; re-aligned roads have consigned others to the wilderness; and men's eyes have come to accept the remainder, to expect them in the places where memory always sets them, even to look through them, unaware of their presence. Nowadays strangers and even residents can drive through the valley from Bamford to the very outskirts of Derby, without even realizing that around them lies one of the pioneer industrial regions of Britain.

The gaunt mill at Calver still dominates the village, but, standing back, as it does, from the road, half-hidden by trees, many people never even see it as they pass; Arkwright's first, grim, gritstone structures at Cromford, tucked away down the old packhorse road that climbs to Holloway, must be glimpsed by millions of travellers every year, but without any conscious appreciation; and families who stroll at weekends through the richly-wooded glory of Lathkill Dale walk by tumbled heaps of stones that were once stores for gunpowder, drainage channels, aqueducts and massive pumping engine houses. Maybe they stop to wonder what purpose these served, but, bemused by the gentle rustle of leaves, they never know they stand amid the soundless relics of a lead mining field.

Most of those who park their cars at Monsal Head to gaze at the deep magnificence of the dale look through and beyond the viaduct that so enraged Ruskin a hundred years ago, and leave without knowing that a few yards behind them lies a busy turnpike junction on one of the most ancient, continuously-trodden trackways in the whole of Britain. To many of those who tramp, bent beneath their rucksacks, up the High Peak Trail, the marvels of Jessop's trans-Pennine railway remain mysteries as distant as the valleys below; those who wander casually out of their way and stumble on the classical ruin of Watts must, lacking the perception that only knowledge can bestow, wonder what it was used for; while to others Millstone Edge is no more than another weathered gritstone face, the stubs of Morley Park a conundrum beside the new A38, and Tideslow Rake an incomprehensible stretch of hummocks and hollows climbing from Washhouse Bottom to the sky.

The mills may still throb, though with different machinery, but time has invested them with familiarity, and familiarity with a kind of respectable anonymity; the shells of engine houses, bleak against the sunset, have acquired a dramatic, rectilinear beauty, and squat, truncated furnaces the fascination of Aztec shrines. Canal beds, quarries and railway tracks, abandoned to nature, are now overgrown and, in places, almost indiscernible; orchids flourish where limestone was blasted; and the shaft hollows and spoil heaps where 't'owd man' once laboured are bright with the blues and yellows and purples of mountain pansies, speedwell and thyme.

Rhodes' lapse of years has introduced his softer graces to the unlovely works of industrial man, as it has in those places where the valley has even more recently been disfigured. In his book, *Highways and Byways in Derbyshire*, published seventy years ago, J. B. Firth echoed Rhodes' words when he wrote that the construction of the Howden and Derwent dams had 'most rudely disturbed the amenities' of the area. He was sorely afraid, he said, that the restoration promised was 'too good to be true'. Yet that same restoration is now completed for all to see and many to enjoy; man and nature, between them, have softened the surface of the gritstone slopes with thick woods of conifer, maple and rowan; great sweeps of water have hidden the massive scars on the face of the land; and the Derbyshire lakes have become as much a part of the Derwent Valley as the Derwent itself.

There is an inevitability about this process, as Edward Rhodes foresaw. Time lends enchantment to even the most discordant works of man. The branches of trees screen them with grace, grasses wave about them, wild flowers dot them with rainbow colours, and wind, rain and sunshine, ice, snow and frost fret and fade their harshness into a constrained and muted harmony. So will it be with the latest of discords. The huge cement works at Hope, which even now Turner, renascent, might have painted—a white *Téméraire* rising from the morning mists of the valley—will one day become an industrial monument, overgrown with time, cossetted and cared for as if its ugliness had never existed. So, too, will the jagged mile-long gash of the quarry face at Tunstead. Abandoned, its days of weathering will come, and orchids will flower where once there was only the hoar dust of limestone blasted from the hills.

Ruskin's Muses of light may no longer tread the pinnacles above Monsal Dale. The grass may rustle no more beneath their classical feet; but other sounds can still be heard by those men and women, and more especially children, gifted with that mystical inner vision which some call historical imagination. The axle of the waterwheel creaks at Alport mill; the Newcomen engines wheeze and sigh and bump on the heights around Winster; 'Baby', 'Alice' and 'Jumbo' hiss and clank above the cavern of Warren Carr Shaft; the Shardlow warehouses ring to the stowage of bar-iron and lead; waggons, enchained, rattle at the foot of Sheep Pasture Incline; locomotives grind around Gotham Curve, and pant smoke and steam as they strive for the summit of Hopton Bank; stage coaches, wheels locked, rasp and grate on the dangerous slope of Whatstandwell hill; and the millstones rumble with a noise like slow thunder across Baslow Bridge.

The gods in fair procession may no longer walk the crags above Water-cum-Jolly, but other sights persist, mirrored in the crystal vault of the years. Molten iron, John Martin's liquid fire, pours from the flanks of the Morley Park furnaces; the ponderous crushing-wheel of the Odin Mine revolves on its circle below Mam Tor; the team of forty horses strains to haul the beam of the Mandale engine up the twisting hill from the bed of Lathkill Gorge; candles burn and powder flashes in the chert mine at Bakewell; long trains of packhorses, panniers swinging, turn across the river at Leadmill Bridge; Brunton's walking locomotive propels itself on its jointed legs down the Butterley Gang Road; and a waggon-load of children peer with frightened eyes through the falling dusk at Ellis Needham's mill.

Apollo may indeed have forsaken the lawns around Derwent and Wye, but other figures still move like shadows through the landscape. Francis Hurt parts the curtains at Alderwasley Hall, and looks through the darkness across the valley to the glow of his flaming furnaces at Heage; George Stephenson climbs his gritstone tower above Milford, and watches his navvies driving the railway north towards Belper; Brindley, on horseback, reconnoitres the shaft of his silver cross from Wilden Ferry along the bank of the Trent; Strutt ponders his epitaph, lifting his gaze to the great cotton mills that proved his true memorial; Sorocold falls from the planks of the Silk Mill, swept by the river beneath his own wheel; and Paxton climbs over the greenhouse gate at Chatsworth to start the first of his many mornings' work, and to meet at breakfast the girl who lies beside him in Edensor churchyard.

Byng strolls, sniffing, through Willersley Castle; Samuel Smiles surveys in wonder the 'curious complication' of water and bridge, railway and canal piled four storeys high near the mouth of the Amber; Ruskin stands beneath the towering viaduct at Monsal, and shudders at its powers of desecration; and William Adam cowers in his cleft at Water-cum-Jolly while the lightning splits the sky above Litton Mill.

The nailers sweat, bare of breast, in their Belper workshops; 't'owd man', lean and pale as the dead, thrusts himself up to the light of day from his climbing shaft on Brassington Moor; the women of Castleton struggle to work across snow-powdered tracks, hobbling down the hillside to Edale Mill from the ridge at Hollins Cross; the needle grinders cough out their lungs in the streets of Hathersage; the men of Pentrich march to the gallows and the hulks; the soughers, like moles, tunnel through the shale and limestone of the hills; and the watchman at Darley Abbey raises his lantern to see the millgirls' petticoats over their heads.

But one shadow seems more solid than the rest, and moves with more purpose through the valley it transformed: that of a bulky, bag-cheeked, asthmatic old man. Arkwright is, as always, about his business; and those who hear the sound of his carriage in the night, as it climbs the road to Wirksworth, are hearing, with the clack of the spinning frames and the roar of the river breaking over its weirs, the elemental sounds of that transformation which set the Derwent Valley, for a moment of time, in the forefront of history.

Bibliography

Adam, W. *Gem of the Peak* (1840) (reprinted Moorland Publishing Co., 1973)
 Dales, Scenery, Fishing Streams and Mines of Derbyshire and Surrounding Counties: Historical and Geological (1861) (Also published under the title *Pleasant Walks in Derbyshire*)
Aikin, J. and Enfield, W. *General Biography* (1799)
Anderson, P. H. *Forgotten Railways: The East Midlands* (1973)
Andrews, C. B. (ed.) *The Torrington Diaries* (1935)
Anthony, J. *Joseph Paxton* (1973)
Arkwright Society *Arkwright and the Mills at Cromford* (1971)
 Local History Trails (1971–6): 1. Cromford Canal and High Peak Railway 3. Lead Mining 4. The Matlocks. 5. Bonsall 6. The Derbyshire Journey of the 5th Lord Torrington 7. Some Local Traditional Buildings 8. Cromford Village 9. Transport and Communications 10. Dethick, Lea and Holloway 11. Wirksworth 12. Belper 13. Around Elton 14. Some Derbyshire Cornmills 15. Youlgreave, Middleton, Alport 17. Ironville 18. Canal—Shardlow
Arnould, J. *A Memoir of Thomas Denman* (1873)
Ashmore, O. 'The Early Textile Industry in the Derwent Valley', *Derbyshire Miscellany* (The Bulletin of the Local History Section of the Derbyshire Archaeological Society) vol. 1, 5 (March 1957)
 'The Early Textile Industry in N. W. Derbyshire', *Derbyshire Miscellany* vol. 1, p. 9 (June 1958)
Ashton, T. S. *Iron and Steel in the Industrial Revolution* (1924)
 The Industrial Revolution 1760–1830 (1948)

Bagshaw, S. *History, Gazeteer and Directory of Derbyshire* (1846)
Bailey, J. E. (ed.) *The Palatine Note Book* (1883)
Baines, E. *History of the Cotton Manufacture in Great Britain* (1835)
Balston, T. *John Martin* (1947)
Band, S. 'Lead Mining in Ashover: A Preliminary Survey', *Bulletin of the Peak District Mines Historical Society*, vol. 6, no. 3, pp. 129–39 (April 1976)
Banks, F. R. *The Peak District* (1975)
Barnes, E. G. *The Rise of the Midland Railway 1844–74* (1966)
Barton, D. B. *The Cornish Beam Engine* (1965)
Baxter, B. 'Early Railways in Derbyshire', *Transactions of the Newcomen Society for the History of Technology*, vol. 26 (1947–9)
 Stone Blocks and Iron Rails (1966)
Belper Historical Society *Belper: A Study of its History Based on Visual Evidence* (1970)
Bessborough, Earl of *Georgiana: Extracts from the Correspondence of Georgiana, Duchess of Devonshire* (1955)
Bird, A. *Roads and Vehicles* (1969)
Bird, R. H. *Yesterday's Golcondas* (1977)
Bowtell, H. D. *Reservoir Railways of Manchester and The Peak* (1977)
Bracegirdle, B. *The Archaeology of the Industrial Revolution* (1973)
Bracegirdle, B. and Miles, P. H. *The Darbys and the Ironbridge Gorge* (1974)
Bray, W. *A Sketch of a Tour into Derbyshire and Yorkshire* (1777)
Brook, F. *The Industrial Archaeology of the West Midlands* (1977)
Brown, J. *A Memoir of Robert Blincoe* (1828) (reprinted Caliban Books, 1977)
Brown, I. J. and Ford, T. D. *The Magpie Mine, Sheldon* (1971)
Bryant, Sir A. *The Years of Endurance 1793–1802* (1942)
Buchanan, R. A. *Industrial Archaeology in Britain* (1972)
Buchanan, R. A. and Watkins, G. *The Industrial Archaeology of the Stationary Steam Engine* (1976)
Burdett, P. P. *Map of Derbyshire* (1767) (1791 edition)
Burke, E. *A Philosophical Enquiry into the Origin of our Ideas of the Sublime and Beautiful* (1757)
Burt, R. *John Taylor: Mining Entrepreneur and Engineer* (1977)
Burton, A. *Josiah Wedgwood* (1976)
 Industrial Archaeological Sites of Britain (1977)
Burton, A. and Coote, C. *Remains of a Revolution* (1975)

Byng, Hon, J. (Viscount Torrington) see Andrews, C. B. (ed.)

Calder-Marshall, A. *The Two Duchesses* (1978)
Cameron, K. *The Place Names of Derbyshire* (1959)
Carlyle, T. *Chartism* (1839)
    Past and Present (1843)
Catling, H. *The Spinning Mule* (1970)
Chadwick, G. F. *The Works of Sir Joseph Paxton* (1961)
Challis, P. J. 'William Bray's Sketch of a Tour into Derbyshire and Yorkshire', *Bulletin of the Peak District Mines Historical Society*, vol. 6, no. 6, pp. 297–302 (December 1977)
Chapman, S. D. *The Early Factory Masters* (1967)
    The Cotton Industry in the Industrial Revolution (1972)
Checkland, S. G. *The Rise of Industrial Society in England 1815–1885* (1964)
Childs, J. 'William Hutton 1723–1815', *Derbyshire Life and Countryside* (February 1979)
Christian, R. 'The Handyside Story', *Derbyshire Advertiser* (7 April 1961)
    Factories, Forges and Foundries (1974)
    The Peak District (1976)
    Derbyshire (1978)
Coleman, T. *The Railway Navvies* (1965)
Coleridge, S. T. *The Friend* (1809)
Collins, W. *Rambles Beyond Railways* (1851)
Cossons, N. *The B. P. Book of Industrial Archaeology* (1975)
Cozens-Hardy, B. (ed.) *The Diary of Sylas Neville 1767–88* (1950)
Cromford Canal Society *The Cromford Canal and Leawood Pump* (1975)
Crowley, T. E. *Beam Engines* (1975)

Darwin, E. *The Botanic Garden* (1789–91)
Davies, D. P. *An Historical and Descriptive View of Derbyshire* (1811)
Davison, A. W. *Derby: Its Rise and Progress* (1906) (reprinted S. R. Publishers, 1970)
Defoe, D. *A Tour thro' the Whole Island of Great Britain* (1724–6) (Penguin English Library, 1971)
de Maré, E. *London 1851* (1972)
Derbyshire Countryside Ltd. *The Garden at Chatsworth* (1978)
Derbyshire County Council Planning Dept. *Middleton Top Engine House* (1975)
Derry, T. K. and Williams, T. I. *A Short History of Technology* (1960)
Devonshire, sixth Duke of *Handbook to Chatsworth and Hardwick* (1845)
Dodd, A. E. and E. M. *Peakland Roads and Trackways* (1974)
'Dowie' *The Crich Mineral Railways* (1976)

Eden, Sir F. M. *The State of the Poor* (1797)
Edwards, K. C. *The Peak District* (1962)
Efford, W. 'Description of Famous Copper Mine Belonging to his Grace the Duke of Devonshire in the County of Stafford', *Gentleman's Magazine* (February 1769) (reprinted, *Bulletin of the Peak District Mines Historical Society*, vol. 1, no. 5, pp. 37–40, 1961)
English, W. *The Textile Industry* (1969)
Farey, J. *View of the Agriculture and Minerals of Derbyshire* (1811–17)
Farey, J. junior *A Treatise on the Steam-Engine* (1827)
Felkin, W. *History of the Machine-wrought Hosiery and Lace Manufactures* (1867)
Fergusson, J. *History of the Modern Styles of Architecture* (1863)
Fielden, J. *The Curse of the Factory System* (1836)
Fiennes, C. see Morris, C. (ed.)
Firth, J. B. *Highways and Byways in Derbyshire* (1905)
Fitton, R. S. and Wadsworth, A. P. *The Strutts and the Arkwrights 1758–1830* (1958)
Flindall, R. 'An Account of a visit to Holme Bank Chert Mine, Bakewell, during 1892', *Bulletin of the Peak District Mines Historical Society*, vol. 6, no. 3, pp. 173–4 (April 1976)
Flindall, R. and Hayes, A. *The Caverns and Mines of Matlock Bath* (1976)
Ford, T. D. 'The Black Marble Mines of Ashford-in-the-Water', *Bulletin of the Peak District Mines Historical Society*, vol. 2, no. 4 (October 1964)
Ford, T. D. and Rieuwerts, J. H. (ed.) *Lead Mining in the Peak District* (1968)

Ford, T. D. and Rieuwerts, J. H. 'The Odin Mine, Castleton', *Bulletin of the Peak District Mines Historical Society*, vol. 6, no. 4 (September 1976)
Fraser, W. 'Some Derbyshire Water Mills', *The Derbyshire Countryside* (January–March 1951)

Gale, W. K. V. *The British Iron and Steel Industry* (1967)
Gaskell, P. *Artisans and Machinery* (1836)
George, M. D. *England in Transition* (1931)
Gibbs-Smith, C. H. *The Great Exhibition of 1851* (1950)
Gilpin, W. *Three Essays to which is added a poem, on Landscape Painting* (1792)
Glover, S. *Derbyshire Directory* (1829)
   A History of the County of Derby (1829)
   The Peak Guide (1830)
Granville, A. B. *The Spas of England and Principal Sea-Bathing Places* (1841)
Grayson, M. *A Short History of Edensor* (1976)
Greig, J. (ed.) *The Farington Diary* (1922)
Grigson, G. and Gibbs-Smith, C. H. *Places* (1954)
Grimes, G. H. 'The Morley Park Iron Foundry, Heage, 1780–1874', *Derbyshire Life and Countryside* (October 1976)
Guedalla, P. *The Duke* (1946)

Hadfield, C. *British Canals* (1952)
   The Canals of the East Midlands (1966)
   The Canals of the West Midlands (1966)
Hadfield, C. and Skempton, A. W. *William Jessop, Engineer* (1979)
Harris, H. *The Industrial Archaeology of the Peak District* (1971)
Heath, J. E. 'Shardlow—Then and Now', *Derbyshire Life and Countryside* (September 1976)
   'The Friargate Line', *Derbyshire Life and Countryside* (September 1978)
Henson, G. *The Civil, Political and Mechanical History of the Framework Knitters* (1831)
Higgens, C. W. 'The Framework Knitters of Derbyshire', *Journal of the Derbyshire Archaeological Society*, vol. 71 (1951)
Hills, R. L. *Power in the Industrial Revolution* (1970)
   Richard Arkwright and Cotton Spinning (1973)
Holland, G. C. *Diseases of the Lungs from Mechanical Causes* (1843)
Hoskins, W. G. *The Making of the English Landscape* (1955)
Hutton, W. *History of Derby* (1791)
   The Life of William Hutton (1816)

Jenkins, R. 'George Sorocold: A Chapter in the History of Public Water Supply', *The Engineer* (18 October 1918)

Keys, R. and Porter, L. *The Manifold Valley and its Light Railway* (1972)
Kirke, H. 'Dr. Clegg, Minister and Physician in the 17th and 18th Centuries', *Journal of the Derbyshire Archaeological Society*, vol. 35 (1913)
Kirkham, N. *Steam Engines in Derbyshire* (1966)
   Derbyshire Lead Mining through the Centuries (1968)
Klingender, F. D. *Art and the Industrial Revolution* (1947) (Paladin edition, 1972)

Landmark Trust *The Landmark Handbook* (1977)
Latham, D. J. 'Shardlow—A Historical Sketch', *Derbyshire Life and Countryside* (October 1978)
Law, R. J. *The Steam Engine* (1965)
Lindsay, J. 'The Butterley Coal and Iron Works 1792–1816', *Journal of the Derbyshire Archaeological Society*, vol. 85 (1965)
Longford, E. *Wellington: Pillar of State* (1972)

Mackenzie, M. H. 'Calver Mill and its Owners', *Journal of the Derbyshire Archaeological Society*, vol. 84 (1964)
Macpherson, D. *Annals of Commerce* (1785)
Malynes, G. *Lex Mercatoria* (1622)

Mantoux, P. *The Industrial Revolution in the Eighteenth Century* (1928)
Markham, V. *Paxton and the Bachelor Duke* (1935)
McKnight, H. *The Shell Book of Inland Waterways* (1975)
Mehew, S. 'Packhorse Bridges in Derbyshire', *Derbyshire Miscellany* vol. 1, p. 11
Merrill, J. *Legends of Derbyshire* (1975)
   'Winster—Past and Present', *Derbyshire Life and Countryside* (October 1978)
Millward, R. and Robinson, A. *The Peak District* (1975)
Morris, C. (ed.) *The Journeys of Celia Fiennes* (1949)
Murray's Handbook for Travellers in Derbyshire (1874)

Nasmyth, J. *Autobiography* (1883)
Neal, J. *The Pentrich Revolution* (1895)
Nicholson, B. *Joseph Wright of Derby* (1968)
Nicholson, C. P. *Branch Lines in the Peak District* (1977)
   Main Lines in the Peak District (1977)
Nicholson, C. P. and Barnes, P. *Railways in the Peak District* (1975)
Nixon, F. 'The Early Steam Engine in Derbyshire', *Transactions of the Newcomen Society*, vol. 31 (1957–9)
   The Industrial Archaeology of Derbyshire (1969)
Noall, C. *Botallack* (1972)

Ormerod, G. *History of the County Palatine and City of Chester* (1819)

Parker, H. M. and Willies, L. *Peakland Lead Mines and Miners* (1979)
Parker, V. 'The Calver Mill Buildings', *Journal of the Derbyshire Archaeological Society*, vol. 84 (1964)
Pecchio, Count G. *Italian Exile* (1833)
Pendred, L. St. L. 'A Note on Brunton's Steam Horse 1813', *Transactions of the Newcomen Society*, vol. 2 (1921–2)
Perkin, H. *The Age of the Railway* (1970)
Peters, D. *Darley Abbey, from Monastery to Industrial Community* (1974)
Pevsner, Sir N. *The Buildings of England: Derbyshire* (1953) (Penguin edition, 1978)
Phillips, Sir R. *A Personal Tour through the United Kingdom; describing living Objects and Contemporaneous Interests* (1828)
Pigot and Co. *Commercial Directory for Derbyshire* (1835) (reprinted Derbyshire County Council, County Library, 1976)
Pike, E. R. *Human Documents of the Industrial Revolution in Britain* (1966)
Pilkington, J. *A View of the Present State of Derbyshire* (1789)
Price, Sir U. *Essays on the Picturesque* (1810)
Pryce, W. *Mineralogia Cornubiensis* (1778)

Raistrick, A. *Dynasty of Ironfounders: The Darbys and Coalbrookdale* (1953)
   Industrial Archaeology (1973)
Raistrick, A. and Jennings, L. B. *A History of Lead Mining in the Pennines* (1965)
Rathbone, H. M. *Letters of Richard Reynolds with a Memoir of his Life* (1852)
Reynolds, J. *Windmills and Watermills* (1970)
Rhodes, E. *Peak Scenery or The Derbyshire Tourist* (1818–23)
Richardson, W. A. *Citizen's Derby* (1949)
Riden, P. *The Butterley Company 1790–1830* (1973)
   'The Butterley Company and Railway Construction 1790–1830', *Transport History*, vol. 6, no. 1 (March 1973)
Rieuwerts, J. H. *Derbyshire's Old Lead Mines and Miners* (1973)
   Lathkill Dale; its Mines and Miners (1973)
Rimmer, A. *The Cromford and High Peak Railway* (1956)
Ripley, D. *The Peak Forest Tramway* (1972)
   The Little Eaton Gangway (1973)
Robbins, M. *The Railway Age* (1962)
Robey, J. A. and Porter, L. *The Copper and Lead Mines of Ecton Hill, Staffordshire* (1972)
Robson, M. E. 'The Nailmaking Industry in Belper', *Derbyshire Miscellany*, vol. 3, no. 2 (June 1964)

Rodgers, F. 'Andrew Handyside—Engineer Extraordinary', *Derbyshire Life and Countryside* (September 1975)
Rolt, L. T. C. *Victorian Engineering* (1970)
Rolt, L. T. C. and Allen, J. S. *The Steam Engine of Thomas Newcomen* (1977)
Rostow, W. W. *The Stages of Economic Growth* (1960)
Rowland, K. T. *Eighteenth Century Inventions* (1974)
Ruskin, J. *Fors Clavigera* (1871–84)

Sanders, L. C. (ed.) *Lord Melbourne's Papers* (1889)
Seymour-Jones, A. 'The Invention of Roller Drawing in Cotton Spinning', *Transactions of the Newcomen Society*, vol. 1 (1920–1)
Sherlock, R. *The Industrial Archaeology of Staffordshire* (1976)
Sissons, W. and G. Ltd., *Sissons at Calver Mill* (1975)
Skempton, A. W. and Johnson, H. R. 'William Strutt's Cotton Mills 1793–1812', *Transactions of the Newcomen Society*, vol. 30 (1955–7)
Smeaton, J. *Experimental Engineering Concerning the Natural Powers of Wind and Water* (2nd edition, 1796)
Smiles, S. *The Lives of the Engineers* (1861–2) (reprinted David and Charles, 1968)
    Industrial Biography (1863) (reprinted David and Charles, 1967)
    Lives of Boulton and Watt (1865)
Smith, D. M. *The Industrial Archaeology of the East Midlands* (1965)
Smith R. (and others) *First and Last: The Peak National Park in Words and Pictures* (1978)
Stevens, J. *England's Last Revolution: Pentrich 1817* (1977)
Stokes, A. H. *Lead and Lead Mining in Derbyshire* (1964)
Storer, J. D. *A Simple History of the Steam Engine* (1969)
Swindin, K. 'The Arkwright Cotton Mills at Cromford', *Journal of Industrial Archaeology*, vol. 2, no. 1 (March 1965)

Thomas, D. St. J. *The Country Railway* (1976)
Thomis, M. I. *The Luddites* (1970)
Thornhill, R. 'The Arkwright Mill at Bakewell', *Journal of the Derbyshire Archaeological Society*, vol. 79 (1959)
Tooke, J. H. *Diversions of Purley* (1805)
Tramway Museum Society *The Tramway Museum: Official Guide* (1972)
Trevithick, F. *Life of Richard Trevithick* (1872)
Twitchett, J. and Bailey, B. *Royal Crown Derby* (1976)

Unsworth, W. *Portrait of the River Derwent* (1971)
Unwin, G. *Samuel Oldknow and the Arkwrights* (1924)

Vale, E. *The Harveys of Hayle* (1966)
Victoria County History of Derbyshire (1905–7)

Wailes, R. *Wind and Watermills* (1970)
Walton, I. *The Compleat Angler* (5th edition, 1676, with addendum by Charles Cotton)
Watson, W. *A Delineation of the Strata of Derbyshire* (1811)
    'Observations of Bakewell beginning 31 May 1774', *Journal of the Derbyshire Archaeological Society*, vol. 11 (1889)
White, R. J. *Waterloo to Peterloo* (1957)
Williamson, F. 'George Sorocold of Derby', *Journal of the Derbyshire Archaeological Society*, vol. 57 (1936)
Willies, L., Rieuwerts, J. H. and Flindall, R. F. 'Wind, Water and Steam Power on Derbyshire Lead Mines: A List', *Bulletin of the Peak District Mines Historical Society*, vol. 6, no. 6 (December 1977)
Wilson, C. *England's Apprenticeship 1603–1763* (1965)
Woodall, F. D. *Steam Engines and Waterwheels* (1975)
Wordsworth, W. *The Excursion* (1814)

Young, A. *A Six Months' Tour through the North of England* (1770)
    Annals of Agriculture, and other useful Arts (1785)

INDEX